THE INTERNATIONAL
WILDLIFE ENCYCLOPEDIA

VOLUME 9

THE INTERNATIONAL WILDLIFE ENCYCLOPEDIA

GENERAL EDITORS

Dr. Maurice Burton

Robert Burton

MARSHALL CAVENDISH CORPORATION / NEW YORK

CONTENTS

Printed in Great Britain
Library of Congress Catalog Card No 78-98713

Horsehair worm

The adults of these long thin worms, which as larvae are parasites in insects, are sometimes found in freshwater. From 4 to 40 in. long but only $\frac{1}{80}-\frac{1}{8}$ in. across, they were once thought in the Middle Ages to be born of horsehairs that had fallen into water. An alternative name is 'hair worms', their thread-like form being reflected also in their scientific name Nematomorpha. The way they become entangled in masses of 2—20 worms has earned them the names of 'gordian worms' or Gordioidea, a reference to the knot tied by Gordius and cut by Alexander the Great.

The adults of a given species vary considerably in length and in colour from yellowish to almost black. The males of some species end at the back in two lobes while those of other species are simply rounded at the hind end like the majority of females. (The hind end of the female ***Paragordius*** *is three-lobed.) Females are generally longer than males. Enclosing the unsegmented body is a tough cuticle covered, according to the species, with a variety of tiny furrows, warts, spines and other ornaments.*

Horsehair worms are related to the much more important nematode worms which include eelworms and roundworms, and are easily confused with another kind, the mermithid nematodes which are also parasites of insects but taper at each end. There are about 80 species of horsehair worm of which four are found in Britain. All but one belong to the order Gordioidea, but there is a single marine species ***Nectonema*** *that is parasitic in its young stages in crabs and which is classified separately.*

Gordian knots are marriage knots

Adult horsehair worms live in temperate and tropical regions in all kinds of freshwater; mountain streams, temporary pools, damp earth, marshes, underground waters, even in dogs' drinking bowls. The females are sluggish and move little, the males swim clumsily by undulating the body by contractions of longitudinally-arranged muscles. They have no circular muscles to give ease and grace to their swimming. The adults do not feed, their digestive tract being degenerate and apparently functionless. Usually they have no mouth, but this means little because food is not swallowed at any time during the life history. In the parasitic stage it is absorbed through the general body surfaces.

The entangled 'Gordian knots' contain mating pairs. The male coils the hind part of his body around that of the female and deposits sperm near her cloacal opening. These migrate into a sperm receptacle where they are stored for a few days until the time of egg laying. The eggs are laid in long, gelatinous strings, a fraction of an inch to more than 1 in. long, which swell on contact with water to produce masses often larger than the parent worm. These masses, often attached to stones or weed, may contain several million eggs $\frac{1}{500}$ in. diameter. Like so many parasites, the horsehair worms lay prodigious numbers of eggs to ensure the survival of the species. The males die after mating and the females after laying their eggs.

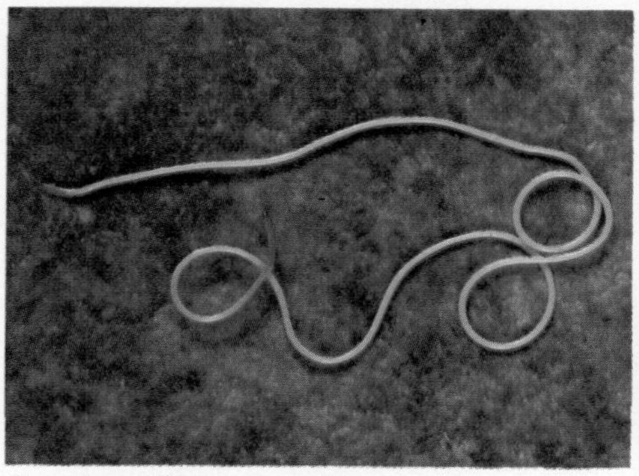

M Tweedie: NHPA

Gordius villoti *— a gordian worm.*

Driving insects to drink

The eggs hatch in 3—11 weeks according to the temperature. The larvae are unlike the adults. Their cylindrical ringed bodies are about $\frac{1}{125}$ in. long and divided into a trunk and, at the front, a shorter muscular region from which they can shoot out a proboscis bearing three circlets of hooks and three long stylets.

Soon after hatching, the larva may encyst on vegetation near the water's edge. Within its cyst, it can survive for several months, even if the water level falls and it dries out. Indeed, exposure by falling water level actually helps infection of the host. The cyst or the free larva may be eaten by an insect or millipede along with the vegetation on which it is lying. The cyst wall then breaks down and the released larva bores through the intestinal wall of the host and into its body. Here the larva gradually digests the surrounding tissues and absorbs them through its surface. Eventually it metamorphoses and develops in a few weeks or months into a long adult, tightly coiled —perhaps with others—in the host's body cavity. If the host insect becomes wetted or falls into water, the mature worm breaks out through the body wall, usually near the anus. Not all adult worms then find themselves in a suitable body of water and so do not live to reproduce. Perhaps the presence of mature gordians in the host insects somehow influences them to seek water.

Harmless to man

The insects normally parasitised by horsehair worms include a wide range of beetles, grasshoppers, crickets and cockroaches, but gordians have also been seen coming out of caddisflies and dragonflies. Different species of horsehair worms probably vary in the range of insects they parasitise. Many larvae are eaten by abnormal hosts such as the larvae of mayflies and stoneflies, but in these they either die or re-encyst in the tissues. In the latter case, the worms may still grow to maturity provided the abnormal host is eaten by a more suitable carnivorous or omnivorous insect. For example, the giant water beetle *Dytiscus* has been known to become infected by eating tadpoles. On rare occasions the larvae turn up in odd places, in a fluke, the intestinal wall of a fish and the faeces of a child who had perhaps swallowed it in ill-chosen drinking water. Sometimes the presence of horsehair worms in water supplies causes great alarm and in some regions there is a belief that cows die soon after swallowing such animals. Horsehair worms are, however, almost entirely harmless to mammals, and the curious case of an adult specimen of *Paragordius* living in the urinary passages of a girl is not only difficult to explain but quite exceptional.

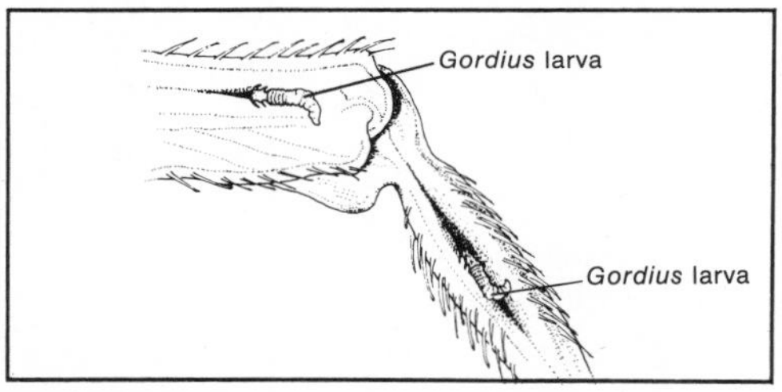

phylum	**Aschelminthes**
class	**Nematomorpha**
order	**Gordioidea**
genera	***Gordius, Paragordius***
order	**Nectonematoidea**
genus	***Nectonema***

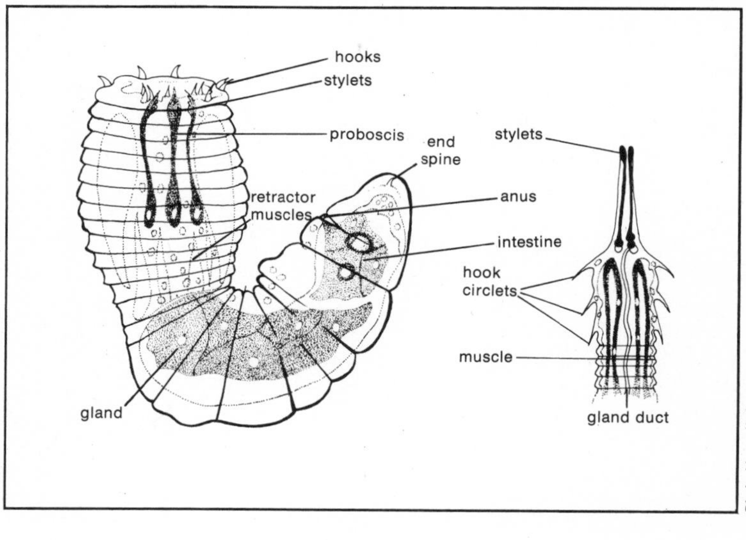

Chris Howell-Jones

Gordius *larvae in the leg of an insect (top left). It is thought that the stylets penetrate the body wall of the host, probably by boring. These hooks and stylets are clearly seen (left) on the extended proboscis of* ***Paragordius,*** *and in the larva (far left). The cylindrical body of the larva is ringed and divided into a trunk and a shorter muscular region from which the proboscis is protruded.*

Horseshoe bat

The horseshoe bats belong to the Microchiroptera but are readily distinguished from others of this suborder by their nose-leaves. This is the name given to the folds of skin on the faces of many bats. In the horseshoe bats the pattern of the nose-leaves includes one part shaped like a horseshoe. This covers the upper lip and surrounds the nostrils. Above it is a narrow pointed flap of skin, known as the lancet. Horseshoe bats differ markedly from other bats in many features of their behaviour, and especially in the way they use echolocation.

Their ears are large and are without an earlet (tragus). Their eyes are small and their field of vision obstructed by the large nose-leaf, so sight probably plays little part in their lives. The females, which are slightly smaller than the males, have two dummy teats on the abdomen as well as the functional teats on the chest, the dummy teats being used by the baby to hang on to the mother when being carried in flight.

There are 50 species of horseshoe bats in temperate and tropical regions of the Old World, all similar in appearance and behaviour. The two European species are typical of the rest.

The greater horseshoe bat has a $2\frac{3}{4}$in. head and body with a $1\frac{1}{4}$in. tail and a wingspan of up to 15 in. The weight varies throughout the year, being heaviest in December when the male weighs up to $\frac{3}{4}$ oz and the female weighs $\frac{1}{5}$ oz. The ears are large, $\frac{1}{2}$ in. long ending in a sharp tip. The fur is thick and woolly and ash-grey on the back and covers both surfaces of the wing membrane for a short way. The fur of the underside has a yellowish or pinkish tinge.

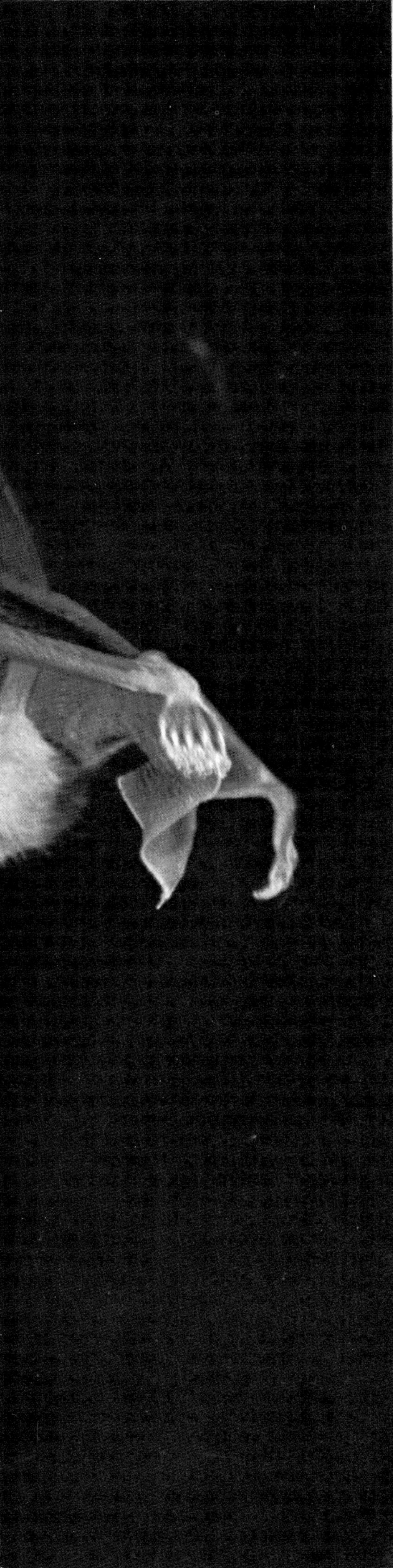

SC Bisserot

SC Bisserot

Late risers

The horseshoe bat comes out from its roost rather late in the evening; it returns to roost and flies out again several times during the night. It flies low on the wing, sometimes only a few inches off the ground and at most 10 ft high. Its flight is heavy and butterfly-like, with frequent glides. By day, in summer, it sleeps in caves, tunnels, dark buildings, lofts and roof spaces, sometimes in hollow trees, usually in colonies but occasionally singly. Males and females occupy separate roosts.

Hibernation

Hibernation, which lasts from October to the end of March, is usually in caves and tunnels. It may sometimes begin in September or be continued until May or June, depending on the weather. It is not as continuous as was formerly supposed. There is much movement in the caves, the bats moving about and some flying from one cave to another as much as 40 miles apart. Movement is influenced by temperature. Normally horseshoe bats sleep singly, in clusters of half-dozens or in larger clusters, typically hanging by the toes of the hindfeet from the ceiling of the cave and with the wings wrapped around the body like a cloak. Should the temperature drop they may cluster more for warmth, each bat holding its wing out to absorb extra heat. They will also move to another part of the cave when the temperature drops below 6°C/42°F, seeking spots where it is up to 8°C/46°F.

Even in a cave hibernating horseshoe bats sense when the temperature outside rises to 10°C/50°F. They will then come out to feed on dung beetles which seem to be active during winter, returning if the temperature falls. Further proof that the hibernation is intermittent is seen in the accumulations of bat guano on the floor of the caves during each winter and the fact that the bats themselves gain weight. The females lose weight rapidly until February then gain weight. The males remain steady until mid-December, when their weight drops sharply but increases in the last month of hibernation.

Feeding on the ground

Horseshoe bats feed more especially on beetles and moths. They have been seen to settle on the ground or on stems of grass to take ground-living beetles. They also eat spiders. Small insects taken on the wing are devoured straight away, the larger ones are carried to a resting place to be eaten there. The bats cannot walk on a flat surface and to alight they turn a somersault in the air to land by the feet, head downwards.

Hanging up the baby

Mating is promiscuous, between October and mid-December but the sperms lie quiescent in the female's reproductive tract until the spring. Then, after a gestation of 6 weeks, the young are born in June and July. The single baby is hairless and blind, and its wings are pale coloured. At first the mother takes her baby with her when hunting. It clings to her fur with its claws and holds one of the false nipples in its mouth. Later she hangs it up in the roost when she goes out foraging. Newly born bats have relatively large heads, ears and feet. They also have the instinct to climb upwards, but should one fall to the ground it dies from inhaling the strong ammonia from the guano. Horseshoe bats mature at 3 years, and are known to live at least 17½ years.

Scientists' snap

In 1938 a young graduate at Harvard University, Donald R Griffin, became interested in ultrasonics and in the next few years had unravelled the story of how bats use echolocation to find their way about and to find their prey. Meanwhile war had broken out in Europe and for the next six years Germany was cut off from the rest of the world as regards the exchange of scientific information. During those years Franz Mohres in Germany was discovering the same story as Griffin. Not until the war had ended and exchange of scientific knowledge had been resumed was it possible to know that two men on opposite sides of the Atlantic had been doing the same work.

Griffin's discovery was made on vesper bats which fly with the mouth open emitting squeaks through it in regular short pulses. The echoes from these, bouncing off solid objects, are picked up by the ears giving the bats a sound-picture of their surroundings. Mohres worked on horseshoe bats which fly with the mouth shut, sending out squeaks through the nostrils. They send out 'explosive' pulses at more infrequent intervals and the horseshoe-shaped nose-leaf forms a movable cup by which the pulses can be beamed. This is best illustrated by the way a horseshoe bat, hanging by its feet, can twist itself on its hips through almost a complete circle scanning the air around, often darting off suddenly to seize an insect that flies within range.

class	**Mammalia**
order	**Chiroptera**
suborder	**Microchiroptera**
family	**Rhinolophidae**
genus & species	***Rhinolophus ferrumequinum*** *greater horseshoe bat* ***R. hipposideros*** *lesser horseshoe bat* *others*

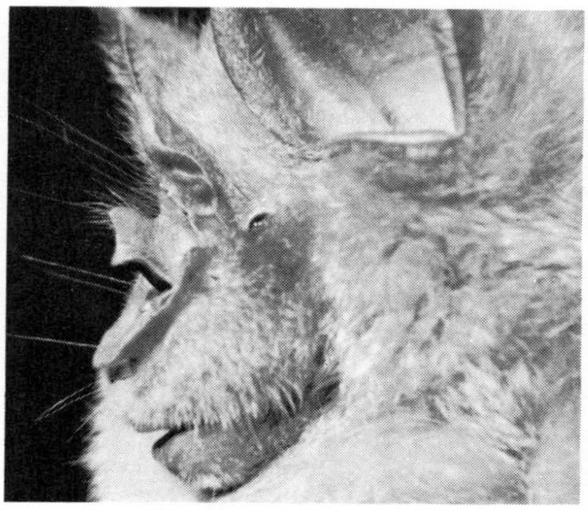

J Hooper

The greater horseshoe bat (left and previous pages) and also the lesser horseshoe bat are easily recognisable by their characteristic nose-leaves. These expansions of the skin consist of a lower part shaped like a horseshoe surrounding the upper lip and nostrils, and an upper part, the lancet, a narrow pointed flap of skin. It is thought the nose-leaves may direct the sounds emitted through the nostrils. These bats roost where they are able to hang freely (below). Unlike most bats that close their wings alongside their bodies the horseshoe bats wrap their wings around their bodies so they are completely enclosed in their flight membranes, looking very much like fruit pods.

SC Bisserot

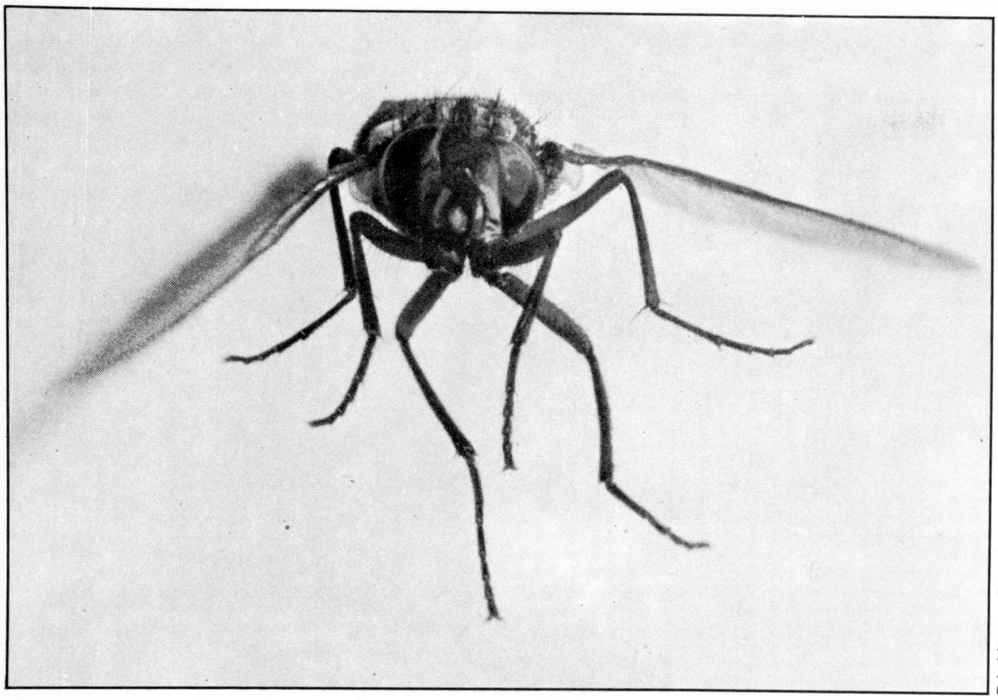

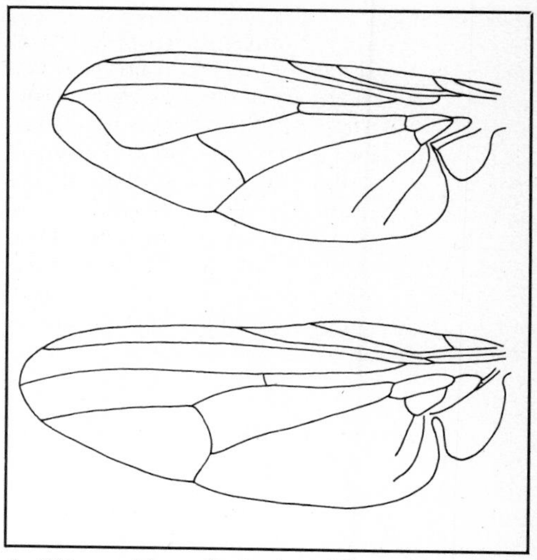

B Leidmann: Bavaria

△ Wings of housefly (top) and lesser housefly (bottom). The differences in venation can be used to distinguish the two types of fly.
◁ Housefly with legs askew just about to land.
▽ Photomicrograph of a leg. The last segment has a pair of claws and two suction pads which help the fly to walk on smooth surfaces (× 60).

Housefly

Many different kinds of flies come into houses. Some are accidental intruders that buzz on the window panes trying to get out into the open air again. Others enter houses in the autumn to hibernate in attics and roof-spaces. But there are two kinds that make our houses their home. One is the housefly, the other is the lesser housefly. The first is stoutly built and in both sexes the abdomen is yellowish or buff. Lesser houseflies are smaller and more slender, the females dull greyish, the males similar but with a pair of semi-transparent yellow patches at the base of the abdomen. The two are also distinguished by a difference in the veins of the wings which can easily be seen with a lens. This difference separates the two species regardless of sex.

Both have a wide distribution, the housefly being found throughout the tropics as well as in almost all inhabited temperate regions.

Kiss-in-the-ring flight

Houseflies pass their adult lives in houses, flying about the rooms and crawling over food that is left exposed. Both species breed in the sort of refuse that accumulates around the dwellings of people who live unhygienically, but their habits differ in detail. Lesser houseflies appear earlier in the season than houseflies, which build up their numbers rather slowly after the winter and are not usually abundant until July. The males of lesser houseflies fly in a very distinctive way. They choose a spot in a room, often beneath a hanging lamp or similar 'landmark', and fly as if they were following the sides of a triangle or quadrilateral, hovering momentarily at the corners and turning sharply at them; a single fly will continue to follow the same course for long periods. If, as often happens, more

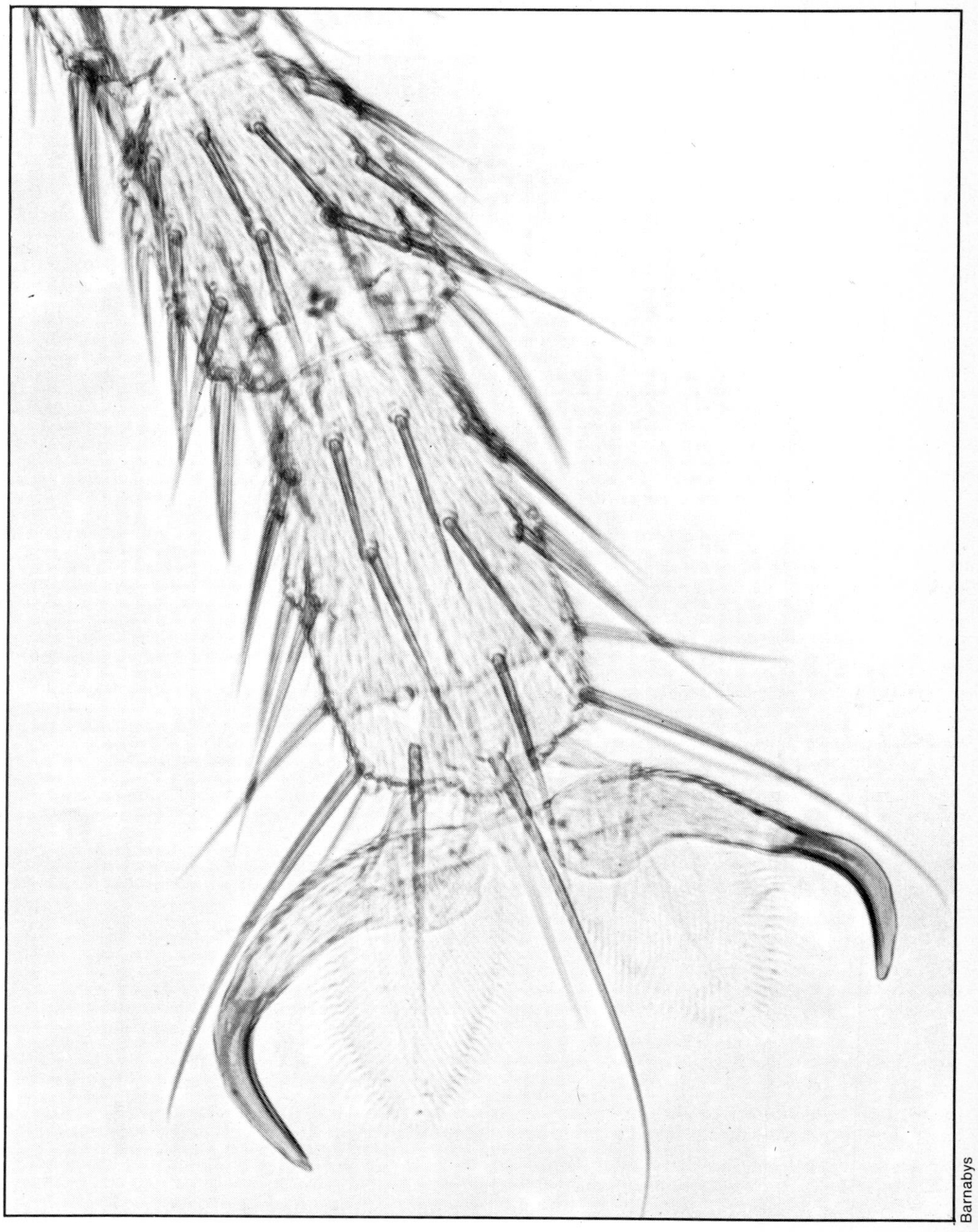

Barnabys

Colin G Butler

A housefly cleans itself by rubbing its first pair of legs together. This common fly spreads disease mainly as a result of its indiscriminate feeding habits. Bacteria may be carried on the legs or body, or in the proboscis and so be exuded onto food with the next flow of saliva.

than one fly is patrolling in the same area, one of them will intercept the other and the two whirl together for an instant and then part again. The expression 'playing kiss-in-the-ring' aptly describes this activity, but they are in fact all males, and always lesser houseflies.

Flies in summer—and winter

The breeding habits of the two species are similar but the larva of the lesser housefly prefers food rich in nitrogenous compounds, such as urine or bird droppings. These flies are nearly always abundant where chickens are kept. The larvae of the housefly are less particular. Manure and compost heaps, the night soil from old-fashioned privies and house refuse of any kind all provide them with breeding-grounds.

The eggs are laid on the larval food, and the adult flies also feed in places of this kind. The eggs are white, about $\frac{1}{25}$ in. long and a female housefly may lay as many as 900 in batches of about 150. They hatch in as little as 8 hours if it is very warm, otherwise in 1–3 days. The white legless maggots feed rapidly and may reach full size in under 2 days, but can live for 8 weeks in colder and less favourable conditions. At 15°C/60°F houseflies will breed continuously throughout the year, taking about 3 weeks from egg to adult, but in the tropics the cycle is completed in a week. The pupa is formed in an oval brown capsule called the puparium, which consists of the last larval skin; instead of being shed at pupation this is retained and plays the same part as the moth cocoon.

The lesser housefly has a similar life cycle, but its larva is very different in appearance, being flattened and beset with rows of short branched tentacle-like processes on the upper surface of the body.

Flies disappear in winter time, and the question where they go is often asked—and it once formed the theme of a popular song. There seems no simple answer to it. Houseflies may hibernate as adults or continue breeding slowly in warm places, especially in buildings where cattle are kept. Probably the fly has different adaptations for wintering in different parts of its range. In warm regions it breeds all the year round.

Sucking up their food

Adults of both species feed by settling on moist organic matter of almost any kind and sucking up nutrient liquid from it. If the material is dry the fly regurgitates a drop of liquid onto it and sucks up the resultant solution. Crude sewage and a bowl of sugar are equally attractive and the insect may fly straight from one to the other. The feeding apparatus consists of a short sucking proboscis expanded at the end into a sponge-like organ with which the fly mops up its liquid food. Flies that have overfilled their stomachs will often regurgitate on any surface on which they happen to be resting, leaving little dirty spots.

People will sometimes assure you that they have been bitten by a housefly. The mistake is excusable because the stable fly *Stomoxys calcitrans* looks almost exactly like a housefly. Its mouthparts are, however, very different, consisting of a stiff piercing organ, and they feed, as horseflies do, by sucking blood. Their bite is quite painful and they can penetrate one's skin through a thick sock. The stable fly breeds in dung mixed with straw and is far less common now than when horses were kept in large numbers.

Bearers of disease

The most important disease-carrying insects are those which feed on our blood, taking micro-organisms from infected people and injecting them into the blood of healthy ones. Examples are the tsetse fly and some mosquitoes. Houseflies do not feed in this way, but by feeding on excrement and exposed foodstuffs they are potential carriers of gastro-intestinal diseases such as dysentery. Houseflies taken from a slum district have been found to carry on average over $3\frac{1}{2}$ million bacteria per fly, and over a million in clean districts. These are not all disease bacteria, but some of them are very likely to be. Infants and small children seem to suffer most from fly-borne disease. In a tropical village infant mortality dropped in one year from 22·7 to 11·5 per cent when flies were controlled by an insecticide.

It is not difficult to kill flies in vast numbers by spraying such substances as DDT and chlordane on the places where they feed and breed but they have a remarkable capacity for developing resistance to specific poisons. No individual fly develops resistance during its lifetime, but some will almost always survive a spraying and these will include individuals having, by an accident of nature, some degree of immunity to the pesticide being used. This immunity is inherited by their offspring, in varying degrees, and the most resistant of these will again survive and breed. Selection of this kind continues with every generation until the insecticide is useless in any concentration at which it is safe to use. The process is exactly the same as the natural selection through which evolution has taken its course. These examples of acquired resistance in insects are in fact examples of very rapid evolutionary change, and they form one of the most compelling arguments against relying too much upon pesticides in our efforts to control harmful insects.

Control of houseflies is best achieved by depriving them of breeding places. The modern civilised way of life has already gone a long way towards doing this. Water-borne sanitation, the use of covered dustbins and the decline of the horse as a means of transport are three obvious factors, but flies will be with us for a long time yet, especially in regions with hot climates. We must still wage war on them by the best means available and try to exclude them from our houses and, above all, keep them away from our food.

class	**Insecta**
order	**Diptera**
family	**Muscidae**
genera & species	***Musca domestica*** *housefly* ***Fannia canicularis*** *lesser housefly*

House mouse

This is probably the most familiar and the most widely distributed rodent. Although often found in woods and fields it lives mainly in or around buildings especially where food is stored—even in large meat refrigerators, in constant darkness and with temperatures below freezing point.

The house mouse has a 3—4in. head and body length and weighs $\frac{1}{4}$—$1\frac{1}{3}$ oz. It has a scale-ringed, sparsely-haired tail about the same length as the body, a pointed muzzle and moderately large ears and eyes. Its fur is brownish grey, slightly paler on the underparts.

It used to be thought that the house mouse, like the common and ship rats, originated in Central Asia. The present view is that its original range probably included the Mediterranean area, both southern Europe and North Africa, and most of the steppe zone of Asia as far east as Japan. Certainly it was known in Europe at the time of Ancient Greece, but it has now spread all over the world, largely through being accidentally carried by man. It is now found wherever there are human habitations, in the Tropics as well as in the Arctic. At first mice were taken from country to country across the seas by ship. Today stowaways go by air as well.

Heather Angel

▷ *A house mouse grooming. This small rodent has a long tail, the same length as its body, that is scale-ringed and sparsely-haired.*
▽ *Making sure all is clear before leaving.*

L Lee Rue III: Photo Res

Swift and silent mover

Mainly but not wholly nocturnal, the house mouse moves quickly and silently. It can also climb well up walls of brick or concrete. When suddenly alarmed, it can leap surprising distances, especially over vertical barriers, and it can squeeze through holes as small as ⅜ in. diameter. Throughout its present range it has become mainly associated with man but not merely in towns. House mice have been found in isolated buildings well away from towns and villages even in the Tropics. They are usually found in buildings in warmer countries but this may be because they are killed off by predators in open country. On islands where predators are virtually non-existent mice have become established in the countryside away from buildings.

Wild origins

According to the experts there were originally four wild subspecies. One of these, the original outdoor form, is small with the tail considerably shorter than the head and body length. The other three which became commensal with man have since given rise to numerous other subspecies. Even these have become thoroughly mixed by interbreeding, with a resulting wide range of colour varieties, dark and light as well as the typical mouse grey. Sometimes these indoor mice will live out of doors but, as a rule, only where there are cultivated crops. There are also the strains of tame and laboratory mice and breeds that are hairless except for the whiskers. One example of how strains of wild house mice can differ is seen in the ease with which mice in country houses can be trapped as compared with the difficulty of trapping those living in London.

The dreaded mousy smell

House mice have territories which they mark with their urine, and this is responsible for the 'mousy smell' from mice kept in captivity. This leads to people cleaning out their cages, but it has been found in animal rooms attached to laboratories that the more the mice cages are cleaned out the more energetically do the occupants mark their cages with urine until the odour from them becomes unbearable. Individuals occupying a territory can be recognized by each other by their odour. Experiments have shown that a 'foreign' mouse introduced into a territory after having been artificially supplied with the odour from those living in the territory is readily accepted by them. Otherwise a 'foreign' mouse wandering into the territory is driven out. The aggressive attitude of the house mouse is to rear up on the hindlegs and hold the forepaws together, with the nose in the air. It looks almost an attitude of prayer, and it can occasionally be seen when a cat is playing with a mouse. The cat drops the mouse, which turns to face the cat as if pleading for mercy. It is, in fact, showing fight—usually with a notable lack of success.

Myopic mice

The senses of smell and hearing are the two most important to house mice. It is commonplace for those writing about small mammals generally, and mice in particular, to speak of their bright beady eyes, implying keen sight. In fact, mice are myopic. It is doubtful whether in daylight they see much beyond a range of 2 in., although how their eyes serve them at night has not been fully studied.

Dominant males

The social structure of the mouse colony is loose until the population builds up to overcrowding. Then a social hierarchy is formed with one male dominant over the rest, and he alone mates with the females. It provides a natural brake to further overcrowding. Nevertheless there are frequent instances, notably in California and Australia, of mouse plagues, when the ground is alive with them in their tens of thousands in quite small areas.

Surviving on flour

House mice are basically seed and grain eaters but they readily adapt to a wide variety of other foods. Those living permanently in the meat cold stores eat meat only. They are larger and heavier than usual, have longer coats and make their nests in the carcases. During the Second World War 'buffer depots' of flour were set up in Britain. Mice invading these were able to live on flour alone and with very little water. House mice that have lived on household wastes and in larders seem unable to revert to natural foods, as shown by the St Kilda mice, which soon died out when the human inhabitants left the island in 1930.

Five litters a year

The success of the house mouse owes as much to its breeding rate as to its adaptability in feeding and finding shelter in buildings. They breed through most of the year. In houses they average just over five litters a year with an average of five to a litter. In cold stores the averages are six litters a year and six to a litter. In grain stores they average 8–10 litters a year. Gestation is 19–20 days, and the young are born blind and naked. They are weaned at 18 days and at the age of 6 weeks begin to breed. The life-span is up to 3 years, although house mice have been kept in captivity for 6 years.

Driven out of home

Mice living outdoors have many enemies. They include the obvious examples of birds and beasts of prey such as hawks and owls, weasels, stoats, foxes and cats, and also the occasional omnivores, such as crows and rats, all of which normally take small animals. Where mice abound, snakes often make them their staple diet. There is a rooted belief in some quarters that rats and mice cannot live together, that if you have mice in a house there will be no rats. It is more likely that when rats take up residence they kill off the mice. Where close studies have been made it has been found that the house mouse cannot compete successfully even with the long-tailed fieldmouse which, although about the same size, is the more active. It is even suggested that the long-tail drives out or kills the house mouse. This can only happen in the wild because the long-tail rarely enters buildings, so there are no encounters.

The dancing mice

One of the famous breeds of house mouse is the waltzing mouse of Japan, a freak breed which runs around in circles. There are also singing mice. These can be heard at a distance of 20 yd literally singing like a bird. This is because they have a diseased larynx or diseased lungs. Another seemingly artistic mouse was the one recorded by the Rev JG Woods, a famous naturalist of the mid-19th century. In his *Natural History* dated 1852 he made the statement that the house mouse 'is said to be greatly susceptible of music'. To support this he told of 'a gentleman who was playing a violin seeing a mouse run along the floor and jump about as if distracted. He continued the strain, and after some time the mouse, apparently exhausted with its exertions, dropped dead on the floor'.

One recent discovery is that house mice and many other small rodents, use ultrasonics. Some of their squeaks can be heard by the human ear but others are too high-pitched. A baby mouse will call in ultrasonics, for example, when its mother sits heavily on it. A mouse's ears are sensitive to high-pitched sounds, which we cannot hear. If you rub your finger round and round over the glass of a cage in which a mouse is confined you see the mouse's ears moving in time with your finger. Then, as the operation goes on, the mouse begins to get restless and in the end it is running and bounding as if in a frenzy (or as if it were dancing to music). The rattling of a bunch of keys near a mouse may have the same effect. There has been a great deal of research on this as a result of which we speak of mice suffering from audiogenic seizures. Not all house mice are affected by this, but in others the audiogenic seizure may be fatal. This, beyond doubt, is the explanation of the story told by the Rev JG Woods, and it is of interest his story, frowned upon for a century, should have received support from modern research.

class	**Mammalia**
order	**Rodentia**
family	**Muridae**
genus & species	***Mus musculus***

▷ *A pretty pair of house mice sitting peacefully at home in a barn. There are commensal and wild forms of this common mouse, the scourge of many housewives. Both have brownish grey fur that is slightly lighter on the underparts, large ears and eyes and a pointed muzzle. Although the eyes look bright and keen these mice are in fact short-sighted and rely on their senses of smell and hearing. The commensal forms often move out from buildings in the spring and summer and return in the autumn for shelter. They will feed on any human food that is available damaging much more than they eat and seeming to survive on very little, hence the saying 'poor as a church mouse'. The wild forms eat mainly vegetables, such as seeds, roots, leaves and stems. These small mammals, pests in the house, are of great importance in research. The albino strains in particular are used in laboratory work.*

Jane Burton: Photo Res

A house shrew surrounded by its meal of kitchen refuse. This shrew originally lived in the forests of India but has taken to living in houses and has been accidentally introduced to other countries.

House shrew

The house shrew, or musk rat as it is sometimes called, is one of about 20 species, belonging to a genus that contains some of the largest shrews and one of the smallest mammals, the dwarf shrew or Savi's pygmy shrew ***Suncus etruscus*** *of the Mediterranean, Africa and Malaya. Savi's pygmy shrew has a 1½in. head and body length with a tail 1 in. long. The house shrew is large, with a head and body length of up to 5½ in. It has a long, pointed snout with long whiskers and minute eyes. Its ears are fairly prominent and the tail has longer fur than is usual in shrews and looks very stout. The coat is black to dark brown.*

Spread by man

The house shrew originally lived in the forests of India but, like rats and mice, it has learned to depend on man and has been introduced accidentally to new places, living in and around houses. It has been taken to East Africa and Madagascar in the west and to many islands including New Guinea, Guam and Japan in the east. House shrews reached Guam after the Second World War and have reached Australia in ships but have not become established there.

House shrews are nocturnal, spending the day in burrows or inside houses and warehouses. They emerge at dusk and forage for their natural food of insects and other small animals and their acquired diet of human food and refuse. As they run about they chatter continuously, sounding like coins being jingled together; in China they have been given the name of 'money shrew'.

Killing chicks and mice

The success of rats and house mice is mainly due to their liberal diet, for they take advantage of any food made available by man. This also seems to be the reason for the house shrew living with man and becoming spread over a large part of the Old World tropics. As is usual when a wild animal lives with man, it becomes unpopular, and so it is with the house shrew. Although it is beneficial to some extent because it kills insects like cockroaches, it eats meat, bread and other foods and will attack crops like melons, where it digs up the seeds after they have been planted, and also damages stored fruit.

Shrews are renowned for a belligerence out of proportion to their size and the house shrew is no exception. It is disliked by farmers because it kills chicks. The damage it does is probably overestimated and many kills attributed to house shrews are most likely the work of rats. This is because rats kill quickly and silently but the house shrew is not as efficient. It grabs the luckless chick by the leg, works its way up the leg and severs a tendon. The chick is now immobilised and the house shrew can attack its body. Meanwhile the farmer has been alerted by the chick's cheeps and has caught the house shrew red-handed. House shrews also capture house mice, seizing them by the tail and, again, working up to the body and head.

Up to five babies

The house shrew has been studied on Guam where it has been found to breed all the year round. In its native India, it breeds mainly during the monsoon season when food is abundant. Some 2–5 young are born in a nest constructed by both parents, where they stay until they are nearly fully-grown.

Smelly shrews

Apart from stealing food and killing chicks, house shrews are unpopular because of their very strong musky odour which is produced by glands on the sides of the body. It is often said that if a house shrew runs over a bottle of beer or wine the contents are contaminated by the musk. One suggested explanation for this rather incredible story is that the musk clings to the outside of the bottle and is smelt by anyone drinking the contents.

Other shrews also have musk glands but not so well developed as those of the house shrew. The musk does not seem to have a deterrent effect on enemies as shrews are eaten by many predators, and cats will often kill them even if they do not eat them.

The glands are not easy to find as they are hidden by the fur, but can be readily seen on the inside of the pelt if a shrew is skinned. They are especially well developed in males and are variable in females. This suggests a sexual function and it may be that the males leave musky trails behind them which discourage other males from following, so spacing the population. When a female is not in season she also leaves a strong trail, and this discourages any male from following her. When in season she leaves little or no odour which enables the sexes to come together for mating. There would be an obvious economy in such a scheme, but as yet there is no proof that this is so.

A further peculiarity is shared with the white-toothed shrews of Europe. A female with her litter will form what has been called a caravan. The young line up behind the mother. The leading youngster seizes her fur with its teeth and the rest of the litter holds on to the fur of the one in front. Then all run off in step. The musk shrew has been seen to do the same and because of its larger size the caravans it forms are sometimes mistaken for snakes.

class	**Mammalia**
order	**Insectivora**
family	**Soricidae**
genus & species	***Suncus murinus***

Hoverfly

Hoverflies are probably the most skilful of all insect flyers. They can hang suspended in the air then glide rapidly to one side or forwards or backwards, or move up or down to hang suspended once more. They are two-winged flies belonging to the family Syrphidae. Many visit flowers in large numbers to feed on nectar and in America they are also known as flower flies. They are second only to bees in importance as flower pollinators.

Most hoverflies have a superficial resemblance to wasps and bees, being either marked with black and bright colours in contrasting patterns or covered with a coat of short, dense hairs, also variously patterned. In some cases there is such close resemblance between certain species of hoverflies and the wasps and bees living in the same area that there seems no doubt mimicry is involved.

Most of the two-winged flies are unattractive to us, including as they do the mosquitoes and houseflies. Hoverflies are almost all harmless and many are useful as well as being attractive to look at. In Britain the most abundant of them are the little yellow-and-black striped species ***Syrphus balteatus*** *and* ***S. ribesii,*** *and the large bee-like* ***Eristalis tenax.*** *They are mainly seen towards the end of the summer.*

Living helicopters

Hoverflies are most active in sunshine and warm weather. They can be seen in large numbers hovering over flowers with exposed nectaries, and feeding from them. When hovering they sometimes make little rocking movements while accurately maintaining their position. This is a more remarkable feat of controlled flight than it first appears, for the air in which the fly is poised is not motionless. There is almost always some lateral drift or 'wind', as well as eddies caused by rising air currents and the breeze passing around branches and other obstacles. The insect must therefore be constantly making minute adjustments of its wingbeats to avoid being carried up and down or to and fro.

It seems most likely that the hoverfly maintains its position through its sense of sight. Insects' eyes are less efficient than ours at forming images, but much more efficient at detecting small movements. The slightest shift in the fly's position is thus instantly perceived and as quickly corrected, so it remains motionless in relation not to the air around it but to the solid objects within its field of vision. Occasionally it is

Syrphus *feeding. Adult hoverflies live entirely on nectar and honeydew which they suck up through their proboscis with its sponge-like tip. This makes them important as flower pollinators, second only to bees, which they also closely resemble with their striking black and yellow markings (10 × lifesize).*

NA Callow: NHPA

slightly displaced and recovery from this is shown in the rocking movements already mentioned.

The eyes of hoverflies are relatively enormous. Other insects with very large eyes, such as the dragonflies and robber flies, need efficient vision to hunt winged prey in the air, but hoverflies feed from flowers and the need for accurate control of their hovering provides the only explanation of their very highly developed sense of sight.

Why do they hover? In a few cases it seems to have some connection with courtship and mating, but in most of them both sexes constantly hover without taking any notice of each other at all. It seems stretching a point to suggest that hoverflies hover because they enjoy doing so, but there is no better explanation at present.

Another curious habit hoverflies have is of continuing to buzz or 'sing' after they have settled and ceased to move their wings. The sound seems to be produced by vibration of the thorax, but why they do this is not known.

Many kinds of larvae

Most hoverflies have a short proboscis that has a sponge-like expanded end with which they mop up sugary liquids. They can feed only on flowers in which the nectaries are exposed, such as those of ivy. Others have a kind of snout which they can push into bell-shaped flowers, and one Oriental genus *Lucastris* has a long proboscis and can feed from tubular flowers. As well as taking nectar, hoverflies also take aphid's honeydew from leaves.

The feeding habits of the adult hoverflies are fairly uniform but those of the larvae are extremely diverse. They may hunt aphids or greenfly, feed on decaying organic matter—often in very foul surroundings, feed on the juices oozing from wounds in trees, burrow into stems or roots of living plants, or feed on the rubbish in the nests of bees, wasps and ants.

The aphid killers include some of the most abundant and familiar hoverflies. Their larvae are slug-like with the body tapering to a kind of neck at the front end. They have no eyes and the head is small and no broader than the neck. They hunt the swarming aphids by touch, crawling among them and swinging the trunk-like neck from side to side. The aphids make no attempt to escape so this method of hunting is very successful. Starting when very tiny with 3–4 aphids a day, a hoverfly larva may be eating 50 or 60 a day when fully grown.

One of the most interesting of the larvae living on decaying matter is that of the drone fly *Eristalis tenax*. The larvae, often called 'rat-tailed maggots', live in the puddles that collect around manure heaps, in water containing little oxygen. At the hind end of its body the rat-tailed maggot has a breathing tube or siphon which is extensible like a telescope. Its length can be adjusted to reach 4 in. to the surface or a small fraction of this when the larva is only just immersed.

Hoverflies that feed on juices from wounded trees do not belong to familiar species and those that burrow into living plants provide exceptions to the rule that hoverflies are harmless. The narcissus fly

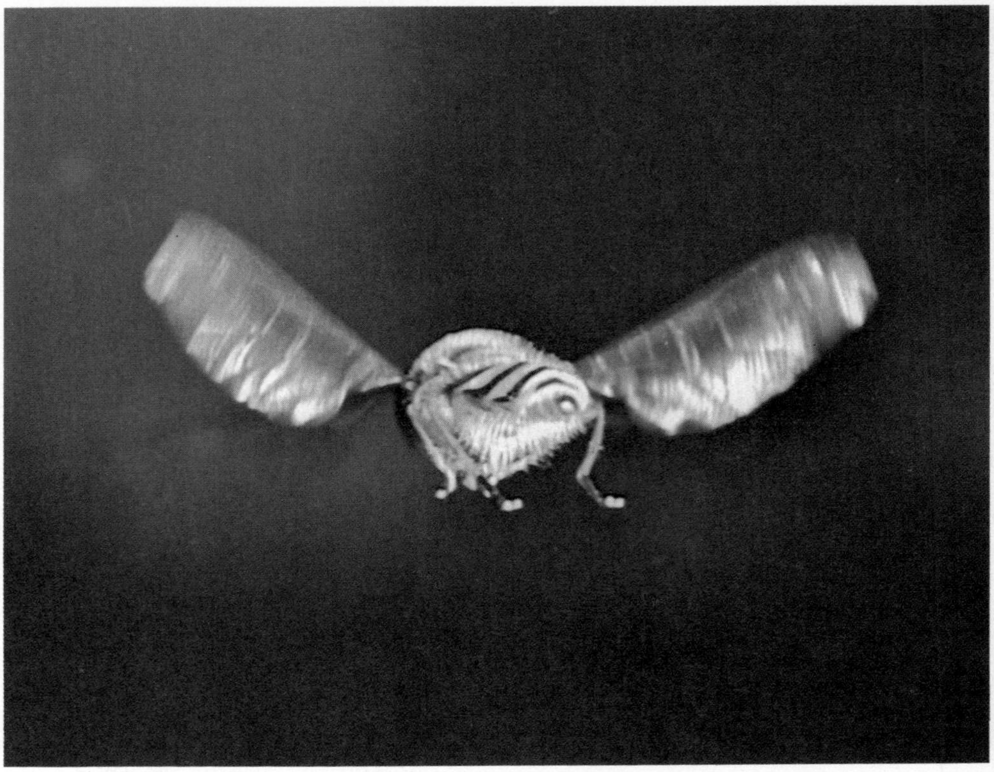

Stephen Dalton: NHPA

Natural History Photographic Agency

△ ***Syrphus luniger*** *hovering (8 × lifesize).*
◁ *Rat-tailed maggot—the larva of* ***Eristalis*** *($1\frac{1}{2}$ × lifesize). The siphon is an extension of the posterior spiracles, an obvious adaptation to life in water or decaying matter. The larva can creep about under water and reach to the air with its extensible breathing tube.*
▽ ***Syrphus*** *larva—an aphid-eater. The larva raises the front end of its body and swings from side to side until it touches and seizes its victim which is literally a sitting target (7 × lifesize).*
▷ ***Volucella zonaria*** *is often mistaken for a hornet because of its yellow-banded abdomen. It breeds in wasp and hornet nests (× 16).*

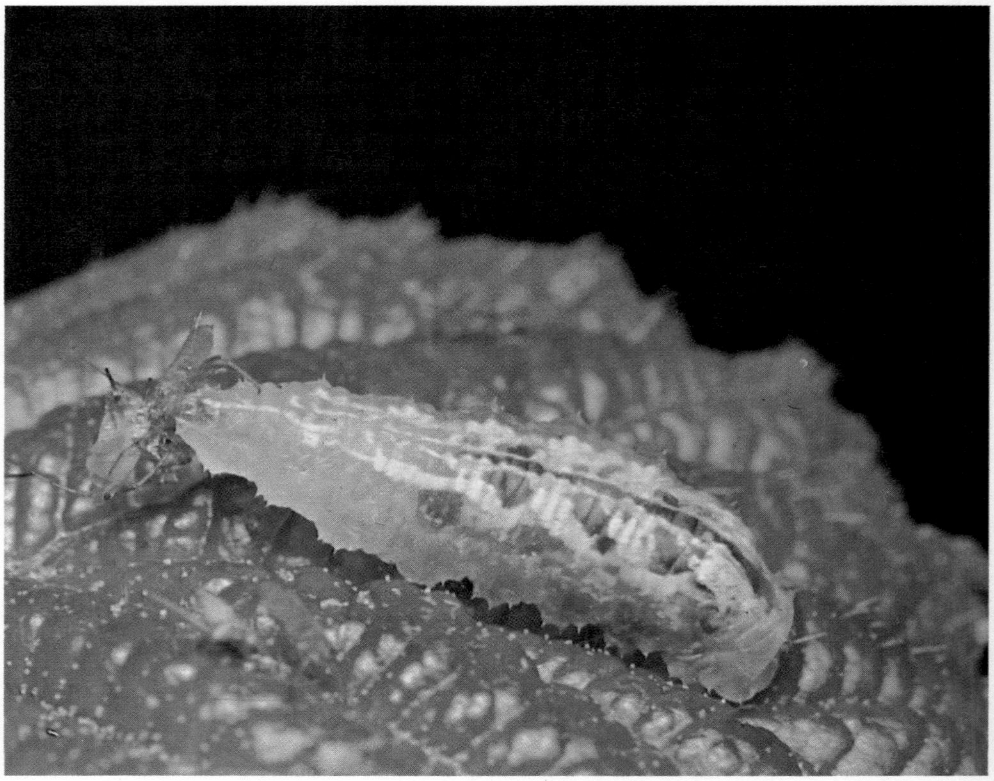

Stephen Dalton: NHPA

F Greenway: NHPA

Merodon equestris spends its larval stage inside bulbs of narcissus and daffodil plants, eating their substance and destroying them. In places where bulbs are cultivated on a large scale they may cause considerable losses. The adult fly is large and hairy and looks like a bumble-bee.

Feeding on bees' litter

The big handsome hoverflies of the genus *Volucella* provide the larvae that feed on rubbish in the nests of bees, wasps and ants. The females enter the nests and lay their eggs, and the larvae from them live in the 'rubbish heap' space beneath the nests where dead bee larvae and adult bees are thrown, living on the bodies and any other edible debris. The exact pattern varies according to the type of nest invaded, but in all cases the egg-laying females and the larvae are accepted by the bees and wasps, which are generally most intolerant of trespassers. In the case of the common species *Volucella bombylans,* which usually lays in the nests of bumble bees, the adult flies closely resemble the bees; furthermore the species occur in two distinct forms, each of which looks like a particular species of bumble-bee. It is tempting to think this helps them get into the nests, but this is far from certain, since they also breed in the nests of wasps which they do not at all resemble.

The Samson legend

The resemblance of hoverflies to wasps and bees led to a queer belief that persisted from the dawn of history right up to the 17th century. We meet it in the writings of the classical Latin and Greek scholars and in the Old Testament, in the story of Samson and the lion, and the riddle, 'out of the strong came forth sweetness'.

People believed that a swarm of honey-bees could be engendered by leaving the carcase of a large animal to rot. An ox was usually recommended, and in the Samson story it was a lion. The truth is that drone flies *Eristalis* breed in a decaying, liquefying carcase, and after a time large numbers of these bee-like flies emerge from it.

Drone flies have only two wings, bees have four; drone flies do not sting, bees do—and not a drop of honey can ever have been obtained from 'bees' conjured up in this way. In those days, however, all learning was in the hands of classical scholars, and their authority prevailed over any kind of evidence. If Aristotle and Ovid said that carcases produce bees, then the insects that appeared had to be bees. Anyone questioning this would risk his reputation and livelihood, possibly his life.

class	**Insecta**
order	**Diptera**
family	**Syrphidae**
genera & species	***Syrphus balteatus*** ***S. ribesii*** ***Eristalis tenax*** ***Merodon equestris*** *others*

Hladik: Jacana

△ *An animal alarm clock set for 5 am. The howler monkey begins his lazy day with a good howl, warning others off his territory.*
▽ *The skull of a male red howler. The thyroid cartilage directs the air to the corniculum which acts as a resonator.*

Howler monkey

These, the largest of the South American monkeys, are named for their loud calls. They have enormously enlarged hyoid bones in the throat which form a bony box or resonating chamber, causing a loud voice. The hyoid is smaller in the female than in the male but is still quite remarkable. This bony box makes the neck thick and heavy and the male has shaggy hair around it, making it look even larger. The whole shape of the skull and throat is modified by the vocal apparatus: the lower jaw is expanded at its angle, the skull is long and low. The colour of the fur is usually black, brown or red, but it differs between the five species. The tail is prehensile, with a naked area on the underside at the tip. The hands and feet are large but like other South American monkeys the thumb cannot be opposed to the fingers, so howler monkeys pick up objects with the second and third fingers. Both sexes reach a total length of nearly 4 ft including the tail, but, partly because of the modified neck region, the male is heavier, 16–20 lb as against 12–18 lb in the female.

The range of howler monkeys extends north into southern Mexico and south into northern Argentina, wherever there are tropical and subtropical forests.

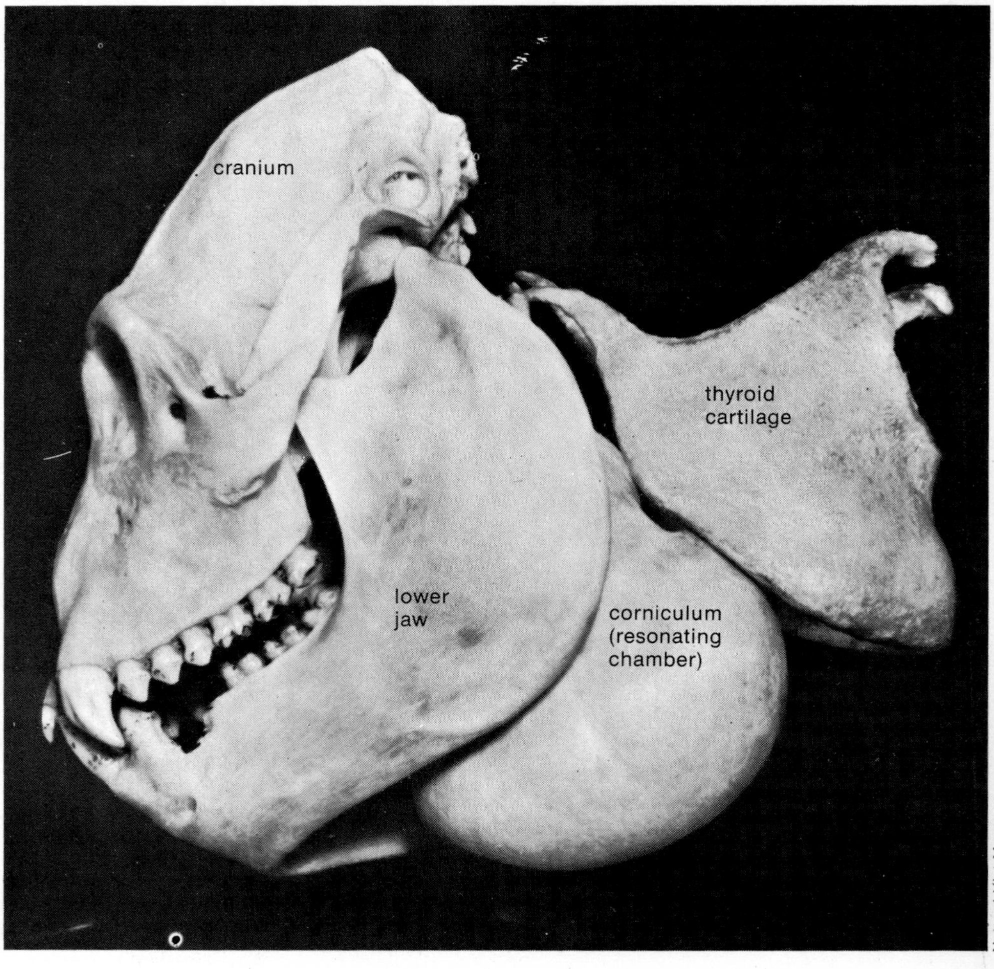

Natural Hist Museum

Howling by numbers

When howler monkeys wake at about 5–6 am, most groups begin the characteristic howl, low and resonant in males and a 'terrier-like bark' in females. One group howling stimulates others to do so, and troops usually howl when they catch sight of each other on the edges of the territory or in the 'no-man's-land' between, warning each other against trespassing. After howling, the group begins to feed and laze around in their sleeping-tree. Then, in the middle of the morning, the animals begin to move out to food trees away from the centre of the territory. They rest up until mid-afternoon when they begin to feed again, and they finally travel around and call again before settling down for the night at 7–8 pm.

The daily round

There may be 2–30 howlers in a troop, averaging about 18, in which are 2–3 times as many females as males. Each troop occupies a territory which varies in size according to the amount of food available, so territories change in size and position over the weeks. The troop occupies some areas of the territory more than others, and has favourite sleeping-trees.

Within the group, the males are dominant over the females, but not aggressively so. There is a fairly well-defined dominance hierarchy or 'peck order' among the males, and a less marked and separate hierarchy among the females. The males act in concert in leading the troop and in howling. When the troop meets a neighbouring troop the monkeys act together, the males roaring, females whining, and the young ceasing to play. On rainy days, howlers are less active, and very little roaring can be heard.

Howlers are slow and deliberate in their movements, except when playing and when excited. They never jump from branch to branch, but form a 'bridge', clinging with their prehensile tails and grasping the neighbouring branch with their hands. Often an adult animal lets a youngster use it in this way as a bridge from branch to branch. When moving through the trees the adult males lead the way in order of rank, and all the troop follow exactly the same pathway through the branches.

Wasting their food

Howler monkeys feed on leaves, buds, flowers and fruit. They also eat nuts—shells and all. They are very fond of wild figs which may be one of the reasons for the competition between groups. Each troop needs to have a territory large enough to contain a sufficient number of fig trees. The fruits are pulled in by hand and eaten directly from the stems, but the females sometimes pick and hold food for the young. Strangely, a great deal of the food—as much as half of it—is dropped uneaten, and no effort is made to retrieve it. The prehensile tail is very useful while feeding, wrapped round a branch for stability.

Breeding the year round

At any one time, approximately one third of the females in the troop have infants, which cling to their mothers' bellies, often with the tail wrapped round the base of the mother's tail. If the infant becomes separated from its mother it makes a little cry of three notes while the mother makes a wail ending with a grunt or groan. When happy the infants purr. The infant is dependent on its mother for about 6 months, when a second baby is born and the first is rapidly displaced. Most of their time is spent playing—swinging, chasing, wrestling and fooling about.

AN Warren

An endearing young male red howler.

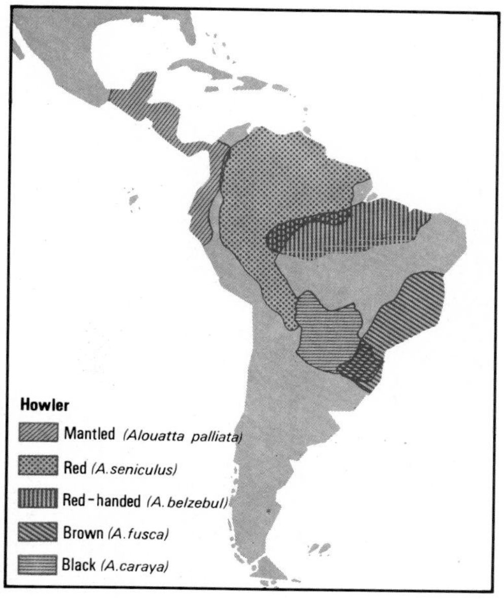

No serious enemies

Ocelots and other small cats occasionally take young howlers but the adults have no serious enemies. The biggest threat is the clearing of forests in such countries as Brazil, but they are not in danger of extinction as yet.

Howler colonies

Howler monkeys have been intensively studied on Barro Colorado island in Gatun Lake, Panama Canal. The island used to be merely a hilltop, but was isolated when the Chagres River was dammed to supply water for the canal. In 1923 it was made a reservation for the Institute for Research in Tropical America and since 1946 it has been administered by the Smithsonian Institute. In 1933 there were 489 howlers in 28 groups on the island, but in 1949–50 the population suffered a severe reduction, probably as a result of an epidemic of yellow fever. A survey in 1951 showed that there were only 237 individuals left, but these were in 30 troops, so it looks as if there had been a redistribution of individuals between the groups, each of which averaged only 8 animals instead of the usual 18. It is reasonable to expect that an epidemic would bear more heavily on some groups than others, even to virtually wiping some out. Significantly, the males were evenly distributed about each troop. This implies that the howler monkey society is very resilient and can be re-grouped and reorganised when conditions demand.

In 1959, the population had increased to well above its original level when there were 814 individuals in 44 groups. How this has come about is not known. The probable explanation is that a superabundance of food following the epidemic had led to a temporary increase of the population but that in time it will come down again. One further point of interest is that the epidemic bore most heavily on the young. After the epidemic, only 13% of the population consisted of juveniles between 2 and 4 years old, instead of the normal 20%.

class	**Mammalia**
order	**Primates**
family	**Cebidae**
genus & species	***Alouatta palliata*** *mantled or Panamanian howler* ***A. seniculus*** *red howler* ***A. fusca*** *brown howler* ***A. belzebul*** *red-handed howler* ***A. caraya*** *black howler*

Hummingbird

There are over 300 species of these minute, beautiful birds living in the New World. The largest is the giant hummingbird, a 8½ in. monster compared with the bee hummingbird of Cuba which is little more than 2 in. long; half this length is bill and tail, the body being the same size as a bumblebee. Hummingbirds are very diverse in form, although all of them are small and have the characteristic rapid wingbeats producing the hum that gives them their name. They have brilliant, often iridescent, plumage which has led to their being given names like 'ruby' and 'topaz'—and also to their being killed in thousands and their skins exported to Europe for use in ornaments. A feature of many hummingbirds is the long narrow bill, often straight but sometimes curved, as in the sicklebill. The sword-billed hummingbird has a straight bill as long as the head, body and tail put together.

Hummingbirds are most common in the forests of South America, but they range from southern Alaska to Tierra del Fuego. Some species are so rare that they are known only from collections of hummingbirds' skin exported to Europe. Loddige's racket-tail was known from a single skin found in 1840 and was not found alive for another 40 years, when it was discovered in a small valley high in the Andes.

Hummingbird stamina . . .

Considering the diversity of habitats and food in the South American forests it is not surprising that there should be so many kinds of hummingbirds living there. It is rather surprising, however, to learn that hummingbirds breed as far north as southeast Alaska, or in the heights of the Andes. The rufous hummingbird breeds in Alaska, migrating to South America for the winter, an incredible journey for so small a bird. The ruby-throated hummingbird also migrates to and from North America, crossing the Gulf of Mexico on each trip. Unlike non-migratory hummingbirds, it stores a layer of fat equal to half its body weight before setting off. At a normal rate of use, however, this would not last through a non-stop crossing of the Gulf. Yet the hummingbirds complete this marathon, so we must presume that they have some method of economising on food reserves.

. . . and speed

Even ignoring the mystery of their migration, the flight of hummingbirds is truly remarkable. Their wings beat so fast they appear as a blur. Small species have wingbeats of 50—80 per second and in courtship displays even higher rates have been recorded. The fast wingbeats enable the hummingbirds to dart to and fro, jerking to a halt to hover steadily. They are also extremely fast in straight flight—speeds of 71 mph have been recorded. Specialised filming has shown that hummingbirds do not take off by leaping into the air like other birds but lift off with rapid wingbeats. The photographs showed that a hummingbird on a thin twig actually pulls the twig up as it rises before letting go.

Flying with such rapid wingbeats requires a large amount of energy, so hummingbirds must either feed constantly or have plentiful reserves. Even at rest their metabolism—the rate at which they produce energy—is 25 times faster than a chicken's. At night when they cannot feed they conserve their food reserves by becoming torpid—going into a form of nightly hibernation. In the Andes a hummingbird's temperature drops from 38°C/100°F to 14°C/57°F, about the temperature of the surrounding air—and their metabolism is reduced six times.

Nectar seekers

Hummingbirds feed on nectar and small soft-bodied animals. To sip nectar they hover in front of flowers and insert their pointed bills down the corolla or, if that is too long, pierce it near the base. The nectar is sucked through a tubular tongue that resembles those of flowerpeckers (p 787). Pollen is often brushed onto the hummingbirds' heads and transferred to other flowers, so pollinating them. To the flowers of the South American jungle, hummingbirds are as important as pollinators as bees are in a clover field. Hummingbirds can readily be attracted to tubes containing sugar-water and they become so tame they will feed at a tube held in the hand.

Small insects are caught on the wing and spiders are taken from their webs. Most hummingbirds are unable to manipulate insects in their bills and have to rush at them so they are forced into the mouth. Some pick insects and spiders from flowers.

Tiny babies

Courtship antics of hummingbirds are difficult to watch as they flit about among dense vegetation too fast for accurate observation. The males fly about in arcs, singing songs that are almost too high-pitched for humans to hear. They are usually promiscuous, mating in the air with several females, but in a few species such as the violet-eared hummingbirds (which have similar plumage for males and females) the male helps rear the family. The nest is a delicate cup of moss, lichen and spiders' webs placed on a twig or amongst foliage. The two eggs are incubated for 2—3 weeks and minute naked chicks hatch out. They are fed by the parent hovering alongside, putting its bill into theirs and pumping out nectar. The chicks grow very rapidly and leave the nest when 3 weeks old.

Hovering skill

When feeding, hummingbirds can be seen hovering steadily and even flying backwards. They can do this because their wings can swivel in all directions from the shoulder. When hovering the body hangs at an angle of about 45 degrees so the wings are beating backwards and forwards instead of up and down. In each complete beat the wing describes a figure of eight. As it moves forwards (the downstroke) the wings are tilted so they force air downwards and the bird upwards. At the end of the stroke they flip over so that the back of the wing is facing downwards and on the upstroke air is again forced downwards. To fly backwards the wings are tilted slightly so air is forced forwards as well, and the hummingbird is driven back.

The flight of a hummingbird can be compared with that of a helicopter with its blades moving in a circle to achieve the same effect of driving air downwards as the hummingbird's wings do by moving back and forth. In the flight of most birds the power is in the downstroke, the upstroke being merely a recovery phase, but in hummingbirds both strokes are powerful. The breast muscles of a hummingbird weigh a third of its total weight and the muscles drawing the wings upward are half as powerful as those driving the wings down. Non-hovering species have comparatively much smaller muscles for the upstroke.

class	**Aves**
order	**Apodiformes**
family	**Trochilidae**
genera & species	***Archilochus colubris*** *ruby-throated hummingbird* ***Ensifera ensifera*** *sword-billed hummingbird* ***Eutoxeres aquila*** *sickle-billed hummingbird* ***Loddigesia mirabilis*** *Loddige's racket-tail* ***Mellisuga helenae*** *bee hummingbird* ***Patagona gigas*** *giant hummingbird* ***Selasphorus rufus*** *rufous hummingbird, others*

▷ *White-tailed hummingbird feeding.*

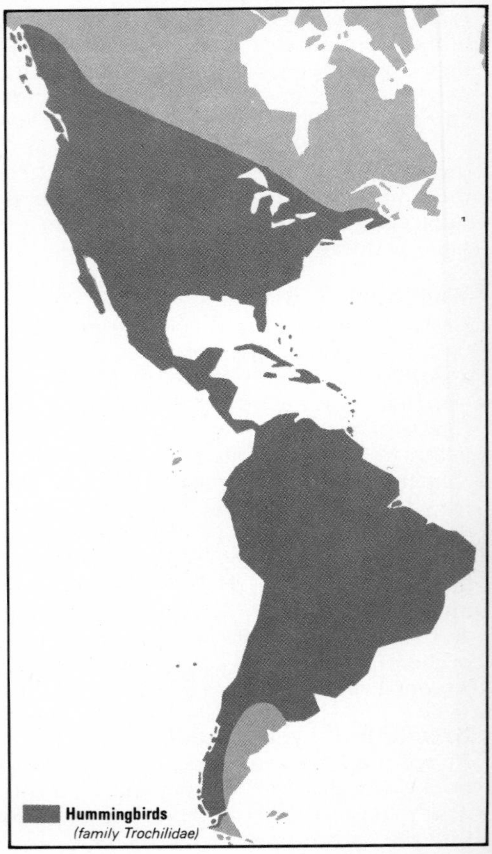

Stones and metals polished by art are not comparable with this gem of nature

The form of individual species of hummingbird is very varied. This male black-throated train-bearer ***Lesbia victoriae,*** *from Ecuador, has long ornamental feathers that do not appear to hinder its aerial acrobatics. Its body is only 2 in. long but the tail is 6 in. with widely forked feathers which help make a marvellous picture when it turns sharply doing its fast manoeuvres in the air. The iridescent throat is absent in the female.*

Top: Banana-boat feeder. A male velvet-purple coronet ***Boissonneaua jardini*** *greedily sips nectar from* ***Heliconia jaquinii,*** *a relative of the bananas. Centre: The white-lipped sicklebill is perfectly adapted for sucking nectar from flowers. Bottom: The tiny ruby-topaz hummingbird* ***Chrysolampis mosquitus,*** *a beautiful Brazilian species, vibrates its wings at about 100 beats per second, fast even for the hummingbirds.*

Photos by Walter Scheithauer

Top: The best helicopter [illegible] in action. There is no other bird which can fly so competently when stationary. Although falcons and sunbirds can hover, only the hummingbirds can hold the body quite still in the air. Species: Blue-throated sylph ***Aglaicercus kingi.*** *Bottom: The sword-billed hummingbird* ***Ensifera ensifera*** *has an extreme 'pipeline' for flowers with a long tube. The bill measures $4\frac{3}{4}$ in., the body, 3 in.*

Skilled construction engineer when it comes to nest design, a ruby-throated hummingbird ***Archilochus colubris*** *feeds its hungry young. The nest is an exquisite cup, less than 2 in. across, made of felted plant, fern or dandelion seed down covered with moss and lichens and fastened with spider webs as to appear a mere protuberance on the twig and lined with a layer of the finest down.*

G Rüppell

R Austing

Humpback whale

The humpback whale belongs to the same family as the better-known whalebone whales but has a number of distinct features that place it in a genus on its own. Its name probably comes from its appearance as it dives, when it arches its back just before disappearing below the surface. Its most characteristic feature is an extremely long set of flippers. Far longer in proportion than in any other whale, they may be as much as one-third of the total body length. The body, far from being streamlined, is barrel-shaped and ugly. Humpbacks migrate a great deal and tend to hug the coastlines as they pass the tropics to waters of high latitudes. Keeping close to the coasts in this way has made their migrations well known but has also made the whales an easy prey for hunters. Humpbacks grow to 40–50 ft in length, the females being slightly longer. The colour is normally black above and white below, but there are a number of variations on this. The back is fairly constantly all black or a very dark slaty grey, but the amount of white on the underside varies very considerably from almost totally white to nearly all black. Some scientists have tried to divide humpbacks into races on the basis of their colour. This has been found unreliable, although it is probable there is some sort of division, as whalers have noticed that they tend to catch all-dark whales and then all-light whales, as they work through various schools passing along the coast.

The long flippers are usually dark on the upper or outer surface and white on the lower or inner surfaces, and in the same way the tail flukes are dark above and pale below. One female caught off the Shetlands was totally black except for her white flippers. The flippers also have a distinctive outline. The lower margins are scalloped and they have a number of irregular humps or tubercles along this edge. These tubercles also occur on the upper part of the head and along the jaw line, and each usually has one or two short coarse hairs growing from it.

On the underside are a number of grooves running as far back as the navel. These number 2–36 compared with an average of 85–90 in the fin and blue whales. Each is separated from its neighbour by as much as 8 in. and sometimes the concave part of the groove contrasts with the body colour around it. The short dorsal fin is set rather far back and is almost triangular in outline. It does not have the concave rear edge as in most of the rorquals. There may be as many as 400 baleen plates on each side of the mouth but the average is around 300. They are up to 2 ft in length and greyish black in colour. Sometimes there are a few white baleen plates. When present these are usually at the

front of the mouth and they are often associated with blotchy white markings on the skin in about the same position as the plates themselves.

Cold-warm migrations

Humpbacks are found in all oceans but are typically whales of the coasts, often coming close inshore even into small bays and estuaries. In spite of this they are very rarely found stranded. In this they contrast sharply with false killers (p 735). They migrate every summer to polar waters to feed and back to tropical waters in winter when the young are born and mating takes place. Although there are separate populations in both Arctic and Antarctic waters, by moving towards the Equator in the winter months there is possibly some interchange between the two.

The humpbacks sometimes seen off the British coasts spend the summer with their calves to the north and east of Norway, feeding. In February and March they move westwards and then south as far as the west coast of North Africa where another generation of calves is born and, in April and May, further mating takes place. After this the whales move north again, passing the Outer Hebrides and the Faeroes and finally reaching northern Norway about July or August. Whalers from the Hebrides and Shetland about 60 years ago used to take some humpbacks, but they are seldom seen now, and none has been stranded on British coasts for a very long time. In 1866 one humpback was seen in the Firth of Tay almost daily for a period of about 6 weeks. Eventually it was harpooned and subsequently Sir John Struthers made a detailed description of its anatomy.

The migrations of the southern stocks of humpbacks have been studied in considerable detail, and these follow the same pattern as those in northern waters. The whales spend the summer in the Antarctic feeding on the abundant krill. As the winter approaches they move gradually northwards. The first to go north are the females that have just finished suckling their calves, which go with them. Next are the immature animals, then the mature males and finally the pregnant females. They all go as far as the warm equatorial waters, where the pregnant females give birth and then mate once more. In the return migration the pregnant females go first, followed by immature animals, then the mature males, and finally the adult females with their newly-born calves. By the time they reach the Antarctic feeding grounds the herds have all mixed together and they stay this way until it is time to travel north again.

Time Life Inc.

Krill is the main food

The food of the humpback consists of krill but they do sometimes take small fish and there is one record of a humpback with six cormorants in its stomach and a seventh in its throat. These were probably taken in accidentally when the whale was feeding on the same shoal of krill as the cormorants. Sometimes cod are found in their stomachs. When the humpbacks are in tropical waters they feed very little. Most of the feeding is done in colder waters and the blubber reserves are built up to last through the rest of the year.

Amorous leviathans

Humpbacks are well known for their amorous antics. They will roll over and over in the water, slapping the surface or each other with their long flippers. This causes considerable commotion in the water, and the noise is said to be audible several miles away. Sometimes they leap completely clear of the water in their play, although it has been suggested that this is done to rid themselves of encrusting barnacles.

Killed on the coast

As is the case with many whale species their greatest enemy is man. Killer whales take their usual toll, but the humpback with its coast hugging habits and fixed migratory routes has been an easy prey for man and when a whale fishery has started it is usually the humpback that is killed first.

Barnacle trouble

Humpback whales are usually heavily infested with barnacles and whale lice, one of the barnacles *Coronula* being typically found in association with the tubercles on head and flippers and this barnacle sometimes has a stalked barnacle growing on it. It was long ago noted that humpbacks passing the South African coast on their way north were heavily barnacled, but those returning from tropical waters were only lightly infested. It was believed that when the whales got to where the Congo river emptied into the sea they moved inshore into much less salty water where the barnacles died and dropped off. The story goes that some of the old sailing ship masters would lie in those waters to rid their vessels of barnacles.

class	**Mammalia**
order	**Cetacea**
family	**Balaenidae**
genus & species	***Megaptera nodosa***

Injecting the poison: a sandwasp ***Ammophila*** *paralyses a huge noctuid moth caterpillar which will be dragged to its burrow and put with other immobilised victims to feed the wasp's larva (about 4 × lifesize).*

Hunting wasp

Wasps can be divided by their habits into social and solitary types. The former are the familiar wasps and 'hornets' which live in colonies or communal nests, may sting severely and often appear very numerous. They are, however, only numerous in terms of individuals; a far greater number of species of wasps are not social insects, but types in which each individual leads an independent life. The hunting wasp is one of these.

Solitary wasps are all, apart from a few exceptions, hunters: the females hunt other insects, spiders and the like and store them in burrows or hollow mud cells, not as food for themselves but as a provision for their larvae. The exceptions are the solitary wasps which have a parasitic or 'cuckoo' mode of breeding, laying their eggs in the burrows of other solitary wasps, or solitary bees. Their larvae then grow by feeding on the store provided by the rightful owner, or by killing and devouring the larvae for which this store was intended. A hunting wasp, then, is a solitary wasp which has not adopted a parasitic mode of life.

Hidden larders

Female hunting wasps spend most of their time providing food and shelter for offspring which, in the great majority of cases, they will never see. These activities follow a fairly uniform pattern.

After mating the female digs a burrow in earth or rotten wood, or seeks out a hollow plant stem, or constructs a receptacle of mud, plastered on while wet and allowed to dry. She then hunts for living insects of some kind, such as caterpillars. When one of these is found it is stung, but the effect of the injected poison is only to paralyse, not to kill it. The caterpillar is then carried to the burrow and put inside, and other caterpillars are sought out, stung and added to the first. When sufficient have been brought to stock one burrow the wasp lays an egg, usually on the wall above the immobilised victims, seals up the burrow and goes on to build and stock similar burrows. After a short time the egg hatches and the hunting wasp larva feeds on the store of living food, sucking the juices of the caterpillars in such a way that they remain alive until almost completely consumed. The residue of skin quickly shrivels and dries and the wasp larva goes on to its next victim. By the time the store of food has been eaten, the larva is ready to turn into a pupa.

Perfect meat store

The provision that the mother wasp makes for her offspring is quite elaborate. She constructs a shelter to protect it from enemies and from extreme temperatures, and she provides a store of food which is kept not merely fresh but alive. There is therefore no danger of the uneaten part of the store putrefying during the development of the wasp larva. On the other hand the tiny,

The potter's larder revealed: the potter wasp ***Eumenes*** *builds a beautifully designed little clay pot and often fastens it, quite high, on plants. Paralysed caterpillars are brought and sealed up after a single egg has been laid which hatches into a larva (above) which devours the caterpillars.*

A pupa awaits adulthood: a fully developed potter wasp pupa is ready for the final change, having eaten all the stored paralysed caterpillars during its development. Below: The adult or imago emerges. Unlike its larva, the adult wasp lives mostly on nectar and sap (about 7 × lifesize).

Series by GS Giacomelli

A mud-dauber wasp ***Sceliphron*** *pushing prey into its nest built from mud as its name suggests. This skilful architect is also noted for its long hind legs and the extremely long 'waist' or stalk of its abdomen (about 6 × lifesize).*

delicate larva cannot be injured by the protesting struggles of its victims, for they are paralysed. (We can only hope they are anaesthetised as well!) Also the wasp provides just enough food for the larva's development, but no excess. If any caterpillars remained after the larva's pupation they would die and putrefy, creating conditions likely to kill the pupa.

Classified by habits

The hunting wasps can be subdivided into two groups, again by reference to their habits: by the prey they hunt and by the sort of nest they make. Hunting wasps do not take their prey indiscriminately; each kind confines itself to a particular type of victim. Also each kind of wasp makes a particular type of nest, and both these features of behaviour are related to the natural classification of the wasps, which is based on careful study of their wings, legs and bodily structure.

Thus members of the genus *Ammophila* dig burrows in sandy soil and stock them with caterpillars. The 'bee killer', *Philanthus,* makes a similar type of nest but stocks it with bees, which it attacks and overcomes easily in spite of their stings. *Gorytes,* another burrower, drags young froghoppers out of their concealing mass of 'cuckoo spit'. The mainly tropical mud dauber wasps *Sceliphron* and allied genera make nests of mud plastered onto any suitable surface, including walls of houses—sometimes, inconveniently, inside the house. They stock their nests variously, but each species is confined to a particular type of prey.

One British wasp makes a clay nest of remarkable beauty. This is the potter wasp *Eumenes,* whose nests look like tiny round flasks, each with a short neck and flared rim. These are stocked with small caterpillars and can be found on heather on dry sandy heaths, although they are less common than they were as heathland habitats are being destroyed.

Victory against heavy odds

The most spectacular of the hunting wasps are the spider hunters of the family Pompilidae. A few small species are found in Britain, including the black-and-red *Pompilus viaticus,* another heath dweller. It hunts wolf spiders, which might be thought a match for any insect of their own size, but the wasp subdues them and stings them into immobility without any trouble. Some of the tropical pompilids are among the biggest of all wasps and they hunt the huge Mygalid spiders or 'tarantulas'. These formidable creatures, which can kill a mouse with ease, live in burrows, and the wasp will sometimes enter the burrow, where she might be thought to be at a terrible disadvantage. When they fight in the open the two may spar around or they may close and tumble like wrestlers. The wasp's only weapon is her sting, which is pitted against eight clutching legs and a pair of powerful poison fangs—the slender sword of St George against the claws and teeth of the dragon! Almost invariably, however, the wasp is the victor, and manages to slip her sting into the under-surface of the spider, where its nerve centres lie. It has been recorded that some spider hunters deliver the first sting into the spider's head to immobilise its jaws, and then close in to finish the battle.

When large prey of this kind is chosen the wasp has considerable difficulty in carrying it, in fact she may only be able to drag it along the ground. In such cases the usual procedure is for the wasp to find her victim, sting it, and then look for a convenient place nearby to make a burrow. When this is ready the victim is dragged to it, pushed in and an egg is laid. One victim suffices for the larva in these cases!

Wasp watchers

Many people amuse themselves by watching birds, sometimes making valuable observations. But hunting wasps are most rewarding creatures to watch as well. Here are some interesting observations that have been made of them.

The species *Ammophila pubescens,* which lives in sandy places in Europe, departs from the general pattern described here in that the female continues to bring caterpillars to the burrow after the larva has hatched, thus revisiting the nest a number of times during its development. Prof Niko Tinbergen found that an individual of this species may be keeping as many as three different nests going at the same time, all in different stages. In one the egg may not have hatched, in another the larva may need a replenishment of food and a third may be ready for final closure, the larva being ready to pupate. The female wasp has a mental capacity sufficient to enable her to memorise the needs of all three nests at the same time.

Whenever she leaves a burrow she closes it with a plug of earth or sand, making its position practically invisible; yet when she returns to visit it she flies straight to the hidden entrance. The same observer demonstrated ingeniously how she does this. He found a burrow at an early stage and put around it a fairly wide circle of pine cones. On her first return the wasp was put off by this addition to the local scenery, but soon discovered her burrow and from then on flew straight to it. After a few days the observer played a trick on her; he moved the circle of cones a little to one side and watched for the wasp's return. She flew, not to the location of her burrow, but to the centre of the conspicuous circle of cones, clearly showing that she was using them as a landmark. The implication of this is that these wasps always mark their nests by imprinting a picture of its surroundings on their memory.

Another observer claims to have seen an allied species of hunting wasp do a most extraordinary thing. He noted that *Ammophila* always closes her nest when she leaves it. This wasp, in finally closing her burrow, is said to have picked up a very small pebble in her jaws and used it as a hammer to tamp down the plug of sand closing the hole. Cases of animals using tools or instruments of any kind are rare, even among the highly developed vertebrates. In a wasp it is something quite remarkable.

phylum	**Arthropoda**
class	**Insecta**
order	**Hymenoptera**
families & genera	**Pompilidae** *spider hunters* **Vespidae** ***Eumenes*** *potter wasps* **Sphecidae** ***Ammophila, Gorytes, Sceliphron, Philanthus***

Hutia

Hutias are rodents related to coypus. Most people outside the islands of Central America have never heard of them—but they have a remarkable history. The coypu is South American and the chances are that the ancestors of hutias were also South American. Indeed, there is a Venezuelan hutia ***Procapromys geayi*** *but only one specimen is known and even this is believed to have been a young individual of the hutia living on the Isle of Pines off Cuba. So this is something of a mystery. Apart from this there were about 20 species, on Cuba, Haiti, Jamaica, Bahamas and other islands lying between North and South America. Of these 20 species most are extinct, having been wiped out during the last few centuries, or had just become extinct when Europeans first reached the New World. The few species still surviving are already becoming rare and are in danger of being wiped out in the fore-seeable future.*

Hutias look very like the hyraxes of Africa and both have the local name of coney. They have the blunt muzzle of the coypu and the coarse coat but in most of them the tail is not so long as in the coypu. The four species of hutias on Cuba and the Isle of Pines are up to 18 in. long with a tail 1 ft long, and they weigh up to 15 lb.

Anthony Maynard

Jamaican hutia ***Geocapromys brownii*** *is rabbit-sized but more stoutly built with short legs and tail. Once common in Jamaica it was an important food for the island's aborigines, but today it is rare.*

No safety in trees

Hutias live in trees, feeding on fruit, leaves, bark, lizards and any other small animals they can find. In the morning especially they bask curled up on leafy branches, looking like clumps of foliage. When in danger they are said to come to the ground seeking safety in holes. The females give birth to 1–3 young after a gestation of 17–18 weeks, the young being born with a reddish-brown fur, which later goes grey; they can run about soon after birth. The hutias of Cuba and the Isle of Pines are hunted with dogs for their flesh. The dogs tree them where they can be caught. They have probably been hunted for a long time as one of the species first became known to scientists from bones found in caves.

Everything against them

The hutias on Jamaica and neighbouring Little Swan Island are slightly smaller than those already mentioned. They live on the broken ground among rugged limestone hills, but even here they are not safe from predators. They are now very rare and the survivors are hunted with dogs. For centuries they have been eaten by the local people and now they are at the mercy of the introduced mongooses as well. They are mainly nocturnal and feed on grass, leaves and fruit, but apart from this little is known about them. Two related species are known, one on Cuba from bones found in caves and one on the Bahamas which became extinct many centuries ago, probably killed off by prehistoric Stone Age hunters.

More extinct than living

There are two species of hutia on Haiti and the Dominican Republic, both very rare, and there are two other species, one known only from bones in kitchen middens—the waste pits of long ago—and the other from bones in caves. They also seem to have been widely used as food for a long time. Two other species on Haiti are known from a few bones only, found in caves, and these must have been extinct when the Spaniards conquered the new Americas. The same can be said of two species on Haiti, the Dominican Republic, Puerto Rico and the Virgin Islands. Their bones are found in middens and in caves and these, like other species, seem to have been preyed upon probably by an extinct giant barn owl as well as being eaten by the local people.

Each island its own species?

Already a picture can be built up of the islands being inhabited by many species of hutias, different species in different areas of the Caribbean, probably all descended from coypu-like ancestors from South America. They were probably very numerous thousands of years ago, with the giant barn owl their only enemy until man arrived. As the hutias grew rare, hunted by primitive man, the giant barn owl probably died out and now the hutias look like dying out, killed first by man for food, and now by imported mongooses as well as introduced rats. And every few years the bones of yet another extinct species of hutia are found, showing that formerly these animals existed in many more species than the score already known.

The West Indies have been the scene of several notable introductions of animals, most of them without thought about the effect. Many of these have disturbed if not destroyed some of the local animals. Examples are the common rat, the mongoose, as well as domestic cats and dogs. There is one, however, worth recalling here, especially as it is harmless. This is the flourishing colony of the greater bird of paradise established on Little Tobago in 1909 by Sir William Ingram (see p 202).

Contrast from Africa

On the other side of the Atlantic, in West Africa, lives the cutting grass or grass-cutter, also known as the cane rat and, to the Africans, as the oya. It is a near relative of the hutias but its story is the reverse of theirs. Up to 2 ft long and 16 lb in weight, the cutting grass looks very like a coypu, swims well and lives near damp ground but it does not burrow although it has been found at times in termites' nests. It lives in family groups and feeds at night especially on young plants, and particularly on grasses. The female may have three litters a year each with up to six babies, in a nest of weeds in a depression in the ground usually concealed in a thicket.

The cutting grass is a pest for which control measures are being sought. Nearly 95% of damage to crops in Sierra Leone, Nigeria and other parts of Africa are due to it. Crops which suffer are maize, rice, young oil palms, sweet potato, cassava and sugar cane, all being attacked when half grown. The Africans used to hunt it for food, beating it into nets but with the industrialization of parts of Africa the local peoples are less inclined to do this. Putting down poison has proved useless as the cutting grass is almost solely attracted by young green plants—not by grain or meal, the most convenient poison bait.

If a ready means could be found of catching the cutting grass—without poisoning it—this would prove a profitable source of animal protein and would preserve the 20–30% of the rice crop at present being eaten by this rodent.

class	**Mammalia**
order	**Rodentia**
family	**Capromyidae**
genera & species	***Capromys pilorides*** *Cuba* ***C. prehensilis*** *Cuba* ***Plagiodontia aedium*** *Haiti* ***P. hylaeum*** *Haiti* ***Thryonomys swinderianus*** *cutting grass*

Hyaena

There are three species of hyaena: the spotted or laughing hyaena of Africa south of the Sahara, the brown hyaena of southern Africa and the striped hyaena which ranges from northern and northeast Africa through Asia Minor to India. They all have massive heads and powerful jaws and teeth with which they can crack even marrow bones. Their ears are large and their shoulders are markedly higher than their hindquarters. Their tails are short and each foot has four toes. The male spotted hyaena may be 5 ft long, head and body, with a 13 in. long tail, and 36 in. high at the shoulders, and can weigh up to 180 lb. The female is slightly smaller. The hyaena's coat is grey to tawny or yellowish-buff with numerous brown spots. There is only a slight mane.

Norman Myers

AJ Sutcliffe

A scavenger's life

The spotted hyaena is a nocturnal animal spending most of the day in a hole in the ground (above) or in a cave or lair in dense vegetation. It is very difficult to tell apart the sexes of this species as both have similar external reproductive organs. A myth has grown up that each hyaena may act as male and female. The gestation period is 110 days after which one or two young are born fully furred. Inside the lair of a spotted hyaena (left) are the spoils of a scavenger. The bones include the lower jaw of a cow and the top of a human skull carried away from a cemetery.

Norman Myers

Okapia

Maxlenz: WWF

The largest and most aggressive of the three species of hyaena is the spotted hyaena and unlike the other two it does not limit its diet to carrion and small prey. But it is cowardly and will not fight if a victim defends itself. It may also feed on the kill of bolder carnivores, forming a pack and rushing on a lion which is enjoying a good meal. The lion is usually driven away in frustration leaving his well-earned meal to the scavengers. When eating carrion such as that of gnu (below left) the hyaena crushes the long bones with its strong teeth and powerful jaws eating all he can of the victim. The sorry remains of a meal are being carried away by a spotted hyaena (below centre) probably to the lair for the offspring.

The three species of hyaena are easily recognised by their coats. That of the brown hyaena (above) is dark brown with greyish neck and lower legs. The coat is exceptionally long and heavy. Both the brown and striped hyaenas (below right) have long haired manes which can be erected. The striped hyaena has a grey to yellowish-brown coat with brown or black stripes. It has strong fore-paws which are well adapted for digging up meat from caches made by other carnivores. The spotted hyaena (right) has a yellowish-grey coat with many brown or black spots. It has no long mane and has shorter ears. Its jaws are probably the most powerful in proportion to size of any living mammal.

Norman Myers

Okapia

RS Virdee

Vultures and a jackal keep a respectful distance while hyaenas take their fill from a zebra carcase.

Spotted hyaena clans

Spotted hyaenas spend most of the day in holes in the ground, in caves or in lairs in dense vegetation. Although typically nocturnal they are sometimes active by day. They live in clans of up to 100 at times, in defined territories marked by their urine and droppings. Members of other clans are driven from the boundaries. They often hunt in packs, can run up to 40 mph and are more aggressive than the other two species. The voice of the spotted hyaena is a howl, made with the head held near the ground, beginning low but becoming louder as the pitch rises. When excited, as during the breeding season, it makes its so-called laugh. The spotted hyaena has also been credited with imitating a man's voice, even with calling men by name—a belief that goes back to the Middle Ages.

Spotted hyaenas eat carrion, crushing the long bones of large animals such as buffalo. They also kill sheep, goats, calves, young antelopes and even smaller prey. They may eat even locusts. Immensely strong in the jaws and shoulders they are said to be able to carry away a human body or the carcase of an ass.

There has long been a legend (quite false) that hyaenas are hermaphrodite because the external reproductive organs are superficially similar in both sexes. One or two young are born after a gestation of 110 days. At the birth the mother takes up a squatting position and the young, born fully furred, are ejected forwards. The life span is up to 25 years.

Striped and brown hyaenas

The striped hyaena is usually smaller than the spotted species, being not more than 4 ft head and body with an 18 in. tail. It stands 30 in. at the shoulder and weighs up to 85 lb. The coat is grey to yellowish-brown with blackish stripes and a mane or crest of long hairs. The diet is like that of the spotted hyaena. Its breeding differs from the spotted hyaena in that the gestation period is 90 days and there are 2–4 in the litter, sometimes 6. Otherwise it is much the same. The babies are born in holes in the ground, blind and with their ears closed.

The brown hyaena is halfway in size between the spotted and striped hyaenas. Its coat is dark brown with indistinct stripes but with dark rings round the lower legs. Its breeding and feeding habits are like those of the striped hyaena, but it lives near the shore and feeds on carrion left by the receding tide, eating anything from dead crabs to the carcases of stranded whales. For this reason it is also known as the strandwolf.

The striped hyaena has given rise to all manner of beliefs about its magical powers and its cunning. One thing that led to such ideas is its habit at times of shamming dead when cornered by dogs. The hyaena lies perfectly still and the dogs, having sniffed around it for a while, lose interest and begin to turn away. At that moment the hyaena jumps to its feet and dashes away—at 40 mph!

Not so cowardly

Another belief that has persisted to this day is that hyaenas are cowardly and live by feeding on the remains of the lion's kill. This has now been finally disproved. Already there had been cause to doubt this when Dr Hans Kruuk, of the Serengeti Research Institute in Arusha, Tanzania, made a close studv of hyaenas by following them on moonlit nights in a Land-Rover. He found that at dusk they came out of their holes, often crevasses in the mud, to walk about slowly, meeting other hyaenas, exchanging greeting ceremonies until a pack of up to 20 was formed. Then they set off, closely bunched or spread out, in a seemingly leisurely way until a family party of zebras or a herd of wildebeest was reached. Then they began to harass their quarry, snapping at them until they had slowed one down, when all the hyaenas concentrated on it. By dawn not even a splinter of bone would be left. Kruuk found that hyaenas are scavengers but at night they go out to kill for themselves, and the belief in their cowardly disposition is unfounded.

In fact, Kruuk found that as often as not it was the lions that partook of the hyaenas' kills, instead of the other way round.

class	**Mammalia**
order	**Carnivora**
family	**Hyaenidae**
genera & species	***Crocuta crocuta*** *spotted hyaena* ***Hyaena brunnea*** *brown hyaena* ***H. hyaena*** *striped hyaena*

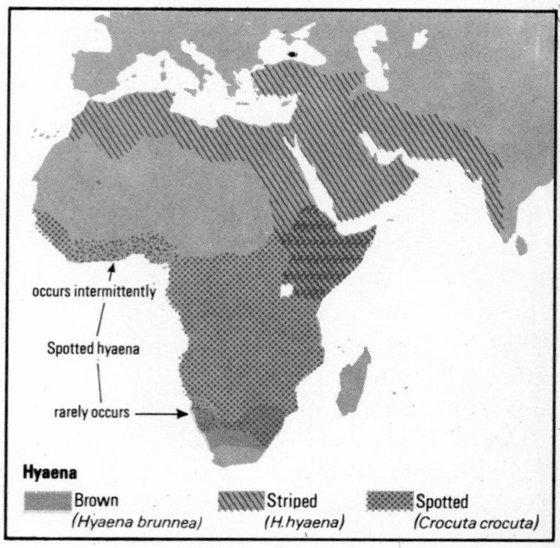

Hydra

The hydra's simple tubular body with its crown of tentacles has earned it a place in every elementary textbook of zoology and made it the object of many detailed studies. It is one of the few freshwater coelenterates, the bulk of which are marine. The body of a hydra is a bag whose wall is made up of two layers of cells separated only by a very thin layer of non-cellular material. The tentacles, which usually number 5 or 6 but may be as few as 4 or as many as 12, are hollow. They surround the mouth, while the other end of the body is a basal disc which normally anchors the hydra by a sticky secretion. Though often abundant in ponds, hydras frequently escape notice

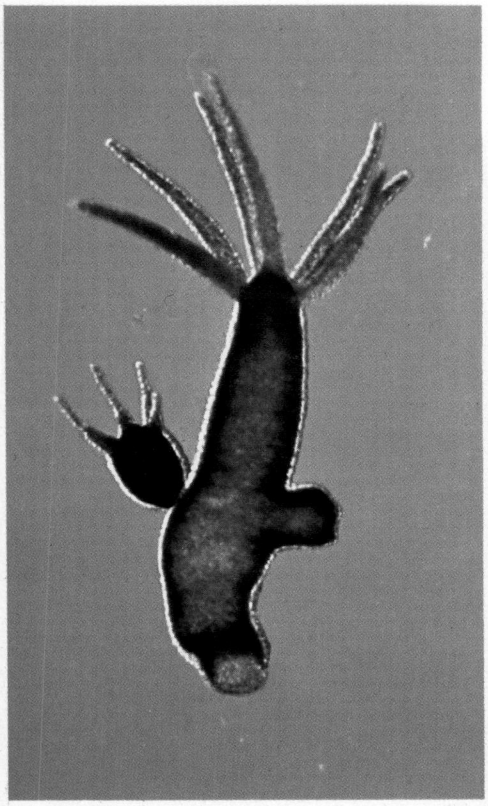

Fritz Siedel

△ *Chips off the old block: a parent hydra with two buds, one advanced, one very very young.*

because of their habit of retracting into a tiny blob when disturbed.

Both tentacles and body are very extensible, for the bases of many of the cells are drawn out as muscle fibres—those of the outer layer of cells running lengthwise and those of the inner layer running around the body. The nervous system co-ordinating the movements is extremely simple, consisting of only a network of nerve cells. There is no brain of any sort.

There are three species of hydra in Britain. The green hydra ***Chlorohydra viridissima****, which used to be called* ***Hydra viridis****, has short tentacles that are never as long as the body. The brown hydra,* ***Hydra (Pelmatohydra) oligactis****, has tentacles 4—5 times the length of the body, which is usually clearly divided into a stomach region and a narrower stalk. These two species are found throughout the world and their colours are caused by single-celled algae living within their cells. When animal prey is scarce the hydra draws nourishment from these algae. In both species the body may be as much as* $1\frac{1}{5}$ *in. long but it is usually much shorter. The third species found in Britain is the slender hydra* ***Hydra attenuata****. Its body is never much more than* $\frac{1}{2}$ *in. in length when fully extended, it lacks a stalk, and its tentacles are never more than 3 times the length of the body.*

The stinging cells

Hydras, like their relatives the sea anemones and jellyfishes, have stinging cells with which they capture their prey. Each stinging cell or nematocyst is a rounded cell with a hollow coiled thread inside that can be shot out at great speed (see anemone p 44).

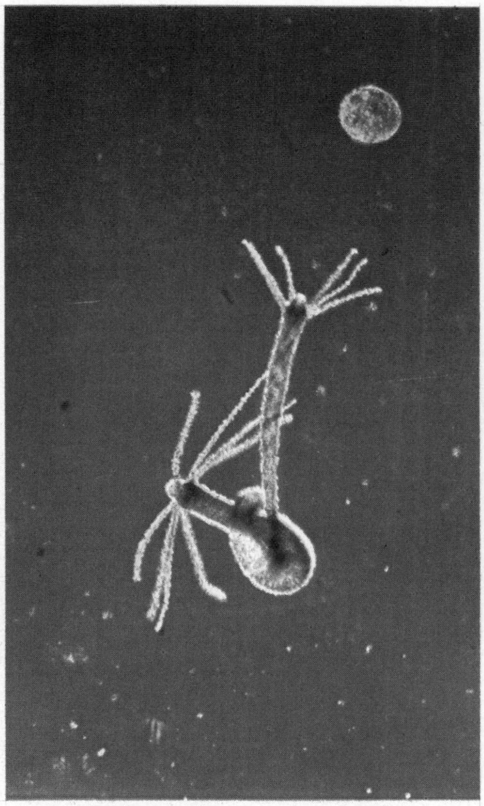

Fritz Siedel

△ *Budded hydra almost ready to break free while a* ***Volvox****-like 'plant animal' just escapes.*

Hydra has four kinds. In one kind the thread is shot into the prey, injecting a poison. In a second kind the thread coils after it is shot out, and if the prey has bristles of any kind these tend to become entangled in it. The third type of nematocyst is probably truly defensive. It is shot out at animals not normally eaten by the hydra. The fourth kind of nematocyst is used to fasten the tentacles when the hydra is walking. This is not strictly a stinging cell although it looks very like it, and is best referred to as a thread capsule. In fact, some people prefer to use the term 'thread capsule' for all of them, simply because some of them do not sting.

When a nematocyst is discharged, its thread is forced inside out like a stocking, except that forces inside the thread itself are responsible for driving it out. The nematocysts used in capturing prey are discharged when the prey touches a little trigger on the side of the cell. Touch, however, is not enough, for the stinging cell must also be stimulated by chemicals in the water that are given out by the prey.

In all types, the stinging cells cannot be used again but are replaced by new ones migrating in from other parts of the body.

Progressing by somersaults

Although normally anchored, hydra can move about by creeping slowly on its basal disc in a sort of sliding movement. It can move more rapidly by a looping movement or a series of somersaults. To do this, a

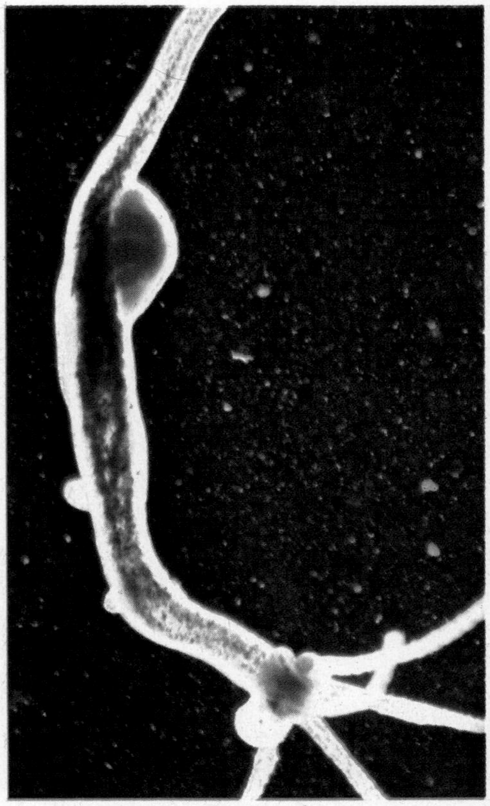

John Clegg

△ *Hydra forming an ovary for sexual reproduction. It does this in harsh conditions.*

hydra bends over and gets a grip with special thread capsules on the tentacles. It lets go with its basal disc and brings this over in turn, very much like somebody doing 'cartwheels'. Hydras can also float at the surface of the water buoyed up by gas bubbles given out by the basal disc. The characteristic feature of the behaviour of hydras is that they suddenly contract into a tight ball every 5 or 10 minutes, for no obvious reason. This happens less often at night than by day.

Snagging its prey

The diet includes insect larvae, water fleas, worms, even newly-hatched fishes and tadpoles. Between meals the tentacles are held outstretched and more or less still, but at the approach of prey they start to writhe and later they bend in towards the open mouth. They will do these things if offered only extracts from other animals without any solids. For example, the juice from crushed water fleas alone will make a hydra go through the motions of putting food into its mouth. In fact a single chemical—glutathione—is responsible. If, however, the prey touches the tentacle the threads of the nematocysts are shot out, it is caught, held and paralysed, then carried to the mouth and swallowed. The mouth can open wide enough to take in animals that are themselves wider than the body of the hydra, which will stretch to accommodate them. Once inside the baglike body of the hydra, the prey is partially digested by enzymes given out by the inner layer of cells. Small particles breaking off are engulfed by individual cells for the final stages of digestion and indigestible particles are rejected through the mouth.

While food is in the body whiplike flagella on the cells of the inner layer are stirring the food around the inside of the body, a churning which aids digestion.

Multiplying in two ways

Hydra reproduce both sexually and by budding. Most species of hydra reproduce sexually in autumn or early winter although some do so in spring or early summer. One thing that can cause sexual reproduction, even out of season, is an accumulation of carbon dioxide in the water—as happens when a number of hydras are overcrowded. There are no special reproductive organs but small cells appear as bulges on the body in the upper half. Ovaries which are borne on different individuals in most species appear lower down on the body, also as bulges, each containing a single large egg-cell, or ovum. The ripe ovum pushes through the outer layer of the hydra's body and the cells around it form a little cup or cushion for the ovum. The male cells or sperms are shed into the water where they swim about and eventually reach the ova and fertilise them. The embryo which results from the division of the fertilised ovum secretes around itself a hard, sticky yellow shell $\frac{1}{50}$ to $\frac{1}{25}$ in. across. The shell may be smooth on the outside or spiny, according to the species. Thus enclosed, the embryo can survive drying and freezing. After lying dormant for 3—10 weeks it breaks out of its capsule, grows tentacles and becomes a new hydra, a perfect miniature of the adult.

Budding technique

New hydras can also be formed by buds. Each bud begins as a little bump on the side of the body. This grows out, and an opening

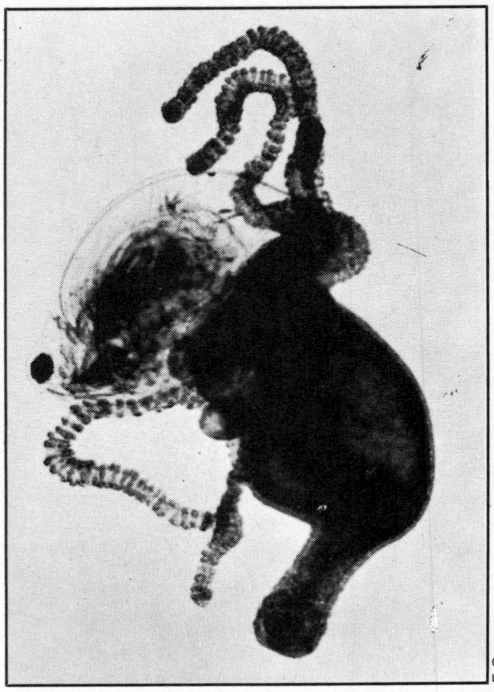

E Grave

△ *Murder in miniature: after paralysing a water flea with stinging cells and drawing it in with sticky threads and tentacles, a hydra stretches its mouth round an outsize victim.*

▽ *Coelenterate mealtime: the green hydra at left is stinging a water flea into submission, the one at right is swollen with similar repast (9 × life size).*

Heather Angel

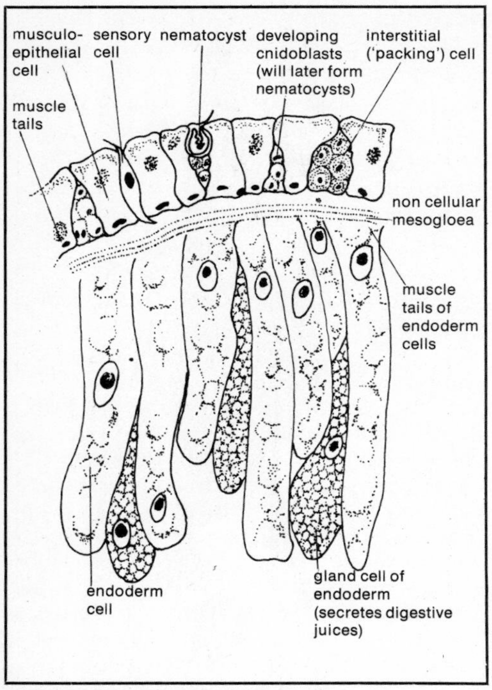

△ *Cross-section through body wall of hydra. It has only two layers of cells. The inner (endoderm) cells are for food breakdown. The outer (ectoderm) cells perform all other functions.*

appears at its free end. Tentacles are pushed out all round the mouth and finally the bud breaks away from the parent, settles down and grows into a new hydra, the whole process occupying 2 days, and a single hydra may bear several buds at once.

Inside-out hydras

In Greek mythology Hercules found himself trying to kill a monster called Hydra which had many heads. As fast as Hercules cut off one head another grew in its place. In 1744, Abraham Trembley, Swiss tutor to the children of the Comte de Bentinck, published his story of another hydra—the animal we are concerned with here. Trembley had found that a complete hydra would be regenerated from only $\frac{1}{8}$th of the parent body. He also succeeded in turning these animals inside out, a remarkably delicate operation which he performed by threading them on horse hairs. Trembley showed that the hydras would survive even this drastic operation. These experiments caught on and for a while became very popular among certain scientists. More recently, they have been pursued in much greater detail. We now know that even tinier pieces of hydra, even a piece only $\frac{6}{1000}$ in. long, will grow into a new hydra provided that cells from both layers of the wall of the parent body are present. Even if the cells are separated into a mush of independent cells, these will come together to form a new hydra. The experiments are called 'Dissociation and Regeneration'.

We also know now that when a hydra is turned inside out it gets back to normal because the cells of the two layers migrate past each other to get into their proper positions. In fact, hydras are continually remodelling themselves and replacing old cells with new. If the tissues just below the tentacles of a hydra are marked with dye, they can be seen to move gradually down to the basal disc, eventually being lost and replaced by growth of new cells in the region from which they started.

phylum	**Coelenterata**
class	**Hydrozoa**
order	**Hydrida**
family	**Hydridae**
genera & species	***Chlorohydra viridissima*** *green hydra* ***Hydra attenuata*** *slender hydra* ***H. oligactis*** *brown hydra* *others*

▽ *Stuck to a water plant by special cells in their basal discs, five brown hydras hang in wait for the touch or taste of prey (7 × life size).*

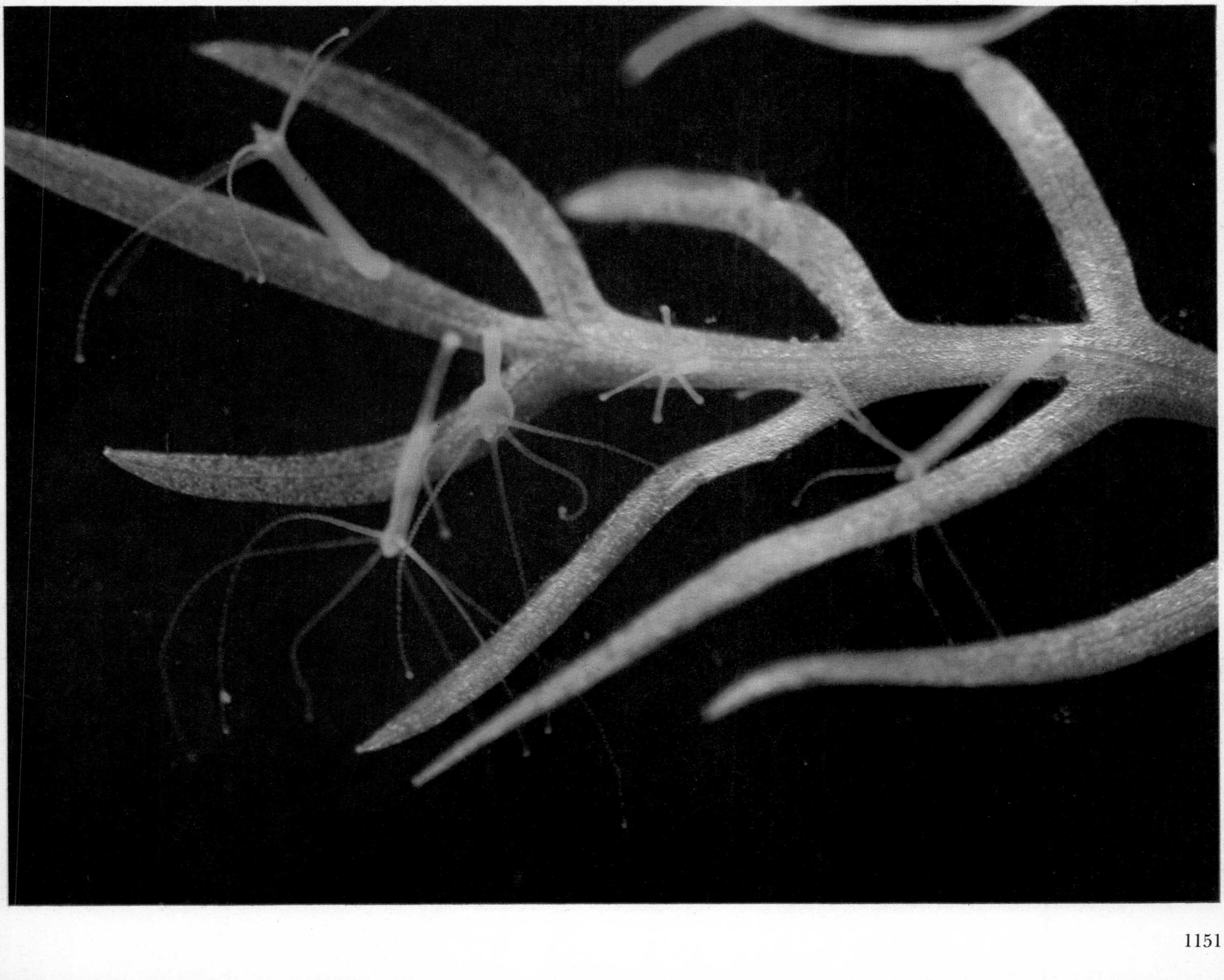

KB Newman

Hyrax

The hyrax has been described as a zoological puzzle, a natural hotchpotch and a museum of antiquities. Although only rabbit-sized, it is usually called the nearest relative of the elephant!

The dozen species of rock hyraxes and tree hyraxes make up a single family in the order Hyracoidea. Small, thick-set, greyish-brown and rabbit-like, tail-less with short muzzles and small round ears, the largest are no more than 18 in. long. The forefeet have four functional toes, the fifth being a mere stump. The hindfeet have three toes, the inner toe having a curved claw. All the other toes have short hoof-like nails. The best known are the Cape hyrax or dassie of Cape Province and Southwest Africa and the daman or cherogil—the conies of the Bible—of Syria to Sinai and southern Arabia. There are many species and subspecies: in the Transvaal, Angola, East Africa, Ethiopia and the Sudan, in the Congo, Nigeria and the Cameroons. Tree hyraxes live in South and East Africa, in the equatorial forests, in Fernando Po and Zanzibar.

Their skeleton has much in common with that of the rhinoceros, but is remarkable for the large number of ribs. The teeth are most unusual, and since teeth are much used in classifying mammals this makes things difficult. The single pair of upper cutting teeth (incisors) are rodent-like except that instead of being flat with chisel edges they are prismatic and end in sharp points. The lower front teeth include two pairs of rooted teeth unlike those of rodents; the outer pair are nearly horizontal and their crowns are divided into three lobes. There is a gap between the front teeth and the cheek teeth like the gap, known as the diastema, in rodents. The upper cheek teeth are like those of a rhinoceros, the lower cheek teeth like those of a hippopotamus.

Noisy family groups

Rock hyraxes are usually timid and inoffensive as well as shy but they can be aggressive at times. Their safety lies in being able to seek shelter quickly. It is said that, when feeding, they have a look-out who gives warning of danger by shrill shrieks. They are noisy and this alone probably gives them protection, for danger or 'all clear' signals can be heard over a wide area. Tree hyraxes seek safety in holes in trees but whereas most tree-climbers have a tail for use as a balancer hyraxes have none. They have no sharp claws nor grasping fingers but they have rubbery pads on their feet. Rock hyraxes use these to scamper over smooth faces of rock and tree hyraxes to run up smooth trunks.

Colonies of hyraxes may contain 6–50 individuals; the larger colonies are made up of family groups of females and young and one old male. When alarmed they scamper for a hole in the rocks or in the ground, the old male bringing up the rear. Although all hyraxes are active mainly by day they are on the alert on moonlit nights, when their calls may be heard. The call is a mewing note which may rise higher and higher to end in a prolonged scream. This may be answered by another hyrax as far as a mile away. The alarm note, as when a bird of prey flies overhead, is a short, coarse bark. The daily pattern is for all members of the colony to come out at dawn to sun them-

◁△ That belligerent look: a hyrax glowers suspiciously from its retreat in the rocks.
◁ Barrel of fur: a thirsty rock hyrax.

Heather Angel

selves on a rock, all clumped together. As the sun warms up they slowly spread out, grooming and stretching. Then they feed for about an hour, the tree hyrax climbing trees, especially acacia, to feed on leaves, rock hyraxes feeding mainly on grass but also on herbs and low bushes. An hour before noon they move into shade to rest and come out again about 5 hours later to feed for a further 2 hours.

Slow breeding, many enemies

There are usually 2–3 in a litter after a gestation of 225 days. The babies are born fully furred and with eyes open. They begin nibbling food at 2 days. They become sexually mature after 2 years and the maximum life span in captivity is nearly 6 years. Slow breeders, they nevertheless keep up their numbers in spite of many enemies. Snakes such as cobra and puff adder, large eagles, Mackinder's owl and the augur buzzard are their main enemies, but hyraxes are also killed by leopard, hunting dog and caracal, and the smaller beasts of prey such as mongooses.

Scientists' joy

When the Bible was translated into English, coney—meaning a rabbit—was the nearest the translators could get to naming this strange mammal. The name 'hyrax' is Greek for shrew, but the first scientific account of the animal was not given until 1766, when it was called *Cavia capensis,* a kind of guinea pig. The first Dutch settlers in South Africa called it *dasje* or little badger, now spelt dassie. It was then called a rodent but Cuvier, the French anatomist, decided it must be related to the hoofed animals. It has, as we have seen, some teeth like the rhinoceros and others like the teeth of a hippopotamus. The bones of its forelegs and feet are like those of elephants; its brain is unlike that of a rodent and more like the brain of an elephant and its stomach is nearer that of a horse. Its hindfeet with the three toes and hoof-like nails recall the hindfeet of the horse's ancestor. The placenta by which the unborn hyrax is attached in the womb is halfway between that of an elephant and that of a horse. And to complete this mixture of rodent and hoofed animal characters, the tree hyrax has a gland in the middle of its back surrounded by white hairs which are erected in moments of excitement. A gland like this is found on the top of the head of the capybara, the huge South American rodent, which also has hindlegs with three toes like the ancestor of the horse, and like the tapir.

The fossil record suggests that horses, tapirs, rhinoceroses, hippopotamuses and elephants had a common ancestor a long way back in time. Although they all look so different today their differences tend to disappear as we trace back along their family tree. The further we go back in time the more their ancestors had in common—and if there is one animal alive today that more than any other shows relationships with the ancestors of all these large hoofed animals it is the hyrax. It may sound absurd to call this animal, the size of a large guinea pig, the paterfamilias of these huge pachyderms but there is a strong degree of truth in it.

class	**Mammalia**
order	**Hyracoidea**
family	**Procaviidae**
genera & species	***Dendrohyrax dorsalis*** *tree hyrax* ***Procavia capensis*** *rock hyrax* *others*

Philippa Scott

▷△ *Alert tree hyrax* ***Dendrohyrax arboreus.*** ▷ *Grazing rock hyraxes. The white back fur covers glands.* ▽ *Hyrax at ease in the sun.*

KB Newman

Donald Paterson: WWF

Ibex

The name 'ibex' is applied to seven high-mountain forms of wild goat. By common consent the markhor is excluded, being somewhat different from the rest. Even so ibexes are a varied lot. It is still not certain whether they are all closely interrelated, or whether some of them may not have been derived independently from the true wild goat or bezoar, which inhabits low-lying but hilly desert country. Most ibexes are larger and more thickset than the bezoar and their horns are broad and rounded in front with evenly spaced knots on this surface, instead of the narrow, keeled front surface of the bezoar. The horns of most ibexes are scimitar-shaped, as in the bezoar, but the Spanish and the two East Caucasus species—locally known as ***tur****—have very divergent horns which turn up, out, back and down, and finally in and up.*

The Siberian ibex, especially those from the Tienshan mountains, have the longest horns. The Caucasian turs have very thick horns compared with their length, while in the bezoar and the Nubian ibex the horns are very slender. In the Siberian ibex and the walia the knots on the front surface of the horns are bold and well-developed; in the Nubian, Alpine and West Caucasus (Kuban) species, however, the outer edge of the front surface is somewhat bevelled-off, and the knots are clear only toward the inner edge. The Daghestan tur has no knots on the horns, while in the Spanish ibex the horns are actually keeled on their front surface like the bezoar. Females in all these species are very similar, with short, backturned horns.

Some species are brownish with black stripes down the outside of the limbs, along the lower flanks, along the middle of the back, and down the nose, while the belly is white. The bezoar also has a black stripe on the shoulders. These markings are sometimes almost or entirely lost. They are always less developed in the females, while in the Siberian ibex they are very faint in winter coat. In some Siberian ibex from the Tienshan and Kashmir there is a large white 'saddle' mark in winter.

Adult males of Siberian ibex weigh 180—220 lb; occasionally, as in the large Tienshan and Pamir race, as much as 290 lb; while females weigh only 70—90, occasionally up to 130 lb.

Up and down the mountains

Thanks to the work of Russian zoologists as well as sportsmen, the habits of the Siberian ibex are fairly well known. It lives between 1 700 and 17 000 ft above sea level, even higher in the Pamir, in steeper country than the wild sheep living in the same mountains. Herds consist of 3—40, in places up to 200, especially during the coldest months. In winter, the ibex move to steeper slopes with less snow, often south-facing. This may involve a downward migration of 1 000—6 500 ft, which sometimes brings the ibex into the forest zone, where some stay the whole year. At night ibex may move down the mountainside to avoid frosts and move up again to feed at 10 or 11 am. They eat mainly grass and herbs in the summer and mainly leaves in winter.

A Molinier: Jacana

△ *An ibex challenges its companions, sure of its ability to master the most precarious of ledges.*

◁ *Room with a view: alpine ibex at rest.*

Enforced celibacy

The rut takes place in autumn, or as late as December or early January in some parts of central Asia. It lasts 7—10 days, the males feeding little at this time. They fight among themselves to form harems, rearing on their hindlegs and clashing their horn-bases together, like wild sheep. This specialised method of fighting causes no injury but ensures that the largest males with the thickest horns win. So a male has not much chance of gathering a harem until about 6 years old, although he may become sexually mature at 1½ years. The old males gather huge harems in which each year 15—20% of the females stay barren. Gestation lasts 170—180 days, and the single young weighing 8—9 lb is born around May. About 5% of females have twins. They are not weaned until autumn, but begin to graze after a month or so. Siberian ibex are thought to live 15—20 years. In the Nubian ibex, the rut occurs in September and October, gestation is shorter, 150—160 days, so the young are born from February to April. In the bezoar, the young are born in May, in dense bush or forest; the young of true ibex hide by day in the rocks.

Fighting with their horns

Young ibex are preyed upon by eagles, jackals and foxes; adults by leopards, snow leopards, bears, lynxes and wolves. They normally seek safety in flight, but can fight with their horns when cornered.

How many species?

There is a division of opinion on whether there are seven species of ibex or fewer than this. Some writers claim there are only five. One sure way to tell if two kinds of animals represent different species is if they remain distinct in the wild state, without forming a hybrid population between them. If there is a hybrid population there will be many intermediates between two 'pure' forms, which will then cease to be separated. Most of the ibex species live in different places and have no chance to interbreed. There is, therefore, no definite way to tell whether they are real species or not. Bringing members of different species together in captivity to see if they will interbreed does not give us an answer because under the unnatural conditions of a zoo paddock things can happen that would not occur in the wild. For example, lions and tigers interbreed in zoos

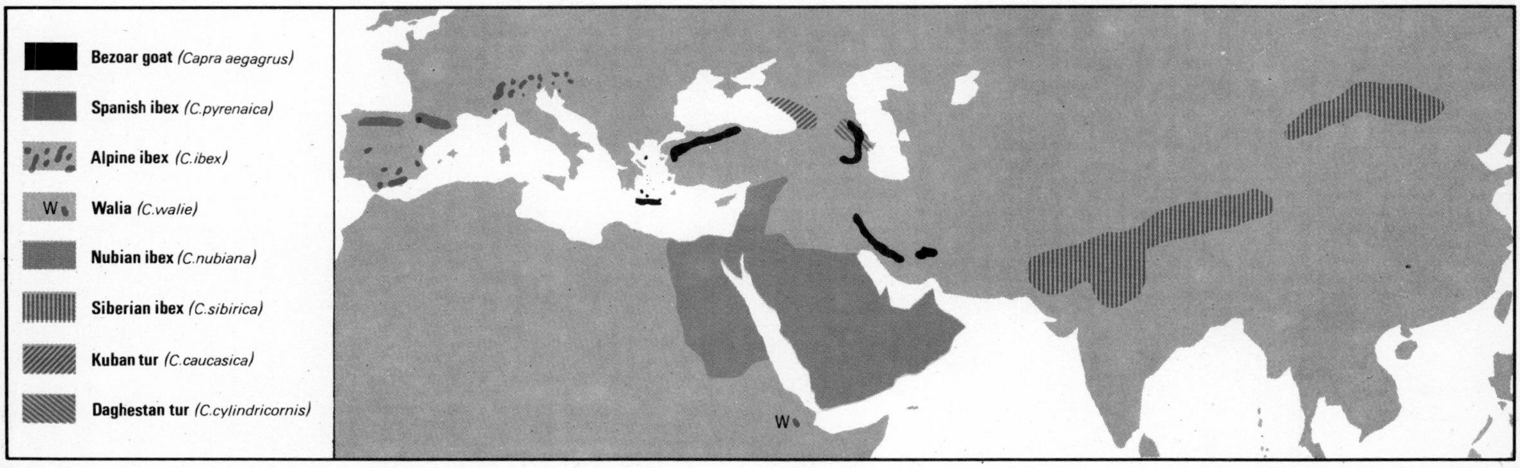

R Van Nostrand

△ *Portrait of a Siberian ibex. The strength of the knurled horns establishes rank in males.*

▽ *Summit conference: male alpine ibexes size each other up from respective stone pillars.*

and although they used to live more or less side by side in the same habitat in India, Iran and Iraq, they did not interbreed.

During the last Ice Age Spanish and alpine ibex co-existed in southern France and apparently did not hybridize. Our evidence for this is that all specimens as well as all cave paintings of these animals show either one or the other, never a mixture. In the central Caucasus today two species of tur live side by side in an area 21 by 24 miles, this area representing 15% of the total range of the Kuban tur and 10% of the range of the Daghestan tur. In that part of the overlap which is on the northern slopes of the Caucasus no hybridization has been found but on the southern slopes hybrids are known. Perhaps a strong male of one species, unable to obtain a harem of his own, drives off a weaker male of the other species and takes over his harem. Even so, the hybrids are only of the first generation, there is no continuing hybrid population. So, although the two species do hybridize, it is only as the horse and ass will hybridize to give mules, which are infertile.

From this and other evidence too detailed to give here it seems reasonable to believe that the seven kinds of ibex enumerated below are all natural species.

class	**Mammalia**
order	**Artiodactyla**
family	**Bovidae**
genus & species	***Capra aegagrus*** *bezoar goat* ***C. caucasica*** *Kuban tur* ***C. cylindricornis*** *Daghestan tur* ***C. ibex*** *alpine ibex* ***C. nubiana*** *Nubian ibex* ***C. pyrenaica*** *Spanish ibex* ***C. sibirica*** *Siberian ibex* ***C. walie*** *walia*

Roebild

Ibis

Peter Johnson

Ibises belong to the same order as herons and flamingos, and have similar long spindly legs, long necks and long bills. Their necks and bills are, however, generally stouter than those of herons and the bills are down-curved. They also lack the powder-down patches of the herons. The smallest is the glossy ibis, about the size of a curlew, with a dark plumage that shines with iridescent greens and purples. It is wide-ranging, being found in southern Europe and Asia, the East Indies, Australia, parts of Africa and Madagascar, and around the Caribbean. It occasionally wanders to the British Isles. The sacred ibis is white with a black head and neck and a black 'bustle' of feathers over the tail as in cranes (p 562). In flight the dark wingtips are prominent. It lives in Africa south of the Sahara, Madagascar and Arabia. The scarlet ibis lives in tropical America from Venezuela to Brazil and the white ibis, wholly white except for red on the bill and the naked skin on the face, ranges from southern United States, where it is called the white curlew, to northern South America. These are the best known of the 25 or so species of ibis. The hermit ibis used to breed in Central Europe but has been extinct there for three centuries. The Japanese crested ibis is extremely rare. In 1966 nine were known in Japan, but the numbers in Manchuria, China and Korea are not known. The wood ibises belong to the stork family, although the name of the African wood ibis is ***Ibis ibis.***

△ Unique photograph of a bald ibis ***Geronticus calvus****. Only about 1 000 of these birds exist, in the mountains of South Africa. ▽ Toes splayed, a scarlet ibis perches, stork-like, on one leg.*

John Tashjian at San Diego Zoo

Picturesque birds

Ibises along with other long-legged and long-necked birds such as herons, cranes, flamingos and storks are among the most beautiful of birds. Their plumage is often magnificent, especially when they are seen in huge flocks. Their poise is statuesque and their flight rhythmically graceful. When roosting on the bare limbs of trees, ibises are heraldic, especially when silhouetted, and scarlet ibises perched in the trees in the evening are an unbelievably magnificent sight. They look like huge blossoms caught in the rays of the setting sun. In flight a group of ibises beat their wings in unison and then glide, the front of the flock stopping first and those behind following suit, so ripples of gliding and wing-beating pass down the column.

Sacred chimney sweep

Ibises live in marshes, shallow lakes and along the shore where they feed on small water animals, such as frogs, fish, worms and small reptiles. The hermit ibis lives in the much drier country of North Africa and the Middle East, where it feeds on beetles and other small land animals. In South Africa the sacred ibis is called the 'chimney sweep' because it eats carrion and 'sweeps' out the insides of carcases for the insects feeding there. These carrion-eating habits were known in mediaeval times. In the 12th century bestiary translated by TH White it is said that the ibis 'enjoys eating corpses and snakes' eggs' and that it looks for 'little dead fish or other bodies which have been thrown up by the waves.'

Trees essential for nesting

Ibises build nests in trees, except for the hermit ibis that nests on cliffs, and the sacred ibis sometimes nests on the ground. The Japanese crested ibis nests in tall forest trees. One reason for its decline is the cutting down of forests, for even if the nesting tree is left intact while the surrounding trees are cut down the ibis will desert it. This species is unusual in that it nests in pine trees. The nests are untidy platforms of sticks and rushes, like herons' nests. The black ibis of India sometimes uses the abandoned nests of birds of prey. This ibis nests in groups of 2 or 3 pairs but the scarlet ibis nests in colonies sometimes 10 000 strong. The colonies are often shared with other birds such as cormorants, herons and egrets. Such concentrations are now much rarer as the scarlet ibis has been slaughtered for its beautiful feathers as well as for its meat.

Both parents incubate the 3 or 4 white or blue eggs, which are sometimes marked with brown, for 3 weeks. When the parents swap places at the nest they indulge in billing and cooing, preening each other and calling quietly. The chicks are fed by regurgitation, placing their bills in their parents'. When a couple of weeks old the young leave the nest and climb out onto the nearby branches. They have two coats of down before growing their dark immature plumage. Adult plumage is attained in 1 – 2 years.

Extinct in Egypt, where it was once held in high reverence, the sacred ibis is by no means endangered; it is still a common bird south of the Sahara. Below: a sacred ibis planes in to join a group in the treetops with herons and a cormorant.

The sacred ibis

At one time the sacred ibis bred along the banks of the Nile and the Ancient Egyptians held it in great esteem, identifying it with the god Thoth who recorded the life of every man. In pictures Thoth is shown with the head of an ibis and ibises were tamed and kept as pets in temples. They were also mummified and buried in the tombs of Pharaohs – perhaps to record their final voyage to the next world?

It is often amusing to inquire why an animal is held in veneration or to investigate its appearance in folklore. The Ancient Egyptians venerated several animals, including crocodiles and cats (see p 390), as well as ibises. Herodotus thought the high esteem accorded to the sacred ibis was due to the toll it took of venomous snakes, but perhaps a more reasonable explanation is that the ibis appeared in Egypt at the time of the all-important annual rising of the Nile, feeding and nesting on the newly flooded land then flying away as the waters subsided. It therefore became associated, together with the flooding of the Nile, with the source of life.

class	**Aves**
order	**Ciconiiformes**
family	**Threskiornithidae**
genera & species	***Eudocimus albus*** *white ibis* ***E. ruber*** *scarlet ibis* ***Geronticus eremita*** *hermit ibis* ***Nipponia nippon*** *Japanese ibis* ***Plegadis falcinellus*** *glossy ibis* ***Pseudibis papillosa*** *black ibis* ***Threskiornis aethiopica*** *sacred ibis* *others*

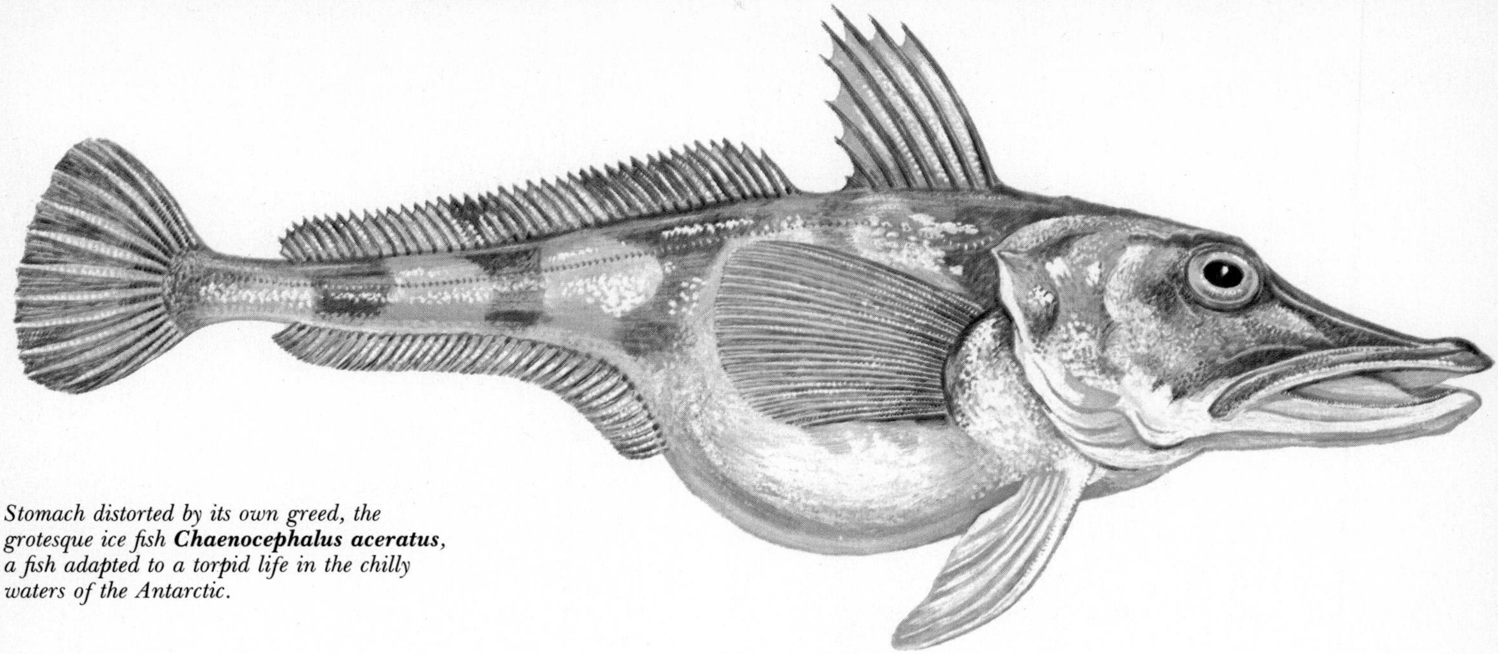

Stomach distorted by its own greed, the grotesque ice fish ***Chaenocephalus aceratus****, a fish adapted to a torpid life in the chilly waters of the Antarctic.*

John Norris Wood

Ice fish

The first reports of ice fish were made by Norwegian whalers working in the Antarctic, who brought back stories of 'bloodless' fishes they caught near their shore factories. The fishes do, in fact, have blood but it is almost transparent with a just perceptible yellowish tint. It lacks haemoglobin, the red pigment that in many other animals carries oxygen from the lungs or gills to other parts of the body. The problem of how these fishes survive without the oxygen-carrying capacity of haemoglobin has led to speculation ever since the fish were discovered but only in the last few years has it been possible, in the remoteness of the Antarctic, to carry out the necessary detailed work for its solution.

The name ice fish was given by British whalers in allusion to the translucent appearance of the body. Ice fish have no scales and the body is very pale brown or white, and slimy. A third (and also descriptive) name is crocodile fish. The front of the head is drawn out into a beak with a large, gaping mouth edged with thick lips. The eyes are large and goggling. The dorsal fin has two parts; the front part in the middle of the back is sail-like and the second part is ribbon-like, similar to the anal fin on the underside. The pectoral fins form paddles just behind the gills and the fleshy leg-like pelvic fins lie in front of them under the belly.

There are about 18 species of ice fish, all but one of them confined to the Southern Ocean. The exception ranges north as far as Patagonia. The largest ice fish ***Chaenocephalus aceratus*** *measures up to 2 ft long and can weigh 2½ lb.*

Sluggish carnivore

The fishes of the Antarctic are now being studied intensively by scientists of several nations but by comparison with other kinds like the Antarctic cod (p 60) little is known of the habits of the ice fish. It has recently been caught with nets at depths of about 200 ft, in some numbers, and so more is likely to be known about it soon. Its muscles are weak and its ribs soft which suggest that the fish is not active. It probably spends much of its time on the sea bed resting on its leg-like pelvic fins, engulfing passing fish or picking up carrion. Like large snakes such as the anaconda (p 41), it probably has big meals at long intervals. The large mouth can close over a fair-sized Antarctic cod and the stomach and skin of its belly can stretch to accommodate a large meal. The proof of this is that ice fishes are sometimes caught when they have engulfed an Antarctic cod already hooked. Ice fish also catch krill, the crustaceans that abound in the cold, oxygen-rich waters, supporting whales and many other Antarctic creatures.

Breeding in the Antarctic autumn

Ice fish spawn in the Antarctic autumn, between mid-March and late April. Each fish lays about 2 000 large yolky eggs, $\frac{1}{6}$ in. in diameter, on the sea floor.

Oxygen problems

The discovery that ice fishes have no haemoglobin in their blood posed several questions. The first was how they manage to transport oxygen to their tissues, for in red blood 90% of the oxygen taken into the body is carried by the haemoglobin and the rest is dissolved in the blood plasma. Ice fishes must carry all their oxygen in the plasma and they must be able to live on very little oxygen. They are helped by the high concentration of oxygen in the Antarctic seas. One of the reasons for the vast amount of plant and animal life in the Southern Ocean, which will be referred to in the article on krill, is that gases dissolve in cold water better than in warm water. As a result the organisms living in the cold seas, where temperatures rarely rise more than a few degrees above freezing point, have a greater supply of oxygen and they oxygenate their bodies more efficiently. Ice fishes are probably able to absorb oxygen through the skin as well as through the gills.

Despite these advantages, ice fish must still absorb less oxygen than other Antarctic fish and it was presumed that this ties them to their sluggish existence. Recent experiments, however, have shown that, weight for weight, ice fish use as much oxygen in their bodies as do Antarctic cod. Some ice fishes and Antarctic cod were caught alive and put in sealed, water-filled containers. Samples of water were drawn off at intervals and the amount of oxygen in them analysed to find out how much the fish were using. It turned out that the ice fish were using as much oxygen as the Antarctic cod, so they do not seem to be labouring at a disadvantage but have a system for carrying quite enough oxygen for their sluggish way of life. The haemoglobin of the Antarctic cod would seem, then, to be an unnecessary luxury, and this may be the case for other fish. Goldfish, for instance, are able to survive indefinitely when their haemoglobin has been put out of action by carbon monoxide.

Ice fishes also have large hearts, about three times the size of the hearts of red-blooded fishes. This must enable them to pump blood very rapidly through the body and so compensate for the small amount of oxygen in the blood. A similar adaptation is found in people living in the rarefied atmosphere of high mountains.

The absence of haemoglobin in the blood of ice fish and the discovery that in other fish haemoglobin appears to be superfluous, raises awkward questions. One can ask either why ice fish lost their haemoglobin, or why so many other fishes have haemoglobin. Even when we know more about the habits and physiology of the fish, these questions may remain debatable.

class	**Pisces**
order	**Perciformes**
family	**Chaenichthyidae**
genus & species	***Chaenocephalus aceratus*** *others*

Ichneumon

This is the name used—usually in a rather imprecise way—for certain small wasps whose larvae live as parasites in the bodies of other insects. They are often referred to as 'ichneumon flies', but 'ichneumon wasp' is a better term since they belong to the insect order Hymenoptera and not to the true flies, or Diptera. Also, the term is often applied to all the parasitic Hymenoptera, including the chalcid and some of the cynipid wasps which we have already described, the cynipids under 'gall wasp'.

The name is restricted here to the superfamily Ichneumonoidea, comprising two main families, the Ichneumonidae and Braconidae.

The word 'ichneumon' has a curious history. The Ancient Egyptians regarded with favour a four-legged animal which helped to destroy crocodiles by digging up and eating their eggs. This story found its way into the early Greek literature, and they used the word 'ichneumon', meaning 'tracker', for the animal. It is generally supposed to have been the mongoose, but this is pure conjecture. It is really more likely to have been a large lizard, the Nile monitor; no clear distinction was made between beasts and reptiles in the confused zoology of ancient times.

A living death

Often the butterfly or moth collector finds a partly grown caterpillar of some particular species he wishes to have, brings it to full growth by careful feeding and is happy to see it pupate, apparently in good health. He may yet be disappointed, however, by the appearance from the pupa of a four-winged 'fly' instead of the beautiful moth or butterfly he was hoping for.

What led to this disappointment was that some time before he discovered the caterpillar, it had been found by a female ichneumon wasp. Having made sure, in some way we do not fully understand, that the caterpillar had not already been visited by another ichneumon wasp, she laid an egg on or under its skin. The caterpillar probably reared up and thrashed about when the wasp settled on it, but once the operation was over it resumed its feeding and growing in an apparently normal way. Meanwhile the egg of the ichneumon hatched into a tiny grub, which then began feeding and growing at the expense of the caterpillar's tissues.

When the time came for the caterpillar to pupate, it was harbouring a parasite of fair size in its body, but not large enough to have destroyed the working of any of its essential organs. As soon as the change to a chrysalis was completed, however, the grub began to grow apace, soon killing its host. It then turned into a pupa itself within the empty shell that should contain a moth. Some time later the ichneumon wasp hatched by splitting the skin of its own pupal covering, and then chewed its way out through the shell of the chrysalis. A moth or butterfly pupa that

Toni Angermayer

△ *Living larder: with ovipositor about to leave an egg, this beetle larva is doomed.*
◁ *With sharp ovipositor, a female* ***Rhyssa persuasoria*** *pierces wood to lay an egg on the larva of a wood-boring beetle (8 × life size).*

has harboured an ichneumon is never split open as it is when it completes its transformation; it has a hole in the side.

If the hatching ichneumon is a female, she finds a male of her own species, mates and then, if summer is nearly over, probably hibernates through the winter. Next spring she will seek out another caterpillar, possibly but not necessarily of the same species that provided her with a living food supply.

No escaping the ichneumon

The very common large rusty-red ichneumon wasps of the genus *Ophion* have this sort of life history, but variations on the theme are numerous. Not all ichneumons parasitize the larvae of moths and butterflies; some attack saw-flies, some beetles, bugs or even spiders, and one sort crawls under the water to lay its eggs on the larvae of caddis-flies. Aphids are also heavily attacked by a small braconid ichneumon called *Aphidius*. The largest British ichneumon *Rhyssa persuasoria* lays eggs on the wood-boring larvae of the big saw-flies called horntails *Sirex* which burrow in pine trees, ruining their timber. The female *Rhyssa* has a very long slender ovipositor—the egg-laying organ—and with this she is able to bore through a couple of inches of solid wood and implant an egg on the horntail grub inside the trunk. The drilling through the wood is a remarkable performance, but the finding and exact locating of the larva within is even more so. Here again we do not really know what sense is employed.

Parasites on parasites

Some ichneumons lay not one, but a number of eggs, resulting in a brood of 100 or more crawling grubs inside the unhappy caterpillar. This multiple parasitisation is characteristic of the Braconidae, most of which are very small insects. One of these *Apanteles glomeratus* is a serious (from our point of view useful) enemy of cabbage white butterflies. In this case the larvae of the ichneumon emerge from the body of the caterpillar just at the time when it has found a place to pupate. On emergence through the caterpillar's skin each ichneumon larva spins a little yellow cocoon, like a tiny replica of that of a silkworm. These little clusters of cocoons are common objects on walls surrounding vegetable gardens. If you collect these carefully and breed them out you will get quantities of *Apanteles* and also, probably, numbers of another even smaller ichneumon. The females of this species are expert at finding butterfly caterpillars infested with *Apanteles* larvae and laying eggs on the parasites, probing through the caterpillar's skin to do so. The word 'hyperparasite' is used to describe this sort of parasite within a parasite.

The stage at which the parasites emerge from the host's body can vary; it may be before pupation or after. The stage at which the eggs are laid may also vary. In the true ichneumons it is usually in the larva, but some of the minute chalcid wasps lay their eggs and complete their metamorphoses in the eggs of the host, and one is known which lays in the newly formed pupa.

Both ichneumon and chalcid wasps (see p 408) have been used in biological control of harmful insects. In New Zealand *Sirex* was accidentally introduced in imported timber and multiplied rapidly, becoming a serious pest in the pine forests and plantations. There is no ichneumon native to New Zealand that can reach it in its burrow in the tree trunks, and so in 1928 and 1929 over a thousand pupae of the big ichneumon wasp *Rhyssa persuasoria* were sent to New Zealand and the insects were released in the pine woods when they emerged. More were sent in 1931 and they all thrived. Horntails are far less abundant.

Parasites or not?

A truly parasitic animal, such as a tapeworm, does not kill the host in which it feeds. On the contrary, it is in its interest for the host to stay alive as long as possible, since if it dies the parasite perishes with it. The association of the ichneumon larva with the caterpillar in which it feeds is quite different. Here the host is doomed to die before it reaches maturity from the moment the egg is deposited in it. Ichneumon wasps really prey on caterpillars, their larvae slowly eating them alive instead of killing them immediately as a normal predator does. For this reason some authorities object to the term parasite to describe ichneumons and call them parasitoids.

phylum	**Arthopoda**
class	**Insecta**
order	**Hymenoptera**
family	**Braconidae**
genera & species	***Apanteles glomeratus*** ***Aphidius***
family	**Ichneumonidae**
genera & species	***Ophion*** ***Rhyssa persuasoria*** *others*

Iguana

The iguana family contains lizards such as the anole, the basilisk, the horned toad and many others, some of which are called iguanas in everyday English. The marine iguana is discussed under a separate heading; here we are dealing with the green iguana, the ground iguana, the land iguanas and the desert iguana or crested lizard.

The ground iguana is one of the most primitive members of the family. It has a crest like the teeth in a comb running down its back starting behind the head and petering out in the middle of the heavy tail. One kind, the rhinoceros iguana, has two or three hornlike scales on its head and a large swelling on either side of the chin. Ground iguanas reach a length of 4 ft, 2 ft shorter than the green iguana which has been introduced to the Virgin Isles and the Lesser Antilles where it has driven out the ground iguana. The native home of the green iguana is Central and northern South America. It is pale green in colour, has a crest similar to that of the ground iguana and an erectable sac under the throat. The males are larger than the females, their crests are longer and their bodies are more orange or yellow compared with the females' light green. The males also have a row of pores on the underside of each thigh, whose function is unknown.

The desert iguana lives in the deserts of North America. It measures 1 ft and is cream coloured with brown or black lines and spots. The land iguana of the Galapagos islands grows up to 5 ft. It is yellow with brown spots on the sides and legs.

High diver

The green iguana is an agile climber and adults are rarely found far from the trees of the tropical forests in which they live. It can scramble from one tree to another providing the twigs are interlaced to give reasonable support for iguanas cannot leap far. Green iguanas will, however, throw themselves from a branch 40–50 ft up and land on the ground unhurt, sprinting away to the undergrowth with barely a pause for breath. For an animal that appears so clumsy, with a heavy tail and legs splayed sideways, an iguana is remarkably fast and is extremely difficult to catch. Its reflexes are very rapid and unless one has nets the only way to catch an iguana is to throw oneself at it and even then a fullgrown iguana will be very hard to hold, as it can inflict nasty bites and scratches. Iguanas often take refuge in water and their favourite haunts are in trees overhanging pools and rivers. If disturbed they leap from the branch where they were lying and dive into the water. They swim underwater, propelling themselves with their tails, and surface under cover of vegetation along the bank.

John Tashjian at San Diego Zoo

▷ *The Barrington Island iguana of the Galapagos* ***Conolophus pallidus****. Local people prize its flesh, goats destroy its home. Only 300 remain.*

John Markham

Brosset: Jacana

◁◁ *The aptly named rhinoceros iguana, with two horn-like scales on the top of its nose.*
◁ *A green iguana pauses, throat sac down and crest erect, to fight or flee an intruder, its partly missing tail witness of a past escape.*

The green iguana comes down to the ground in cold weather and hides under logs or in holes, but the other iguanas are usually ground-living and only occasionally climb trees. The desert iguana is a very fast runner and races about on its hindlegs.

Vegetarian lizards

As adults green iguanas eat a variety of plant foods, including young shoots, fruits, flowers and leaves, but the young ones also eat insects. Other iguanas are also vegetarian. The desert iguana prefers the yellow-flowered creosote bush but also eats other flowers, and after the flowering season is over it eats insects and carrion. Land iguanas feed on cactus and the larger species eat small rodents.

Eggs and constant temperature

Male land iguanas of the Galapagos form territories which they defend against other males. Each keeps watch from a rock and if another male intrudes he climbs down from his vantage point, walks slowly over to his rival and displays at him, pointing his snout at the sky and jerking his head up and down. If this does not scare the intruder into running away a fight breaks out, each trying to grab the loose skin on the other's flanks.

The female land iguanas live in the same burrows as their mates or in separate burrows alongside. Iguanas generally lay their eggs in nests well separated from each other but on a small island in Panama green iguanas were found nesting in great numbers close together on a sandy beach. Each female spent up to 2 weeks on the shore. For the first few days she probed the sand and dug small holes seeking a suitable site. Then she dug a large burrow 1–2 yd long and 2–3 ft deep. Because the beach was so crowded some were seen digging up other nests and scattering the eggs. Eggs were laid at the bottom of the burrow which was filled in afterwards. The females spent some time filling the hole and at the same time filling in adjacent holes. Sometimes this meant filling in the burrows of other females who might be trapped and buried.

The green iguana lays 20–70 eggs in a clutch. The eggs are spherical, white and about 1½ in. diameter. They hatch in 3 months and it has been found that an almost constant temperature is needed for their development. A few degrees too high or too low and they fail to hatch. Although the female abandons her eggs after they are laid she ensures their survival by burying them in a suitable part of the beach. She chooses a spot where the temperature fluctuates only 1°–2° either side of 30°C/86°F. The young iguanas measure about 10 in. when they hatch and grow to 3 ft in one year.

Fooling the iguanas

Man and his domestic animals are the iguanas' worst enemies. Their flesh is relished in many parts of the world. Hawks

Okapia

are also serious enemies, for they catch iguanas as they lie basking in trees. In parts of South America iguanas are hunted by men imitating the screams of hawks. The iguanas' reaction to the cries is to 'freeze' and they are then easily caught. Snakes also hunt iguanas; a 6 ft boa constrictor has been found with an adult green iguana in its stomach.

Vanishing iguanas

When Charles Darwin visited the Galapagos islands in 1835 land iguanas were extremely abundant. Darwin wrote 'I cannot give a more forcible proof of their numbers than by stating that when we were left at James Island, we could not for some time find a spot free from their burrows to pitch our single tent.' Since then man has settled on the island, bringing with him dogs, cats, pigs, rats, goats and other animals and the iguana population is now a fraction of its former size. On some islands, however, where there are no goats, there are still large numbers of iguanas. The link between goats and iguanas is that goats strip the vegetation, depriving iguanas of cover. Some islands seem to be populated by adult iguanas only. They can survive in the open but young iguanas need cover to protect them from the Galapagos hawk. Without this cover they are killed off, and when the old lizards die there will be none left.

△ *Flowers on the menu: although it eats mainly insects when young, this green iguana seems to be interested in the more adult diet of tender young buds. They often clamber in trees.*

class	**Reptilia**
order	**Squamata**
suborder	**Sauria**
family	**Iguanidae**
genera & species	***Conolophus subcristatus*** *land iguana* ***Cyclura cornuta*** *rhinoceros iguana* ***Dipsosaurus dorsalis*** *desert iguana* ***Iguana iguana*** *green iguana*

D Hughes

Impala

The impala is one of the most graceful of the antelopes. About 30–40 in. high, weighing 140–160 lb, it is chestnut brown with a lighter brown area on the flanks and a sharply defined white belly. The male has lyre-shaped, ribbed horns, 20–30 in. long, which make one spiral turn; the female is hornless. The neck and limbs are slender and delicate. The impala occupies a rather isolated position in the family Bovidae. In the past there have been divided opinions on whether it was more nearly related to the gazelles or to the reedbuck. Recently Alan Gentry has suggested, on a study of the skull, teeth and horn-cores, that the impala is more nearly related to the hartebeest and gnu.

Taking to cover

Impala inhabit a wide area of East and South Africa. They seem to like being near water and they avoid open country, being more usually found where there are low trees and tall shrubs, without much ground cover, in scrub and thornbush country especially. Their distribution is patchy because they do not venture much into either overgrown or open land. So, although abundant in most of the Kruger National Park, they are absent from much of its northern end.

△ *Poise in triplicate: a female impala trio nose down in their local river. Impala seldom stray far from water, and will not venture into arid surroundings or bushy thickets.*

According to its suitability for the impala, an area may have a density of anything from seven to over 200 per square mile; the usual figure is 50–70. Concentrations are highest in the dry season, as with most African ungulates; this also happens to be the time of the rut. In the wet season, impala are more scattered, and occupy small home ranges; but they may wander as much as 15 miles for water.

Impala both graze and browse, but in most areas they eat mainly grass.

Born when the grass sprouts

The rut takes place in the beginning of the dry season. The lambs are born, one to each ewe, after a gestation of 180–210 days, early in the wet season when there is most food for them.

In Rhodesia, the first lambs are dropped in early December and the peak of lambing is from December 15 to January 1. Two-year-old ewes, breeding for the first time, give birth later in the season than older ones. The young grow rapidly—in young males the horns begin to sprout in late February—and are usually weaned before the next rut, at which time they may form separate bands. In the rut nearly all ewes breed, at least 97% of the older ones, and 85% of the two-year-olds.

The rut begins when the males set up their territories in late May or early June. Surplus rams attach themselves to small groups of ewes, and the yearlings form small bands by themselves. The ewes live in herds the year round. At the end of the lambing season these may number (including lambs) as much as 100. At Fort Tuli, Rhodesia, herds of 200–300 have been counted. These large herds stay together from January to May, and only a few males associate with them; then in May they break into smaller groups, which pass through the rams' territories and are covered by them. After the rut, the ram groups re-form but groups of mixed sex and age predominate. By December, the groups are reduced in size to ten or less; the ewes become secretive, separating off for a while to give birth.

The main predator is probably the leopard. Existing populations of impala are often subject to poaching, but this does not severely affect their numbers.

Andrew Anderson: NHPA

△ *The roving eye: a handsome male runs a casual glance over the scrubland.*
▷ *A herd of mothers and lambs straddles a road. Males join them only for the rut.*
▽ *Poetry in motion: female in full flight.*

Switchback fugitives

Impala rams become quite aggressive in the rutting season, especially when setting up territories. At this time, fighting and chasing are common. The rams, once the territories are set up, leave their bases to drink at the waterholes, which are a no-man's-land. But the most conspicuous piece of impala behaviour is their alarm reaction. When disturbed, the whole group indulge in a magnificent display of leaping. They jump forward, straight up or with side turns, as much as 10 ft into the air, up and down, round and in all directions. What is the function of this behaviour? It has been suggested that in reality its purpose is to confuse a predator, such as a big cat who is trying to single out one animal from the group it is attacking. The leaping impala, helped by their contrasting colours, seem to be wholly successful in preventing this, and completely confuse the attacker.

A number of animals show this sort of behaviour when alarmed by a predator. Instead of putting as much ground between themselves and their adversary they jink to and fro to cause confusion. The jinking of hares is an example that readily comes to mind and it has been suggested that continually changing direction prevents an enemy from cutting off its prey.

class	**Mammalia**
order	**Artiodactyla**
family	**Bovidae**
genus & species	***Aepyceros melampus***

A Visage: Jacana

Indian buffalo

The buffaloes are a distinctive group of cattle. They are stockily built with large hoofs and large shaggy ears. The horns are triangular in cross-section instead of oval or circular like those of true cattle and bison. The head is carried horizontally and the muzzle is broad and hairless. The back is straight but slopes down towards the hindquarters. The hair is sparse. The two genera of buffaloes are **Syncerus**, *the Cape buffalo of Africa (p 360) and* **Bubalus** *the Indian or water buffalo of Asia.*

The Asiatic buffaloes differ from the Cape buffalo in the shape of the skull, in the horns, and the forward-lying hair in the middle of the back. The Indian buffalo is by far the largest of the Asiatic buffaloes and is an important domestic animal, noted for its docility, in contrast with the aggressiveness of its wild relatives. It is 5–6 ft in height and weighs ½–1 ton. It is black in the wild but the domesticated animal may be grey, black, pink or white with white spots on the chin, throat and limbs. The horns are semicircular, spreading out sideways and then backward, in a line with the back. There are localised populations of wild Indian buffaloes in Ceylon, Nepal, Assam, Indo-China and Borneo. A smaller species is the tamarau, restricted to the island of Mindoro in the Philippines. It is only 3½ ft high with short, thick horns which turn mainly backwards and are only slightly semicircular. It is jet black with a few white spots, very bull-necked and weighs 600–700 lb. In historic times, the tamarau occurred on Luzon as well as Mindoro.

The other two Asiatic buffaloes, known as anoas, are found only on the island of Celebes. They are small and rather antelope-like with short, conical backward-pointing horns and more slender necks. The lowland anoa, the larger, is about 3½ ft high, black, with white spots on jaw, throat and legs. The mountain anoa is about 2–3 ft in height, with shorter tail and horns, golden to dark brown in colour with no white marks except a few white spots above the hoofs. The hair in both is long, soft and woolly. Although these have always been treated as separate species it is now thought that the two are just variants of the same species, and that the tamarau is really a dwarfed island form of the big Indian buffalo.

Shy but pugnacious cattle

Wild buffaloes are so unapproachable that their way of life has not been studied in any detail. In the Kaziranga Game Reserve, in Assam, where there are about 400 wild Indian buffalo, they live in herds of 10–20, in swampy regions and grass jungle, where the elephant grass grows 10–15 ft high. The tamarau is more solitary, but has been seen

▽ *Buffalo bath: a contented soak, away from the intense heat of the tropical sun.*

Toni Angermayer

associating in groups of up to eleven. It inhabits rugged country, on the forest borders and in bamboo. Recently it has become scarce as the forest and bamboo is cut down, and perhaps only 200 or so now survive. It is often shot by cattle farmers. As recently as 1964, tamarau could be seen grazing in the open in morning and evening, but today they have become more nocturnal.

Cattle harems

The wild bulls of the Indian buffalo round up the cows into harems, they then become particularly aggressive. Both the wild and the domesticated animals may breed all the year round, but in the wild there is a breeding peak that occurs at different times, in different areas. In Asia most of the young are born between October and December, after a gestation of 310 days.

In Europe, for example, in Italy where there are semi-wild Indian buffaloes, the young are born between February and April. Buffalo become sexually mature at 2–3 years and in Italy, they often breed at this age, but in parts of the Far East, such as Cambodia, the domesticated animals may not mature until they are about 5 years old, either because they are prevented from doing so or because the poor feed they get delays maturity. Physical maturity does not come until 3½ to 4 years.

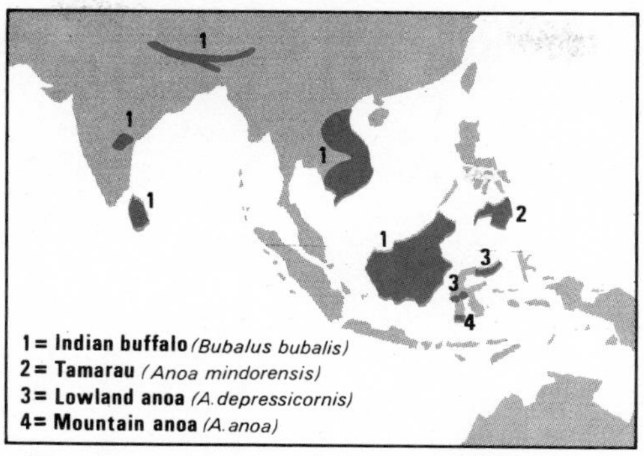

◁▽ *Aggressive cousin: the anoa of Celebes has a well-founded vicious reputation—it will even kill other animals enclosed with it.*
▽▷ *Beast of all work: an Indian buffalo being used to thresh a pile of corn.*
▽▽ *Mother and child, cool in flooded pasture.*

Domestic Indian buffaloes, bred partly at least for milk, have a long, overdeveloped lactation, like domestic cattle. In India and Pakistan they give 40–50% of the countries' milk. In these countries, people tend to buy a female buffalo for a small sum, keep her for one or two lactations, and then get rid of her, since they cannot afford to keep a herd. Meat is forbidden to Hindus but, unlike the humped cattle or zebu, buffalo are not in themselves sacred. Males used for draught are often castrated, and commonly the tail is cut off as well. About half the old animals provide meat for non-Hindus.

Man—the worst enemy

Wild Indian buffaloes may occasionally be preyed on by tigers, but in general they have no serious enemies except man. Anoas live on an island quite free of carnivorous mammals which might prey on them, but they have, nevertheless, a reputation for being extremely aggressive. In captivity they cannot be kept with any other large animals as they will stab them in the belly with their short horns.

Cyr Colour Agency

Peter Hill

Tomsich: Bavaria

Widespread buffalo

The domestic buffalo, usually known as the water buffalo, is one of man's most important and widespread servants. Various breeds are classified as either swamp or river buffaloes. Swamp buffaloes can work in marshy land and humid jungle. They are stocky, heavy creatures, very strong, but have the drawback that they suffer in hot sun, and must bathe or wallow regularly. They are used on a large scale as draught animals in the rice-fields of Malaysia, Indonesia, Indo-China, southern China and the Philippines, where they are called kerabau or carabao. River buffaloes are more specialised, preferring dry pastures, and clear rivers and canals. Used especially in India and Pakistan, they are very docile, and are kept for their milk.

There are about 78 million domestic buffaloes in the world. Over half are in India, with about 10 million in southern China and 5 million in Pakistan. The milk-giving river buffalo of India has been fairly recently introduced into southeast Asia, and is gradually replacing the swamp-buffalo although it is not such a good worker. The present distribution of domesticated buffaloes is of very long standing: in the Philippines, for example, they were there well before the Spaniards arrived.

Domestic buffaloes are also found in smaller numbers in Europe, North Africa and West Asia: in Turkey, Iraq, Syria, Transcaucasia, the Lenkoran plain in the south of Soviet Azerbaijan, Egypt, Eritrea, Greece, Bulgaria, Hungary, Rumania, Yugoslavia, Italy and Andalusia (Spain). In Egypt, they were unknown in the time of the Pharaohs and were probably introduced there in the 9th century AD via Iraq and Syria. Now there are 1¼ million in Egypt. It was only in 1933 that a small number were taken from Egypt to Eritrea.

The European domestic buffalo is of a type very close to the Surti breed of Gujerat, Bombay and Baroda in Western India. Buffalo were probably introduced into Italy from Hungary in the 6th century AD. In 1900, there were 50 000 there; in 1930, only 15 000; now there are still fewer. The draining of the Pontine Marshes has mainly eliminated the buffalo, besides which their state of domestication was never as close as it is in India or the Far East, and the Italian buffaloes, in effect semi-wild, were considered rather dangerous. From Italy, they have been introduced into Guyana, Cayenne, Trindidad, and Brazil; also into the lower Congo.

From the island of Timor—where at present there are 90 000 buffaloes but only 4 000 true cattle—three buffalo were imported to Melville Island, North Australia, in 1825. In 1827, a further fifteen were taken there, and in 1829 another sixteen. They were released on the island to serve as food for settlers and aborigines. In 1838 a few from Melville Island were introduced to the vicinity of Port Essington, and have since spread south to the swamps and grasslands of the Mary, Adelaide and Alligator rivers, and west to the Darwin coast. Some also got ashore from a shipwreck on the Ord river, in Kimberleys district. So, in 1885 there were 6 000 on Melville Island and 60 000 on the mainland of Australia. They have certainly contributed, by overgrazing, to the present scarcity of most Australian indigenous fauna even if they have made their contribution in the form of good leather from their hides. They also provide meat for a few of the aborigines and white hunters in the coastal districts.

△ *Indian buffaloes pause to graze on their journey from a working site. Buffaloes are the mainstay of most of Asia's agriculture—they are even bred to suit varying terrain.*

class	**Mammalia**
order	**Artiodactyla**
family	**Bovidae**
genus & species	***Anoa anoa*** *mountain anoa* ***A. depressicornis*** *lowland anoa* ***A. mindorensis*** *tamarau* ***Bubalus bubalis*** *Indian buffalo*

Indri

The indri is the largest of the lemurs, reaching a head and body length of 30 in. It has a very short tail, only an inch long, and very long hindlimbs with a strong grasping foot and very divergent great toe. The face is short and the muzzle more blunt than in other lemurs. The general effect of its colour is black and white. Usually, the head, neck, shoulders, back, arms and hands are black; and the rump, extending into a wedge-shape up the back, is white, washed with reddish; the flanks and insides of the thighs are grey, but the outside of the hindlimbs are black. The face is also black. There are, however, variations in the colour. In one type, the top of the head is white, the throat and legs grey, and the flanks and heel are bright red. In another, there is a grey patch over each eye, and the forelimbs, shanks and underside are grey. Pure white albinos, with pink eyes, are also known.

A related form is the woolly indri, or avahi. This is much smaller, only 1 ft long, but its tail is longer than the head and body together.

The indri is confined to the two high ranges in northeastern Madagascar, between the Bay of Antongil and the River Masora, where it goes up to nearly 6 000 ft above sea-level. The woolly indri is found in a larger area around the coast, mainly in southeast Madagascar.

Time Life Inc.

△ *Agile ghost of the Madagascar treetops.*

Heard but not easily seen

An indri moves by leaping, making impressive jumps from one trunk to another, pushing off with its hind feet. When climbing, it uses both its feet together, not one at a time like monkeys. By day, the indri sits in the fork of a tree with its legs dangling. Otherwise little is known of the behaviour of either species. Both are purely vegetarian, feeding largely on leaves, of which they eat huge quantities which are digested in their complex stomachs. Each group of indris occupies a territory which seems to consist of an entire hill. The group is made up of two parents, probably monogamous, with their offspring, yet the members of a group are always well spaced, feeding and moving around some way apart from each other, even in different trees, but always in sight of one another. Occasionally, two individuals will come together for mutual grooming, but they do not seem to huddle together like most other primates.

An indri group can be located by its call, a long, mournful, modulated wailing. Though rarely seen, indris can often be heard and their presence pinpointed by this call, which seems to be used by the animals themselves as a means of locating each other. By playing back their calls, David Attenborough drew a group of indris to him so he could film them. Members of a group also communicate with each other by short grunts. They also make a honking call, the purpose of which is uncertain.

The large indri is diurnal, but the woolly indri is nocturnal, and spends most of the day rolled up in a ball in the foliage. It, too, seems to live in family parties. Probably because, being active at night, it cannot rely on sight like its larger relative, it keeps in touch with its fellows by rubbing its face against branches, marking them with scent from glands at the angle of the lower jaw. Its call consists of a very high frequency whistle, almost inaudible to man.

There are few serious predators on Madagascar. Possibly some of the indigenous viverrids, such as the fossa, may eat woolly indris, but the large indri would seem to have no natural enemies, except for birds of prey which might take young ones. At any rate, the local tribes consider the animal sacred and will not harm it. It is, however, being threatened by the destruction of the forest over much of Madagascar.

'There it is!'

'Indri' is not the native name for the animal. The Malagash name for this animal is *babakoto,* meaning 'boy' or *amboanala* meaning 'forest-dog', from its howls. The 18th-century zoologist Sonnerat was the first European to see it. When they first came upon it his Malagasy guide shouted 'Indri' meaning 'Look' or 'There it is!'—so indri it is to this day. The local Malagasy tribes regard the indri with awe. Some believe the indris carry the souls of their ancestors and that the bark and wood of the trees where they live provide remedies for illness. It is also said that if one throws a spear at an indri, the animal catches it in mid-air and throws it back with unerring aim. The baby indri, they believe, is subjected to an ordeal that determines whether it shall live or not. The mother and father toss it back and forth a dozen times, and if it is dropped they simply abandon it; otherwise they rear it carefully. The Betsimaraka tribe recount how the indri are descended from men who went into the forest to hide to avoid working for them. The Betanimena, on the other hand, tell how they (the Betanimena) long ago fled into the forests, where their enemies chased them. Following what they thought were human cries these enemies came across a troop of indri and fled in terror, thinking the Betanimena had changed themselves into animals. So the tribe now treat the indris with the greatest respect—almost as one of them.

class	**Mammalia**
order	**Primates**
suborder	**Prosimii**
family	**Indriidae**
genus & species	***Indri indri*** *indri* ***Avahi laniger*** *woolly indri*

Jacamar

A family of about 15 species of small birds related to woodpeckers, having two toes facing forwards and two facing backwards, jacamars have long, fine bills and often long tails. Their plumage is iridescent and they look like large hummingbirds. The females are less showy than the males, often having a brown instead of a white throat.

The rufous-tailed jacamar is starling-sized with a sharp, black bill and a beautiful plumage mainly of metallic green with a copper and gold iridescence. Alexander Skutch, the American ornithologist, was unable to describe its plumage accurately as its hues were continually changing as it moved. Eventually he merely noted: 'Plumage wonderfully iridescent'. He also recorded that jacamars are among the most exciting birds to meet. The largest is the great jacamar, nearly 1 ft in length, which is also largely metallic green. A less striking species is the white-eared jacamar which is mainly chestnut with a white patch behind each ear.

Jacamars live in the humid forests of Tropical America, ranging from southern Mexico to southern Brazil.

Rufous-tailed jacamar ***Galbula ruficauda*** *a mixed-up bird. It perches like a woodpecker, with two toes forwards, two back, hunts like a flycatcher, and nests in a burrow.*

Flashy flycatchers

The most common places to find jacamars are in tangled secondary growth, in clearings, along the sides of streams and roads, rather than in the dense jungle. They are solitary, spending much of their time perched on prominent branches overlooking open spaces. From here they watch for insects which they fly out to catch. The insects are seized with an audible snap of the pointed bill and carried back to the perch to be eaten. A variety of insects is caught, ranging from bugs, flies and beetles to moths, butterflies, bees, ants and wasps. The jacamars that have been studied feed entirely on insects, most of them caught in the air, and it is presumed that other jacamars do so as well. Large insects are battered against the perch until they are dead and their wings have fallen off. The soft bodies can then be swallowed easily.

In the early years of this century FW Chapman gave us a detailed description of the red-tailed jacamar's flycatching: 'They are the most expert flycatchers I have ever seen . . . Their watchfulness permits no insect to pass in safety. They maintain a constant lookout, turning the head quickly from side to side, above, or even halfway round. The dart into the air is made with wonderful celerity. Sometimes it is straight up, again at various angles, and they go as far as thirty or thirty-five feet from their perch.'

Nesting in burrows

Jacamars are noisy birds and some of them have melodious, quiet songs as well as squeaking call notes. They nest in burrows in banks or steep slopes which both sexes dig by chipping out soil with their bills and scraping it out with their feet. The completed burrows are about 1 ft or so long and 2 in. diameter. At the end is an unlined nest chamber where four white eggs are laid. Both parents incubate the eggs, the female staying on the nest all night. After 3 weeks the chicks hatch. Unlike the naked chicks of woodpeckers and their other relatives, jacamar chicks hatch with a coat of white down. The developing feathers are enclosed in membranous sheaths giving the baby jacamars a prickly appearance. At first all four toes face forwards, then two turn round to face backwards.

The young jacamars spend three or four weeks in the nest. They are fed by both parents who bring insects to the nest, but do not remove droppings as do so many other birds. As a result the nest chamber soon becomes cluttered with beetle wing cases and other debris. At first the parents crawl right into the nest chamber, feed the chicks, turn and crawl out. Then as the chicks become more active they move down the tunnel, and the adults crawl in then back out again. When they are nearly ready to fly the chicks appear at the entrance and the parents need only land at the entrance to feed them.

Is camouflage useful?

The favourite prey of jacamars are the large dragonflies and butterflies of the South American forests, whose colours almost match those of the jacamars in brilliance. To see a jacamar hunting them on rapidly-moving wings is a wonderful sight, yet it raises an interesting question. Most accounts of jacamars refer to their catching colourful insects in preference to the more inconspicuous kinds. So often we hear that a dully-coloured animal is camouflaged to prevent its enemies finding it—and if camouflage is so important to animals, why do some of them exhibit brilliant colours, like these South American butterflies? Some insects have brilliant colours which warn other animals that they are harmful but this is not the case here.

Perhaps there are two answers. No animal has a perfect defence system—bees, despite their warning colours, fall prey to bee-eaters, for instance. It also seems that often camouflage is not really effective. Many hawks, for example, have extremely good eyesight that enables them to find inconspicuous prey and, as jacamars also feed on inconspicuous insects, the butterflies and others would gain no advantage in being drab. If there were any advantage in an inconspicuous colour this is presumably offset by some unknown advantage of having bright colours.

class	**Aves**
order	**Piciformes**
family	**Galbulidae**
genera & species	***Galbula ruficauda*** *rufous-tailed jacamar* ***Galbalcyrhynchus leucotis*** *white-eared jacamar* ***Jacamerops aurea*** *great jacamar* *others*

Jacana

These are water birds that look like long-legged coots, but are in fact waders related to the curlew, avocet and snipe. Jacana is a Spanish word derived from the name given to the birds by South American Indians. In English the soft 'c' is usually pronounced as 'k'. Lily-trotter, lotus-bird and water-walker are alternative names, and describe the jacana's habit of walking on floating vegetation, supported on extremely long toes. On the 'wrist' of the wing there is a knob or spike sometimes 1 in. long. This is said to be used in fighting.

There are seven species of jacana living in America, Africa south of the Sahara and including Madagascar, Asia from India to the Malay Archipelago and in eastern Australia. The American jacana is found in Mexico and the West Indies south to northern Argentina. Its plumage is reddish-brown with yellow-green undersides to the wings. Some American jacanas have completely black plumage or a black head. They have a yellow frontal shield like that of coots. The Australian lotus-bird, which is also found in the East Indies, is brownish with black on the chest and back of the neck and white on the throat and under the tail. The white patch on the throat is bordered with orange and there is a shield of scarlet. Most jacanas have very short tails but in the breeding season the pheasant-tailed jacana, of India to the Philippines, grows a long, curving tail of black feathers. The rest of the plumage is brown with white on the head and neck except for a golden patch on the neck surrounded by a band of black.

Peter Hill

△ *The lily-trotter: an African jacana* ***Actophilornis africanus*** *uses long, widely-splayed toes to run over floating water plants.* ▽ *Mystery: why do jacanas flip up their wings after landing?*

Wolfgang Lummer

Walking on water

Jacanas are found on ponds, lakes and slow-moving rivers where there are abundant waterlilies, water hyacinths and other floating plants. Outside the breeding season they may gather in flocks of hundreds or thousands. A little over 10 years ago their range in Australia moved south when aquatic plants invaded lagoons near Sydney. They can run over the soft water plants because their long toes spread their weight like snowshoes. Sometimes they appear to be running over clear water but they are being supported by perhaps two or three stems. Their gait is a dainty high-stepping, lifting the feet high so the toes clear the surface and jerking their tails at each step. Jacanas can swim but rarely do so and if pressed flutter across open water with legs and toes dangling. They feed on water plants and small animals.

Silence until the rain

Jacanas are usually silent, but in the mating season they give voice to a variety of calls: piping, churring, clucking and grunting are used by most species when breeding, with a scolding chittering when alarmed.

Like most waterfowl, they breed in the later stages of the rainy season. Courtship display consists of showing off the wings, weed carrying and bowing.

Floating nests

Jacana nests are extremely flimsy. The four eggs are laid on a coil of weed or a few rush stems piled together, or even on a water-lily leaf. The eggs are very glossy and look as if they are varnished. They have so much marking that the brown background is often lost. The gloss may make them unwettable—a useful condition, as the nest may submerge as the parent steps onto it.

The adults are very much alike but the female is often larger than the male. In some species at least, the female plays little or no part in rearing the young and she may have several mates. Observations on the bronze-winged jacana of India from a floating hide revealed that both adults collected nest material but that the female took an active part in courtship and left incubation of the eggs and care of the young to the male. The male left the nest only to feed while the female stood guard, driving away moorhens and herons that came too near. Later another male arrived at the pool and, although attacked by the first male it was able to set up a territory at the far end of the pool. The female would peck the two males when they fought; she mated with the second male and laid a second clutch which he raised.

The chicks hatch out after 2 weeks or more and are able to run about immediately. When danger threatens they lie motionless or dive under water while the parents lure the enemy away with a distraction display, attracting attention to themselves by flapping their wings and calling.

Holding the babies

Some jacanas incubate their eggs by holding them under their wings. This seems strange until it is realised that this will keep the eggs clear of the water when the jacana sits on its flimsy floating nest. The eggs are scooped up with the wings and carried two on each side. After the eggs have hatched the chicks will take refuge under their parents' wings. They raise their heads and stretch their tiny wings above their backs to invite their parent to pick them up. Jacanas have one bone in the forewing flattened to form a plate or blade, and this may help in scooping up the eggs.

class	**Aves**
order	**Charadriiformes**
family	**Jacanidae**
genera & species	***Jacana spinosa*** *American jacana* ***Metopidius indicus*** *bronze-winged jacana* ***Irediparra gallinacea*** *Australian jacana* ***Hydrophasianus chirurgus*** *pheasant-tailed jacana* *others*

Sven Gillsäter: Tio

△ *Anticipation: a pair of jackal cubs await their parents' return to the termite mound den.*

Although few fossils of golden jackals have been found, suggesting a limited range in the past, jackals now live in North Africa, a large part of Asia and even in a small area of southeast Europe, partly in Russia and partly in the Balkans. The few fossils there are of the golden jackal date from the Late Pleistocene period (up to 100 000 years ago) and show that it once lived in Italy. Jackals similar to ***C. aureus*** *lived in North Africa in the middle Pleistocene and fossils of other species of jackals have been found in Africa which date back to 3 million years ago. The distribution of the three modern species is shown on the map below. The divisions between these is obscured by the existence of many races and subspecies.*

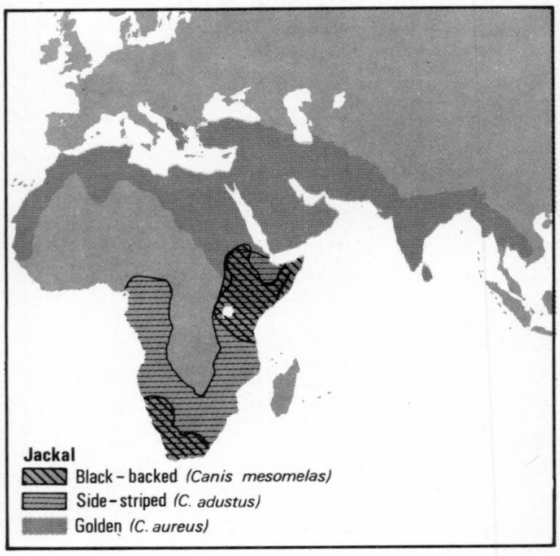

Jackal

There are three species of jackal, distinguished by their colouring. The golden or Indian jackal is a dirty yellow with black and brown hairs and has a black-tipped reddish-brown tail. The black-backed jackal is black shot with grey on its back and neck and pale underneath, there being a very distinct boundary between the two. The tail has a black tip. The side-striped jackal has a pair of light and dark stripes on each side of the body and a white-tipped tail. The jackals are alike in size; the head and body is 22—29 in. long and tail 9—14 in. and they stand about 16 in. at the shoulder.

Jackals once ranged throughout Africa, Europe and southern Asia; now they are found over most of Africa but only the golden jackal is found in Asia and southeastern Europe. Until recently it ranged as far north and west as Hungary.

No competition

Jackals live in wooded and open country and often come into towns and cities, scavanging for refuse and carrion. They are usually seen singly or in pairs, foraging mainly at night. Packs of jackals are sometimes seen but are now much rarer than they used to be. The pairs hold territories, sometimes 2 miles across, marked with urine by both sexes and defended against other jackals. Fights are rare and territorial disputes are settled by aggressive displays.

In the Serengeti, black-backed and golden jackals have different habitats. Most of the black-backed jackals live in bush country while the golden jackals live on the open plains. Hence competition is reduced and where the two species do live side by side, as along the borders of the bush, a jackal will not interfere with another of a different species that wanders through its territory. There is also a separation in their feeding and breeding habits.

Not only scavengers

It used to be thought that, like hyaenas, jackals were scavengers and the name jackal was used as a term of contempt. Jackals are indeed carrion eaters and scavengers feeding on the remains of prey left by lions and leopards, but they are also hunters. Their main prey is gazelles, especially young gazelles, which they chase in a typically dog-like fashion, tiring an animal then slashing at it with their teeth. The black-backed jackals generally bite at the throat, whereas golden jackals go for the belly. The success of the attack depends very much on whether the jackal is hunting by itself or with its mate. In a study made in the Serengeti, single jackals were successful in only 16% of their attacks. Jackals working in pairs were successful in 67% of their attacks. The attacks are sometimes frustrated by female gazelles coming between the jackals and their prey, butting at the jackals and driving them away. Any food that a jackal cannot eat immediately is carried away and buried to be eaten later.

When feeding in open country, black-backed and golden jackals feed on the same food. This includes young gazelles, insects, carrion, rats, hares, ground-nesting birds, and even fruit. In South Africa jackals have become a pest of pineapple plantations and in India they eat sugar cane and ripe coffee beans. In the bush country, however, the two jackals have dissimilar diets. The black-backed jackals feed more on gazelle and the golden jackal more on insects such as termites and dung beetles.

Young born in dens

Some 2—7 pups are born in a burrow that the female digs herself or takes over from another animal and enlarges. Black-backed jackals often enlarge holes in termites' nests, while golden jackals convert the holes of warthogs and other animals to their own needs, often making several entrances. If disturbed, jackals carry their young to new burrows.

As is usual in the dog family there is a strong bond between the parents and both male and female bring food back for the pups. Whenever one returns there is a ritual, the pups running out with tails wagging and ears pressed back. They run alongside their parent keeping their noses just by the corner of its mouth. The parent who has been guarding the cubs also behaves in the same way and the returning parent regurgitates lumps of meat, which are snapped up by the pups or picked up by the second parent and redistributed. When the pups are 8 months old they begin to forage for themselves, catching insects, but they are dependent on their parents for another 2 months.

MJ Coe

△ *Canine manners: a side-striped jackal seeks 'permission' to sit down.* ▽ *Not just scavengers: jackals often hunt and kill their own prey.*

MJ Coe

Norman Myers

The lion's lackey?

Hyaena and jackal are both used as terms of contempt for hangers-on. They are synonyms for parasites, spongers or sycophants. This unpleasant association is derived from the original idea that hyaenas and jackals were scavengers, hanging around the large carnivores for a free meal. In Shakespeare's time the jackal was described as the lion's usher or forerunner. It was believed that two or three jackals would run ahead of a lion like hounds in front of the huntsmen. They followed the scent of the prey and when finding it would bark or howl to alert the lion who would then attack. After the lion had finished eating its attendants picked over the remains.

Such stories were made up on the basis of hearing jackals howling at night and finding them around the remains of large animals at daybreak. Now that zoologists are studying animals at night, they are finding that hyaenas and jackals are hunters in their own right and that lions are not above scavenging the hyaenas' prey.

These studies have not completely cleared the jackal's name. It scavenges a great deal, especially around human settlements and is often credited with digging up bodies—its blood-curdling howl must help reinforce any ideas people may have based on the jackal's grave-robbing habits.

class	**Mammalia**
order	**Carnivora**
family	**Canidae**
genus & species	***Canis adustus*** *side-striped jackal* ***C. aureus*** *golden jackal* ***C. mesomelas*** *black-backed jackal*

No honour among thieves: despite vicious beaks and overwhelming numbers a jackal clears its meal of vultures (above) and threatens all who come near.

Norman Myers

Jackdaw *Corvus monedula*

Jane Burton: Photo Res

Stop thief: the jackdaw's habit of stealing bright objects is immortalised in many stories. One concerns an ex-sailor's jackdaw which would snatch lighted cigarettes from his lips and fly away.

Jackdaw

*The jackdaw is a bird renowned for its talkative and thievish nature. It is familiar to many people as it spends much of its time around buildings such as church towers. It was called **monedula** by the Romans, its Old English name was daw; in the 16th century it became known as Jack daw. The two words later became joined to make one and both daw and jackdaw were used as names of contempt for foolish, thievish and over-talkative people.*

The jackdaw is a member of the crow family. It is 13 in. long, and has black plumage shot with blue on the back and head and with a grey nape and pale blue eyes. Its short but strong bill is black and so are the legs and toes. It ranges across Europe except for the extreme north, across into northwest Africa, and into much of west and central Asia.

Sociable jackdaws

The original home of jackdaws was probably on cliffs but they readily adopted buildings when the opportunities arose, for their nooks and crannies were good substitutes for cliffs and craggy hills. By taking to buildings they also found plenty of food, especially around farms. Capacious chimneys, once fashionable, provide a good substitute for hollow trees in which jackdaws readily build their nests. They also frequent park land and cultivated land.

On the ground a jackdaw walks with a jerky, swaggering strut. Gregarious, it lives in flocks and will join flocks of its larger relatives, the rooks, whose roosts it often shares. It flies with rapid wingbeats, on a somewhat erratic course and often goes in for aerial displays, the whole flock joining in, although individual members tend to keep to pairs within the flock. While flying the characteristic call note *tchack* (or 'Jack!') is used, together with other variations on this note. The birds call in a clamour, especially in the evening when flying around a roost.

Stealing anything bright

Jackdaws feed on insects, especially grubs, and any small vertebrates as well as fruits and seeds. Chicken runs are visited for grain and other foods and jackdaws will scavenge rubbish heaps and feed from bird tables. They are virtually omnivorous and at times will rob the nests of small birds, taking eggs as well as nestlings, but tastes vary from one district to another. In one place, for example, the local jackdaws will visit cherry trees with ripening fruit day after day until the crop is gone, but in another place will ignore a similar crop. Nevertheless, ripe and highly-coloured soft fruits generally seem to be attractive and this may be linked with the birds' habit of stealing bright objects and hiding them. The habit is immortalized in many stories, from the 'Jackdaw of Rheims' to the tale of the ex-sailor whose tame jackdaw would snatch lighted cigarettes from his lips and then fly away, followed by a torrent of nautical oaths.

Like the ex-sailor, jackdaws themselves are voluble. Their native vocabulary includes a wide range of notes, many of them melodious and warbling. Jackdaws are also good mimics of many sounds, including human speech. It used to be thought that slitting a jackdaw's tongue made it a good talker and many thousands of tame jackdaws have been mutilated in this way. It makes no difference, of course, because birds do not use the tongue as we do to form words. Some jackdaws readily learn to talk, others do not, and cutting the tongue does not alter this.

Huge, messy nests in chimneys

Jackdaw courtship consists largely of the male bowing to the female and at times pressing the beak onto the breast to show off the grey head, as well as flicking the wings and jerking the tail. Both build the nest, usually no more than a small platform of sticks with a lining of wool, fur, hair, grass and paper in any kind of hole, in a tree, chimney or church tower, or in a rabbit burrow. Where there is room there may be a deep layer of sticks with the nest proper on top of it. In late April 4–6 light blue eggs with a few dark spots are laid. The female incubates for 17 days, being fed by the male. Both bring food for the young in throat pouches for 30–35 days.

Jackdaws often nest in trees reduced by age to a hollow bole. They fill this with sticks to a depth of several feet and then build a nest of fur, hair or wool on this column. In the chimney of one old house, for example, nesting jackdaws brought in so much material that sticks gradually poured out into the fireplace, covering the wide hearth as well as filling the chimney. To clear the chimney and fireplace a waggon-load of sticks had to be carted away! More surprising, a pair of jackdaws have often built in the space containing a spiral staircase, filling it with sticks.

Feathered fire-raisers

The fire service records in many parts of the world tell of firemen being called to put out fires in the upper parts of trees. In many of these the burning tree stood on its own, far from a highway and the point at which the fire started was too high for anyone to have thrown a lighted cigarette or match into it to start the fire.

Some years ago a man walking through the woods in Surrey, in the south of England, ducked his head to pass under a low bough of a yew tree and felt a burning sensation on the back of his neck. He found it was a red-hot ember and looked up to see a fire starting halfway up the tree. He ran to the nearest telephone, called the fire service and the fire was put out, but not before the upper half of the tree had been reduced to bare and blackened branches. At the point where the fire had started was a small hollow in the yew trunk containing the sticks of a jackdaw's nest. The lining was burnt to ashes. The chances are that one of the jackdaws had carried a burning cigarette to the nest.

class	**Aves**
order	**Passeriformes**
family	**Corvidae**
genus & species	***Corvus monedula***

Aquatic boxer: because of the ritualised fighting which occurs between males during the breeding season, the Jack Dempsey, when it first became popular, was named after the world heavyweight boxer. During display the large black spots become masked as other colours heighten.

Jack Dempsey

This dazzling fish once enjoyed, among aquarists, a high popularity which still persists, but to a lesser degree. It is very aggressive and can create havoc in a mixed tank, with other kinds of fishes so it needs to be kept in a separate aquarium and to be made a special pet. The fighting between males is, however, ritualized and has the appearance of a boxing match. The fish was accordingly named after the world heavyweight boxer at the time it first became popular.

Young fishes are brown but mature males, which are up to 8 in. long, are deep brown to black peppered with light blue spots, and some yellow spots, all over the body. They also have a round black spot at the centre of the body and another at the base of the tail. The upper edge of the dorsal fin is red and the iris of the eye is also red. The females are slightly smaller than the males and have fewer blue spots and shorter fins. The body of both is deep and slightly flattened sideways. The head is large, with a jutting lower jaw. The forehead of the male bulges as it gets older.

The Jack Dempsey lives in slow flowing waters of the basins of the Amazon and Rio Negro in South America.

Queensberry rules

Almost nothing is known about how the Jack Dempsey lives in its natural habitat. It has, however, been closely studied as an aquarium fish, especially in regard to its rules of fighting and its breeding. These two aspects of its behaviour are closely linked, as they are in other species of animals. When a male Jack Dempsey comes into breeding condition he establishes a territory. Should another male swim into that territory the owner faces the newcomer, swims over to him and begins what is known as a lateral display; swimming beside him so the two are nose to tail and lying alongside each other, separated by only a short distance. At the same time he raises his dorsal and anal fins, spreads his paired fins and raises his gill-covers. From the side he now looks very much bigger. At the same time his colours grow brighter, and this makes the two black spots stand out much more. The total result is that he looks much more terrifying to his opponent.

His opponent may do one of two things. He may retreat, in which event he is chased across the boundary of the territory. He may, and usually does, respond to the display by raising his own fins and his own colours grow brighter. In that event the two circle each other, trying to butt each other with the sharp edge of the jaw. The two may later seize each other by the mouth in a trial of strength. In the end it is almost invariably the intruder that finally gives up and retreats, being then chased by the owner of the territory. Slight injuries may be sustained in the fight—very occasionally these may be serious.

Feminine pacifism

Should a female wander into the territory something of the same sort takes place, but everything depends on how near she is to being ready to spawn. In any case, the male displays at her as if she were a male, but instead of raising her fins she lowers them. This indicates to him that she is a female. It is what is called a show of symbolic inferiority. It does not prevent him attacking her, butting her with his jaw, but she accepts these blows and does not fight back. In the end she leaves the territory, chased out, if she is not ready to spawn, but if she is ready to spawn the male's aggressiveness dies down and he accepts her as a mate. Given plenty of space, as they would have in the wild, a female not ready to mate would have room to get away. In a tank a female, in these circumstances, would be beaten up. The usual procedure, in bringing a male and a female together in an aquarium, is to put a sheet of glass in the tank to separate them. They do all their displaying through the glass which prevents them harming each other. In due course this turns to courtship as the female comes into breeding condition, and when the glass is finally taken out they come together peacefully as a pair to spawn.

Working off energy

'Coming into breeding condition' means more than merely getting ready to spawn. Especially in the male there is a build-up of energy which is largely dissipated in fighting. In many cichlid fishes he digs pits in the sand, as described for the firemouth (p 764). Instead of digging several small pits as some cichlids do, the Jack Dempsey digs one big pit. This is interpreted by some scientists as the result of the female taking a long time to come into breeding condition. They compare it with the way some birds build extra large nests when their mates are slow to reach mating condition.

Eventually, both male and female Jack Dempsey choose a flat surface and start cleaning it with their mouths. Then the female moves over this surface laying her eggs, the male following her and fertilising the eggs as they lie stuck to the surface. The eggs take 51 hours to hatch, during which time both parents fan them with their fins. For some 96 hours after hatching the babies are feeding on their yolk sacs, unable to swim. They are then known as wrigglers, and the parents take each wriggler in turn in their mouths and place it in a pit in the sand, where they guard their family. As the babies begin to swim out of the pit the parents pick them up in their mouths and spit them back into the mass. There comes a time, however, when the young swimmers are too big for the parents to keep spitting them back and so they give up doing so. Instead, they direct their efforts to keeping their family of several hundred bunched together for protection. Some 1 000 or more eggs may be laid in a season.

Family cannibalism

One thing scientists have tried to find out is whether Jack Dempseys recognize their own babies. They have taken away their eggs and replaced them by eggs laid by a related species. From these experiments it seems that provided the foster broods grow at the same rate and are about the same size all will be well. So it seems the Jack Dempseys are not recognizing their own babies but are recognizing that the family they are guarding are the same size and have the same growth rate as they should have. Sometimes, in swapping the clutches of eggs, the scientists have overlooked a batch of eggs on the underside of a slab of rock. When, therefore, hatching time comes the wrigglers are half Jack Dempseys and half the babies of another species. All goes well at first but after a few weeks the two sets of babies begin to differ in size, one set growing slightly more quickly than the other, and these larger babies eat their smaller foster-brethren. Although they have lived with them all the time these babies can recognize when one of their foster brothers or sisters is slightly smaller than themselves and so can be overpowered.

class	**Pisces**
order	**Perciformes**
family	**Cichlidae**
genus & species	***Cichlasoma biocellatus***

Training session: young immature 3in. Jack Dempseys circle one another in their aquarium. Almost nothing is known of their behaviour in the wild, but from observations in the aquarium their rules of fighting and their breeding are now known. These two aspects of their behaviour are closely linked as in many animal species.

Jane Burton: Photo Res

Jack rabbit

*The jack rabbits of the western United States are hares belonging to the genus **Lepus**—they are close relatives of the brown hare, varying hare and snowshoe rabbit (p 1019). The white-tailed jack rabbit, also known as the plains or prairie hare, has a brownish coat in the summer which changes to white in the winter. Only the 6in. black-tipped ears and 4in. white tail remain unchanged all the year round. This jack rabbit, which weighs up to 10 lb, lives in the prairies of the northwest, but to the south lives the smaller black-tailed or jackass hare. The latter name is derived from the 8in. black-tipped ears. The coat is sandy except for the black upper surface of the tail. It does not turn white in winter. This species lives in the arid country from Oregon to Mexico and eastwards to Texas. There is also a small population in Florida which has come from imported jack rabbits, used in training greyhounds, that have gone wild.*

The remaining jack rabbits, the two species of antelope or white-sided jack rabbits, live in restricted areas of Arizona and New Mexico.

Safety in bounding leaps

Like all hares, jack rabbits live on the surface of the ground and do not burrow. The exception is the white-tailed jack rabbit which in winter burrows under the snow for warmth and also gains protection against predators such as owls. Otherwise jack rabbits escape detection by crouching among the sparse vegetation of the prairies and semi-desert countryside. They lie up in shade during the day and come out in the evening. Each jack rabbit has several forms, hollows in the ground shaded and concealed by plants, within its home range. If flushed, jack rabbits will run extremely fast, sometimes reaching 45 mph in a series of 20ft springing bounds like animated rubber balls. Every so often they leap up 4 or 5 ft to clear the surrounding vegetation and look out for enemies.

Water from cacti

Jack rabbits feed mainly on grass and plants such as sagebrush or snakeweed, and often become serious pests where their numbers build up. To protect crops and to save the grazing for domestic stock, hunts are organised or poisoned bait put down. In the arid parts of their range, when the grass has dried up, jack rabbits survive on mes-

Hare of the plain and prairie: the jack rabbit of the western United States has two obvious adaptations for grassland life—very long ears, useful for detecting predators at a distance, and long hind legs with which it runs up to 45 mph in a series of bounding leaps.

Joe Van Wormer: Photo Res

quite and cacti. They can get all the water they need from cacti providing they do not lose too much moisture in keeping cool. To eat a prickly cactus a jack rabbit carefully chews around a spiny area and pulls out the loosened section. Then it puts its head into the hole and eats the moist, fleshy pulp which it finds inside.

Born in the open

The length of the breeding season varies according to the range of the jack rabbit, many as eight. The babies weigh 2–6 oz and can stand and walk a few steps immediately after birth, but they do not leave the nest for about 4 weeks.

Radiator ears

Large ears are a characteristic of desert animals, such as bat-eared and fennec foxes, and it is usually supposed that as well as improving the animal's hearing they act as radiators for keeping the body cool. as a means of cooling. In hot weather jack rabbits make use of every bit of shade and in their forms the ground temperature is lower than the air or body temperature and so acts as another heat sink.

The heat balance of a jack rabbit is, however, very precarious. On a hot day it is possible for two men easily to run down a jack rabbit. By continually flushing it and keeping it in the open the jack rabbit soon collapses from heat exhaustion and is soon ready for the pot!

Meston

L Lee Rue III: Photo Res

being shorter in the north. At the onset of breeding jack rabbits indulge in the typical mad antics of hares. The males chase to and fro and fight each other. They rear up, sometimes growling, and batter each other with their forepaws. They also bite each other, tearing out tufts of fur or even flesh and occasionally violent kicks are delivered with the hindlegs. A carefully-aimed kick can wound the recipient severely; otherwise the fight continues until one of the combatants turns tail and flees.

The baby jack rabbits are born in open nests concealed by brush or grass and lined with fur which the female pulls from her body. The litters are usually of three or four young but there may be as few as one or as

There is, however, a drawback to this idea. If heat can be lost from the ears it can also be absorbed. The problem has now been resolved because it has been realised that a clear sky has a low radiant temperature and acts as a heat sink. In the semi-arid home of the black-tailed jack rabbit a clear, blue sky may have a temperature of 10–15°C/50–59°F to which heat can be radiated from the jack rabbit's ears that have a temperature of 38°C/100°F. Only a slight difference in temperature is needed for radiation to take place and the large difference between ears and sky allows efficient heat transfer.

Jack rabbits rely on radiation to keep them cool, for, as we have seen, they do not get enough water to be able to use evaporation

◁△ *On the look-out. White-tailed jack rabbit crouches by sparse vegetation of the prairies.*
△ *Black-tailed portrait. Named jackass hare, after its 8in. black-tipped ears, this jack rabbit does not change to white in winter as does the white-tailed jack rabbit.*

class	**Mammalia**
order	**Lagomorpha**
family	**Leporidae**
genus & species	***Lepus californicus*** *black-tailed jack rabbit* ***L. townsendi*** *white-tailed jack rabbit* *others*

Jaguar

This is the largest of the American cats and is known as **el tigre** *in South America. The jaguar is no longer than a leopard but is more heavily built; head and body are 5–6 ft long and the tail is about 3 ft. It may weigh up to 300 lb. The ground colour of the coat is yellow, becoming paler underneath. All over the body is a pattern of black spots up to 1 in. diameter. The jaguar's coat is usually easy to distinguish from the spotted coat of a leopard because the spots on the jaguar skin are arranged in a rosette of 4–5 around a central spot. These rosettes are not so marked on the legs or head where the spots are more tightly packed. Black and albino jaguars are known.*

Jaguars range from the southern United States to Patagonia. In places it is still quite common but elsewhere it has been shot as a cattle-stealer and for its beautiful coat and is now rare or missing altogether.

Zool Soc London

▷ *'Jaguara'—the South American Indian name for the jaguar—is said to mean the 'carnivore that overcomes its prey in a single bound'.*

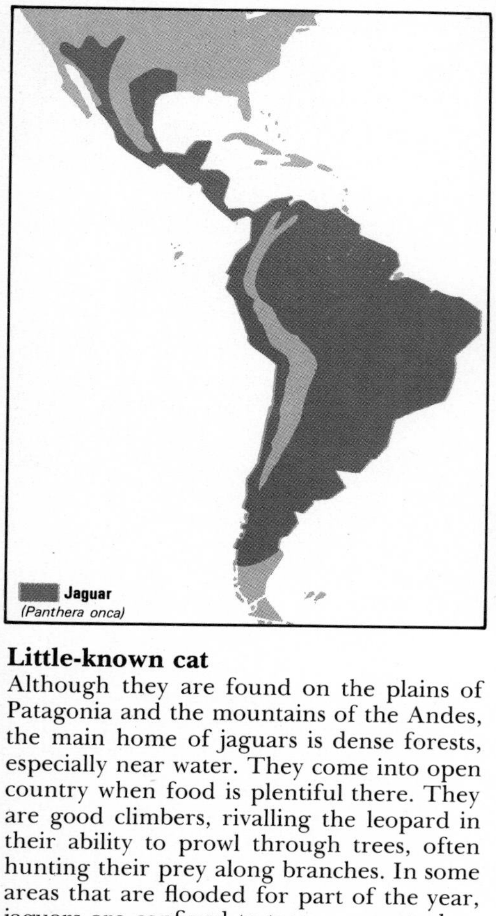

Little-known cat

Although they are found on the plains of Patagonia and the mountains of the Andes, the main home of jaguars is dense forests, especially near water. They come into open country when food is plentiful there. They are good climbers, rivalling the leopard in their ability to prowl through trees, often hunting their prey along branches. In some areas that are flooded for part of the year, jaguars are confined to trees—except when they take to water for they are extremely good swimmers as well. Jaguars are difficult to find in their forest haunts because their spotted coats blend in so well with their surroundings. As a result less is known about jaguars than about other big cats. Our knowledge is based mainly on the stories of South American Indians and the accounts of explorers and hunters.

It is likely that jaguars have territories or ranges which they defend against other jaguars. This explains reports by travellers in the South American forests of being followed by a jaguar for many miles, then suddenly being abandoned. Apparently the jaguars had been seeing the men off their territories.

Man-killers

Jaguars take a wide variety of food. Their main prey is capybaras and peccaries and they also capture large animals such as tapirs and domestic cattle as well as sloths, anteaters, monkeys and deer. They fight, kill and devour alligators and wait for freshwater turtles to come ashore to lay their eggs. The turtles are tipped onto their backs and the jaguars rip open their shells. Their eggs are also dug up.

Another favourite food is fish, which are caught by the jaguar lying in wait on a rock or a low branch overhanging the water and flipping the fish out with a quick strike of the paw. It is sometimes said that jaguars flip their tails in the water to act as a lure. Their tails may hang into the water and attract fish accidentally, and as cats often flick their tails when excited this could be especially attractive to fish. Having done this by chance and met with success it would

not be beyond the mental powers of a jaguar to learn to do it deliberately.

Inevitably there should be stories of man-eating connected with the jaguar, as there are with any big carnivore. According to some accounts it is more dangerous than the lion or leopard, partly because of its habit of defending a territory and partly because it becomes possessive about its prey. When the prey is domestic stock men living and working nearby are likely to be attacked. In these cases, however, the jaguars are man-killing rather than man-eating. Another cause of attacks is the wounding of jaguars by hunters. Jaguars are hunted with dogs that bring them to bay after tiring them, and an enraged jaguar may charge, killing dogs or hunter. In exoneration of the jaguar, the famous explorer and naturalist Humboldt tells of two Indian children playing in a forest clearing. They were joined by a jaguar who bounded around them until it accidentally scratched the face of one child. The other seized a stick and smote the jaguar on the face; the wild beast slunk back into the jungle. How much truth lies in the story is impossible to say, but it is not the first account of a large beast playing with children.

Year-round breeding

Jaguars breed at any time of the year and have cubs every other year. Gestation lasts about 100 days and 2–4 cubs are born in each litter. Virtually nothing is known of courtship or care of the young in the wild because of the difficulty of making observations. Jaguars have lived in captivity for 22 years.

Peccary foes

It is thought jaguars 'take possession' of their prey and defend it. Indians in Guyana have told of jaguars attaching themselves to herds of peccaries and following them about, preying on those that get separated from their fellows. It is also said that the peccaries, which can be very savage, will attempt to rescue their companions and send the jaguar running to the nearest tree. This is supported by the account of an English explorer in Brazil who, hearing a great commotion one evening, found a jaguar perched on an anthill surrounded by about 50 furious peccaries. Inadvertently the jaguar lowered its tail which was immediately grabbed by the peccaries, who pulled the jaguar down and tore it apart. This may be a tall story—but at the moment much of our knowledge of jaguars has to rest on such stories.

class	**Mammalia**
order	**Carnivora**
family	**Felidae**
genus & species	***Panthera onca***

Prowling around—jaguar cubs. The spotted coat has groups of black rosettes similar to the leopard's, but in jaguars each rosette has a central spot.

Walt Disney Productions Limited

Jaguarundi

Although a member of the cat family the jaguarundi is more like a large weasel in shape and habits. Its body is long, its legs very short and its head is flattened with small ears and sloping face. A jaguarundi, sometimes spelt jaguarondi, may be up to 50 in. head and body with a tail of 21 in. but its height at the shoulder will not exceed 12 in. Its weight may be up to 20 lb. Its short fur is uniformly rusty-red or grey, these being distinct colour phases of the same species, although at one time the red was believed to be a separate species with the common name of the eyra or eyra cat and a separate scientific name ***Felis eyra****. Its name is derived from the name used for this animal by the Tupi, an aboriginal people in Brazil. Jaguarundis live in grasslands, on the edges of forests or in dense brushland, especially near water, from the southern border of the United States southwards to northern Argentina in South America.*

Otter-like cat

Jaguarundis are extremely shy and secretive. They are seldom seen and from what little is known of their habits they are more like otters than cats. In some parts of America they are called otter-cats. Instead of stalking their prey or lying in wait they pursue it. Excellent runners despite their short legs, they will sprint for a mile or more if necessary, even through dense undergrowth, running down rodents and ground birds. They readily take to water, another uncatlike trait, and they can climb trees. They do this in search of fruit and have been seen feeding, in company with howler monkeys, on green figs. The gestation period is said to be 9 months, which is unusually long for a member of the cat family, but as jaguarundis are not easy to keep in captivity this figure is unverified.

Colour phases

The jaguarundi is a species showing colour phases. In all species there is a variation from one individual to another in the coat, the plumage and so on. Colour phases, however, are rather special. In dealing with the blotched genet (p 859) we saw that a related form, the rusty-spotted genet, was believed to be a colour phase of it. There are several species of the cat family in which this is more definite. In the jaguarundi there may be red individuals or grey individuals. The African tiger-cat of the tropical rain forests may be red or grey and the colours are interchangeable. A red-coated individual may be grey after the next moult and vice versa. Temminck's cat, also known as the golden cat, of southeast Asia, may be uniformly red or uniformly grey, or it may be red with black spots or grey with black spots and a single litter may contain kittens showing two or more of these four colour phases. The colours are quite distinct and do not grade into each other.

class	**Mammalia**
order	**Carnivora**
family	**Felidae**
genus & species	***Felis yagouaroundi***

The Jaguarundi has yet to be studied closely in the wild. In South America it frequents grasslands, edges of forests or dense brushland, especially near water. It is also known as the otter cat—not for any particular affinity it has for swimming—but for its long, low profile and otter size. To date specimens have not been kept in captivity with great success. The two captive youngsters on this page, however, seem to be pictures of health and liveliness.

Heinz Schrempp

Java sparrow

Java sparrows are known the world over as popular cage birds which breed well in the right conditions. There are several varieties, including pied, cinnamon and white. The natural plumage is bluish-grey with a pink belly and black rump and tail. The head is black with large white ear patches and the bill is pinkish white. The total length is 5 in., 1 in. less than a house sparrow.

The original home of the Java sparrow was on the islands of Java and Bali but it has been introduced to many parts of southeast Asia. It is also called the Java finch, ricebird and Java temple bird.

Rice-eating sparrows

Java sparrows are such a pest in southeast Asia, where rice is the main crop, that even their scientific name *Padda oryzivora* means 'paddy field rice-eater'. In captivity they feed on paddy rice alone largely ignoring other food unless the rice is not available. They may also take other seeds such as canary and millet and green food as substitutes and they eat mealworms and termites. This variation in diet seems to depend on the conditions they are kept in and whether they are breeding.

Old World courtesy

Pairs of Java sparrows live amicably together, sharing the same roost and greeting each other on meeting. If the pair has been separated and then allowed to meet again they perform an elaborate and charming ceremony. The first stage is a low bow, trilling at the same time. Then they perch side by side and each in turn twists sidewards and rests its head over that of its mate. This is followed by more bowing and the birds continue sitting very close to each other for some time.

The male Java sparrow's song is a fluting, sometimes whistling, note which varies between individuals. Writers have given quite different descriptions of the song, which can be heard when the female is out of sight of the male as well as during courtship. At the start of the courtship display the male bows in a 'hunched' posture, different from the meeting bow, and jumps up and down on the perch, waving his bill from side to side and twisting his tail towards the waiting female. As he nears her he begins to sing. Sometimes the female bows and bounces as well, the pair of them making a very pretty sight, before crouching with tail quivering. If the female rejects the male's advances she may put her head over his as in the meeting ceremony or even attack him, pecking at his bill.

Female finishes the nest

The nest is built from grasses and other plant materials, that are long, flexible and tough. They are woven into a loose ball and the chamber so formed is lined with feathers. In captivity the male has been seen to do all the nest building. The female accompanies her mate on his trips for collecting material but helps him only at the end when she collects feathers for the lining.

Both sexes incubate the eggs, taking turns of 20–30 minutes. The chicks hatch after about 3 weeks' incubation. They are completely naked at first and are brooded and fed by both parents.

*'Paddyfield rice-eater'—scientific name **Padda oryzivora** means this. It results from the raids the Java sparrows make on the rice fields of southeast Asia.*

Feather beds

In the *Avicultural Magazine* Derek Goodwin has recounted how his pet Java sparrows took to roosting with turtle doves. Each evening they would nestle against the much larger turtle doves and if possible climb between their legs. When the turtle doves nested the Java sparrows climbed under the incubating bird. This behaviour has been reported by other cage bird fanciers. Sometimes the Java sparrows roosted on top of the doves instead of underneath them. Why they should do this is a mystery. They do not clump like avadavats (p 100), except with their mates, so the doves are not being used as imitation gatherings of Java sparrows. Neither are they nestling against the doves to keep warm—this behaviour has been seen in temperatures of 32°C/90°F in the shade. It would be very interesting to know if wild Java sparrows make use of a wild species of dove in this same way.

class	**Aves**
order	**Passeriformes**
family	**Estrildidae**
genus & species	***Padda oryzivora***

Constance P Warner

◁ The beautiful blue jay of North America. This bird has an unmistakable black collar around its neck and blue plumage on the back.
◁▽ Mouths forever open—the common jay has a full-time job keeping the fledglings happy.
▷ Cayenne jay lives in South American forests.

André Fatras

Jay

Unlike most other members of the crow family jays are highly colourful. They make up a very varied subfamily of over 40 species, 32 of which are in America and all but four of these are South American. The most widely ranging is the common jay of Europe and Asia, which is selected here to represent the subfamily.

The common jay, 13½ in. long, has a reddish brown plumage, darker on the back and wings than on the breast. It has a white head streaked with black and the feathers are raised in a crest in moments of excitement. There is a conspicuous black moustache running from the corner of the bill. The most noticeable feature is the patch of blue feathers barred with black on each wing. Jays are very shy and the usual view of them is a black tail and white rump in full retreat.

The next most common jay is the beautiful blue jay of North America. Its plumage is blue on the back, white on the front, with black bars on wings and tail and a black collar. The turquoise jay of the Andes is blue all over, with conspicuous black markings on the head running down to the chest and outlining a gorget of slightly lighter blue. The Siberian jay is brown and grey, reddish on the wings, rump and sides of the tail. The Canada or grey jay is similar but lacks the red. It has a white forehead and black nape.

Jays are considered to be more primitive than other members of the crow family. The pattern of their distribution suggests a former wide distribution that is now breaking up. For example, the North American scrub jay is found on the western side of the Rockies but there is a small population in distant Florida.

Shy but garrulous

The common jay lives in woods and forests but comes out onto the open scrubland around to feed. Highly secretive and shy, its harsh cries can be heard among trees for long periods without the bird showing itself. Its flight is heavy and appears to be laboured. The raucous cries and cat-like mewing are the best known of its calls, but it uses a very soft and melodious song in spring. Jays are also good mimics and a tame jay can mimic a wide range of mechanical sounds, bird song and human speech. Even wild jays use vocal mimicry. For instance one always hooted like a tawny owl when it flew past the tree in which an owl was known to roost.

Caches of buried food

The jay's diet is very varied and includes seeds, fruits and small invertebrates such as insects, spiders, earthworms, snails and slugs. Soft fruits as well as apple, cherry and plum are eaten. They also take eggs and nestlings of small songbirds, wood pigeons, mallard and pheasant. In autumn the main food is acorns and large quantities are eaten. A young jay, hand-reared and isolated from its own kind will strip an acorn of its husk in a way that suggests it knows instinctively how to deal with it. Jays also bury acorns, pecking a hole in the ground, placing the acorn in it and then covering it up. Tests have shown that, surprisingly, jays can find these acorns again. They seem

▽ *The shy bird with the comical moustache. Common European jay anting. This behaviour is frequent among the crow family and songbirds. They take an ant in the bill and rub it on the wing feathers; but jays often go through the same motions without an ant in the bill.*

Jane Burton: Photo Res

Des Bartlett: Photo Res

to remember where each acorn is buried and will return unerringly to it even when the spot is covered with leaf litter or snow.

Courtship gatherings?

In spring jays indulge in what are called 'ceremonial assemblies' the significance of which is not yet clear. A dozen or more chase each other from tree to tree or among the branches of the trees uttering a chorus of soft warbling notes, delightful to the ear and in strong contrast with their usual harsh notes. It has been suggested that these assemblies may have something to do with the birds pairing off but this has not been confirmed. The breeding season is April–May, when a nest is built 5–20 ft from the ground in a tree. It is made of sticks with a little earth and lined with fine roots. In this 5–7 eggs are laid, green to buff coloured with fine dark mottlings, and scrawled with fine hairlines. Probably both parents incubate for 16 days and the young are fed for 3 weeks after hatching. It has yet to be proven that the two parents share the incubation. Male and female look alike and can only be distinguished by their behaviour when courting and mating.

Sharp eyesight

Experiments with a tame jay have shed light on the use of its eyes including the keenness of its sight. When linked with what is also known about jays' ability to find each acorn it has buried we get a striking picture of the extent to which birds depend on their eyesight. The owner of the tame jay in question noticed that when he went close to the bird's aviary and stood so that his own nose was only a few inches from the bird's beak the pupils of the jay's eyes were brought forward so that the bird was looking down its beak with both eyes. Whether this gives the jay stereoscopic vision is not known, but subsequent observation showed that many birds use their eyes in this way, when taking a close look at an object.

It was while he was looking at his jay in this manner that the owner saw the bird catch an insect. The jay, apparently looking its owner 'straight in the eye', suddenly flew to another perch in the aviary, 6 ft away and somewhat to the rear, pecked at the perch and flew back with a tiny insect in the tip of its beak. The insect was so small that the human eye would have difficulty in picking it out at a range of 6 ft. Yet the jay, with its pupils directed forwards, had detected a slight movement, to the side and to the rear, had flicked one eye round and immediately flown over to take its prey.

class	**Aves**
order	**Passeriformes**
family	**Corvidae**
subfamily	**Garrulinae**
genera & species	***Aphelocoma coerulescens*** *North American scrub jay* ***Cyanocitta cristata*** *blue jay* ***Cyanolyca turcosa*** *turquoise jay* ***Cyanocorax cayanus*** *cayenne jay* ***Garrulus glandarius*** *common jay* ***Perisoreus canadensis*** *Canada or grey jay* ***P. infaustus*** *Siberian jay* *others*

Jellyfish

Jellyfish are free-swimming relatives of sea anemones, corals and hydroids, all belonging to the phylum Coelenterata. In the life cycles of many coelenterates there are two distinct phases. One is a free-living jellyfish, or medusa, that reproduces sexually, while the other develops from an embryo and is an anchored, or sessile, polyp, or colony of polyps, that in turn buds off jellyfish. One or other phase may be dominant and the other less important or even non-existent. The large jellyfishes make up one class, the Scyphozoa (or Scyphomedusae), in which the polyp stage is very small. Attention will be concentrated here on this group.

Upside-down hydra

The typical jellyfish is umbrella-shaped, globular or conical with 4 or 8 tentacles around the margin, or many tentacles may form a ring around the margin. Under the umbrella, and like a handle to it, is the mouth, leading into the digestive cavity. The mouth is drawn out at the corners into four long lips. The basic form of the body can best be understood by comparison with that of hydra (p 1148). The body of hydra, as we have seen, consists essentially of two layers of cells forming a sac and separated by a very thin layer of non-cellular material, mesogloea. In the jellyfish the mesogloea is very thick. Although the body of a jellyfish is more elaborate than that of hydra it still has the same two-layered structure and ring of tentacles around the mouth.

Some common jellyfish

A jellyfish found in seas throughout the world and which is common off the coasts of Europe is *Aurelia aurita*. It grows to nearly $1\frac{1}{2}$ ft across, with many very short tentacles. The blue, yellowish, reddish or brown jellyfish *Cyanea,* also known as sea blubber, can reach 6 ft across in Arctic waters but is usually less than half that. The jellyfish *Chrysaora* has 24 tentacles, and these may be 20 yd long in one species. Around the centre of its white or yellowish disc there is often a brownish ring from which streaks of the same colour radiate. Another common jellyfish is *Rhizostoma,* or 'the root-mouthed', named for the shape of its lips. It is a whitish dome, about a foot across, with a deep purple rim. It has no tentacles but is easily recognized by the cauliflower-like oral lips. In the United States it is called 'cabbage blebs'. Some jellyfish are luminescent and one of the most intense, which is occasionally found in north European waters, is *Pelagia noctiluca.*

Different ways of feeding

Jellyfish swim by rhythmic pulsations of the umbrella or bell. The movement is very like an umbrella being opened and shut slowly. It is co-ordinated by a very simple nervous system and by sense organs around the edge that are sensitive to light, gravity and chemicals in the water. Jellyfish are carnivorous and many of them capture fish, shrimps and other animals on their trailing tentacles, paralyse them with their stinging cells and transfer them to the mouth. *Aurelia* catches fish when young, but once grown to about 1 in. across feeds in quite a different way on small planktonic animals. These are trapped in sticky mucus all over the surface of the body and are driven by cilia to the rim. There the accumulating blobs are licked off by the 4 long oral lips. Further cilia propel the food in currents of water into the digestive cavity, from which a system of branching, cilia-lined canals radiate out to the rim, carrying food to all parts of the body. *Rhizostoma* feeds in the manner of a sponge, drawing in small planktonic animals by means of ciliary currents through thousands of separate mouths on the greatly elaborated oral lips. It is these mouths and the many little sensory palps on the oral lips that give the jellyfish its characteristic cauliflower appearance. Another plankton feeder is a tropical jellyfish *Cassiopeia* which lies mouth upwards on the sea bottom in shallow water, pulsating its bell gently and capturing plankton with its lips as it is wafted by. It has symbiotic algae in its oral lips which benefit from the sunlight falling on them (see also anemone *Anthopleura,* p 45, and clam, p 450).

Piles of saucers

The common *Aurelia* is readily recognised by the four nearly oval purple or lilac reproductive organs, ovaries in the females, testes in the males. These lie in pouches in the digestive cavity but show through the transparent bell. The male sheds his sperm into the sea and these are wafted to the female and taken in along with her food. The eggs are fertilised and develop for a while in pouches on the oral lips. They are eventually set free as tiny planula larvae which soon attach themselves to seaweed or stone and develop into small polyps, known as scyphistomas or hydratubas, each with 16 tentacles. From the base of each, stolons, like runners of strawberry plants, grow out and new polyps develop on them. Each polyp eventually gives rise in the following winter to a number of young jellyfish called ephyra larvae, not round like the adult, but with the edge of the bell drawn out into 8 arms, notched at the tips. To do this, the polyp becomes pinched off into segments so it resembles a pile of lobed saucers. Then the tissue connecting these saucers contracts and snaps and each one swims off as a little ephyra. The growing ephyras transform gradually into adults by filling in the spaces between the arms.

An alternation of forms like this is typical of these jellyfish, though, in *Pelagia,* the egg develops directly into an ephyra.

Sea wasps

Jellyfishes are practically all water. A jellyfish stranded on the shore will soon vanish under the hot rays of the sun leaving little more than a patch of water in the sand. Their bodies are nearly 99% jelly and the whole body contains less than 5% organic matter. Yet jellyfishes can be extremely venomous as anyone knows who has hauled on a rope covered in long trailing tentacles. The stings of jellyfishes come from the many stinging cells or nematocysts which shoot out a poisonous thread when touched. The severity of the sting depends very much on the number of nematocysts discharged and also on the type of jellyfish. The most venomous jellyfishes are those living in the coral seas and the least troublesome are those in temperate seas, but even these, if enough tentacles are allowed to touch our bodies, can sometimes lead to a loss of consciousness and, in the case of one bather to drowning. This kind of accident is happily very rare. The most venomous jellyfishes belong to what are known as the Cubomedusae, so called because of their somewhat squarish shape. They range in size from as small as grapes to as large as pears and have four tentacles or four groups of tentacles. Some of these, like bathers, seem to prefer quiet shallow waters in the warmer seas, and are particularly troublesome around the northern Australian coasts, the Philippines and Japan. They have been called sea wasps and they can kill in as short a time as half a minute, usually in a quarter of an hour, the victim dying in excruciating pain.

phylum	**Coelenterata**
class	**Scyphozoa**

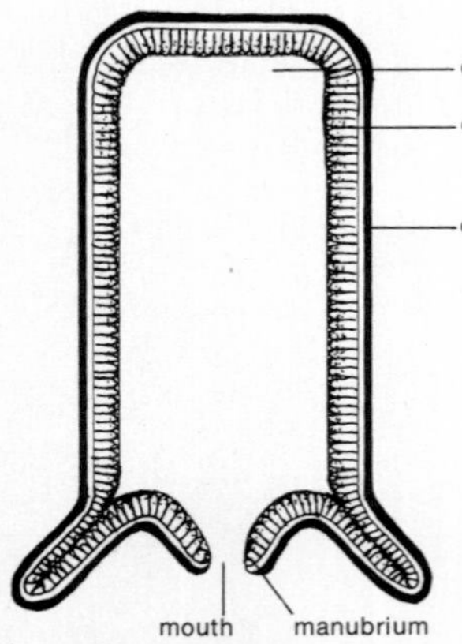

Diagram to show the relation between the sedentary polyp (left) and the freely drifting medusa (right). The intermediate form (centre) is an imaginary stage showing the transition from polyp to medusa. The common jellyfish is a medusa stage.

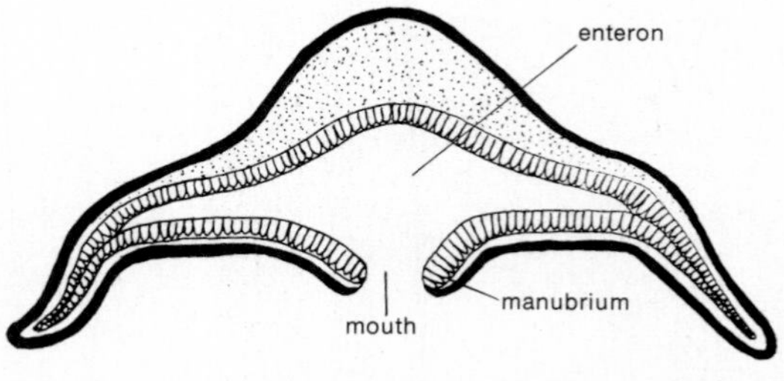

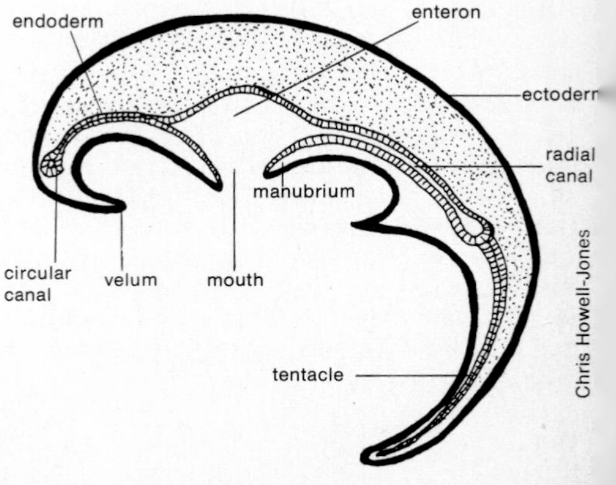

Chris Howell-Jones

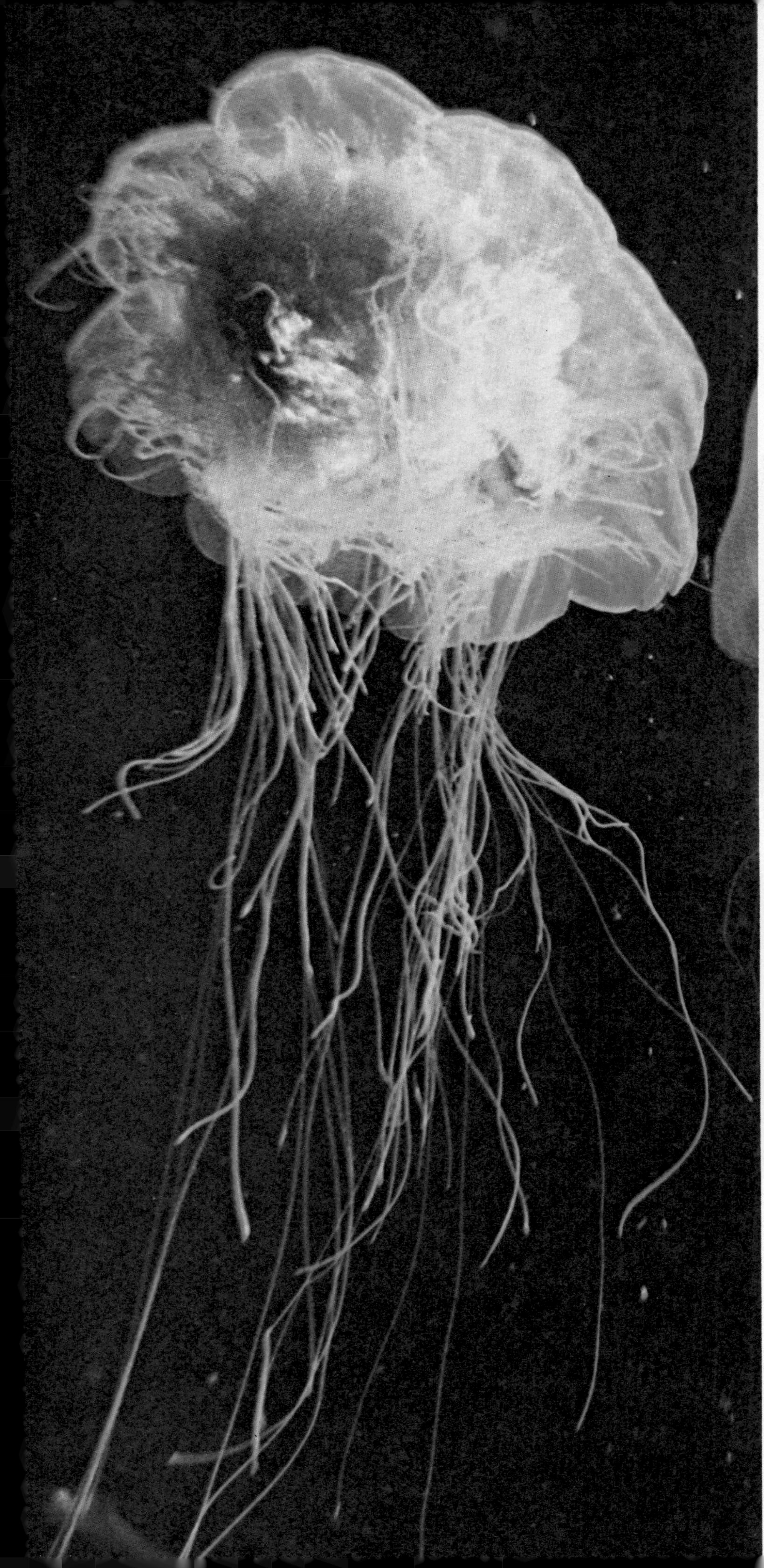

Natural History Museum, London

△ *Plaster cast of a 600 million year old* ***Mawsonites spriggi****, a jellyfish-like animal.*

▽ *Beautifully luminescent—* ***Pelagia colorata****.*

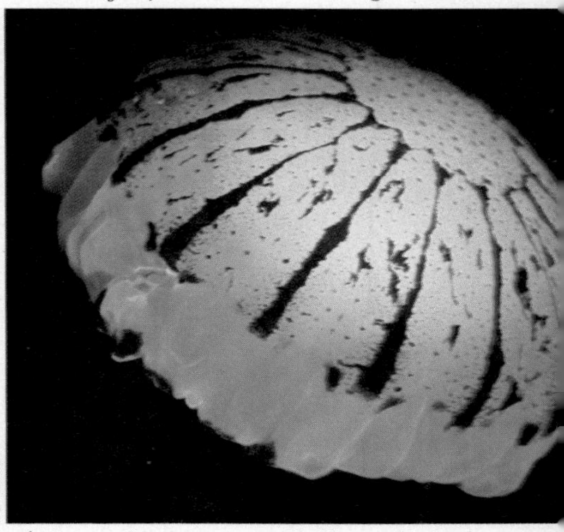

ES Hobson

◁ *Young* ***Cyanea*** *or sea blubber. This is the giant among jellyfish sometimes growing up to 6 ft with trailing tentacles 200 ft long.*

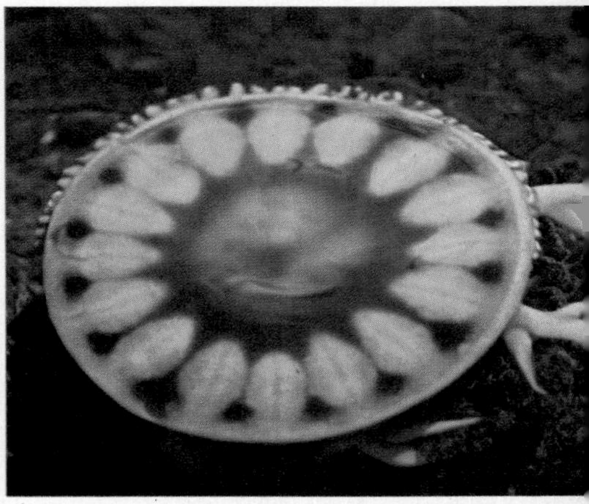

Jane Burton: Photo Res

△ ***Cassiopeia****—a tropical rhizostome medusa. Beneath the flat top protrude the white arms with thousands and thousands of grey mouths.*

▽ ***Rhizostoma****—section showing the mouths.*

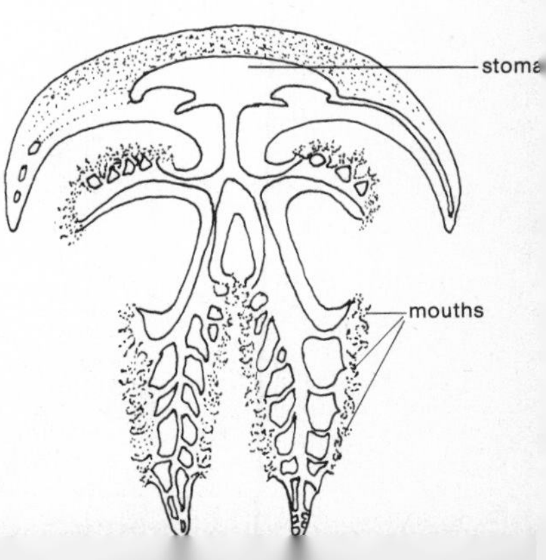

Chris Howell-Jones

Drifting splendour, great . . .

*This association between **Aurelia** and **Pugettia**, a spider crab, has only been seen in the last decade. The habits of these two animals are so different, the jellyfish is planktonic, the crab benthonic (bottom living) that the association is thought to be of chance contact and not where one animal is dependent on the other. Crabs have been seen clinging to medusae, penetrating into the mesogloea and feeding on medusan tissue without any apparent lasting harm to crabs or jellyfish.*

HH Stellrecht

***Chrysaora isosceles**. This jellyfish is like **Aurelia** in shape and general plan except it has 24 long trailing tentacles around its margin which are used to capture food and the lips are extended into four frilly 'oral arms'.*

JM Clayton: NHPA

. . . and small

*The polyp generation of **Aurelia aurita**, like all other jellyfish, is a small sedentary phase passing the winter hanging from a rock. In spring the polyp becomes divided by transverse grooves, a process known as strobilisation, until it looks like a pile of saucers. Each 'saucer' is called an ephyra, a young medusa which eventually breaks off from the top of segmented polyp or scyphistoma and swims away, growing finally into a large free-floating adult jellyfish.*

*The free ephyra (top) a few mm in diameter is beautifully symmetrical and looks very graceful in profile (centre). Equally awe-inspiring is the bell of this moon jelly, the adult version of **Aurelia aurita** (bottom).*

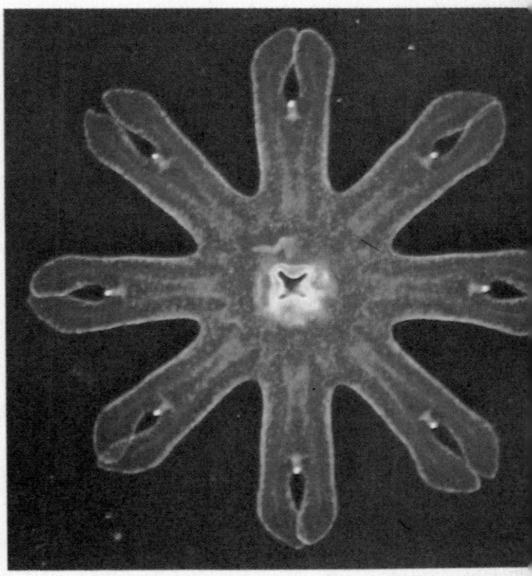

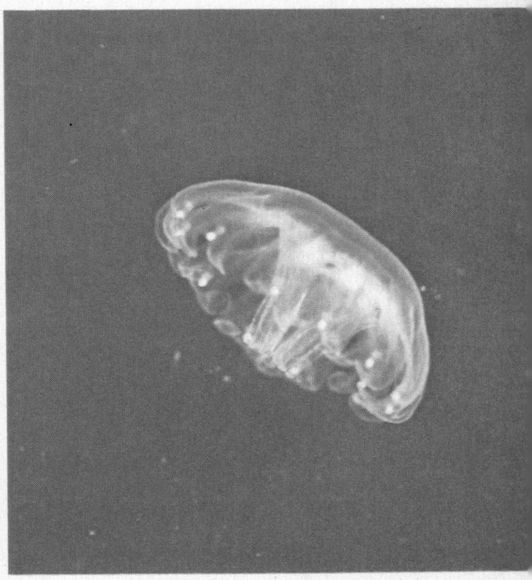

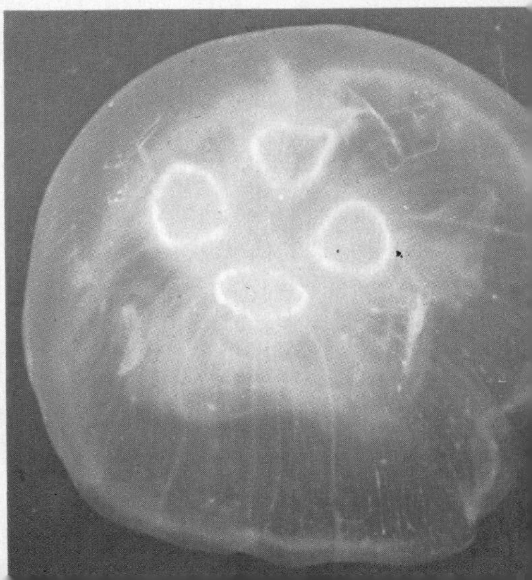

Series by GS Giacomelli

Jerboa

Jerboas are small desert-living rodents, the 'desert rats' of the Second World War. They look rather like kangaroos, having long hindlegs, very short forelegs and long tails. Like kangaroos they travel by hopping. Other desert-living rodents have developed hopping as a means of travelling across sparsely covered ground but in none are there such great differences between fore and hindlegs as there are in the jerboas, where hindlegs are four times longer than the forelegs.

The head and body lengths of jerboas range from $1\frac{1}{2}$ to 6 in., the hindlegs from 1 to 3 in. The tail is longer than the head and body, ranging from 3 to 10 in. and often bears a white tuft at the tip. It is used as a balancer when hopping and as a prop when the jerboa is sitting upright. The fur is fine and usually sandy coloured, matching the ground where jerboas live. Some species have long rabbit-like ears and others have short mouse-like ears. Jerboas are found in northern Africa and Asia east to northern China and Manchuria.

Avoiding the heat

Jerboas survive the desert heat by living in burrows and coming out in the cool of night to forage among the sparse vegetation. Their burrows are usually found near vegetation, especially along the edges of fields, but in the rainy season they make burrows in mounds or in the sides of hills where they will escape flooding. At this time of year the entrances to the burrows are left open but during the hot summer occupied holes have plugs of soil blocking the entrances. The plugs keep out hot air, and, probably, predators. Jerboas' burrows often have an emergency exit that ends just below the surface or opens at the surface but is filled with loose earth. When disturbed the jerboa bursts through this exit and escapes. The Asiatic jerboas dig winter burrows, 10 ft or more long, which may be plugged, and are consequently very difficult to trace. Except when a female has a family, usually one jerboa lives in each burrow.

The burrows are dug very rapidly, the jerboas scraping at the sandy soil with their sharp-clawed forefeet and pushing it back with the hindfeet. Even the nose is used, for pushing earth back or tamping the walls of the burrow. Some species have a fold of skin on the nose that can be drawn over the nostrils to keep sand out.

When chased, jerboas can move very fast, covering up to 10 ft at each bound and reaching speeds of up to 15 mph. Otherwise they 'trot', jumping 4–5 in. at each bound and often stopping. The only time they walk on all fours is when feeding. It is a very awkward movement with nose down, rump in the air and tail dragging on the ground.

Feeding on succulents

Jerboas feed on desert plants, both succulent and dry. During the rainy season there is plenty of fresh, sprouting greenery. As the plants dry up the jerboas dig out roots in which water is stored, but in the dry season they survive on dry seeds. In some places jerboas attack crops of water melons and rubber, and certain species feed on beetles and other insects. The jaws of jerboas are weaker than those of gerbils so they cannot eat hard seeds.

The jerboas' bounding gait allows them to cover a large area in search of food with the minimum loss of energy. This is vital in the dry season when food is scarce. Unlike gerbils (p 862) jerboas do not store food.

Slow-growing babies

Jerboas are mainly solitary animals; each jerboa has its own burrow and forages by itself, although sometimes loose colonies are formed. Some species appear to have communal burrows but the function of these is not known.

Breeding probably takes place twice a year in most species and some may have more than two litters, but the young of the last litter may die before reaching maturity if they are born too near the start of the dry season. Litters are of 2–6, usually 3 babies. Very little is known about the jerboas' breeding habits, partly because the animals are nocturnal and elusive and partly because they have failed to breed in captivity. Pregnant females have been captured and have given birth to their young, but all too often they have then ignored them. The few families that have been raised show that jerboas develop more slowly than laboratory rats. They are born naked and crawl with their forelegs, the hindlegs not developing until they are 8 weeks old, and they cannot jump until 11 weeks old. They are weaned at 8 weeks and are sexually mature at 14 weeks, twice the age at which rats mature. Jerboas, however, live longer: 6 years compared with the rat's 3 years.

Escape by speed

Unlike other rodents jerboas do not dash for their burrows or other cover when pursued but make their escape by bounding away at high speed with frequent changes of direction and occasionally leaping vertically. They have many enemies and are probably eaten by every predator that comes across them, especially foxes, fennecs, owls and perhaps snakes. Bedouin Arabs catch them by flooding or digging out their burrows and by setting traps.

A dry diet

By living in a cool, humid burrow and emerging at night jerboas can escape the worst of the desert heat, but conditions are still severe by comparison with those in temperate climates and like other desert animals jerboas face the problem of water shortage. They economise on water by living in burrows and, in the hottest weather, becoming dormant. So efficient are they at conserving the water in their bodies that they can survive the summer on dry seeds containing very little moisture, while in the laboratory jerboas have lived for 3 years on a diet of dry seeds. By comparison, rats could survive for only a few days. The jerboas' survival on this diet is due to their ability to hold water in their body and pass a very concentrated, acidic urine, although in these circumstances jerboas are much less active so less body waste is formed and water can be conserved.

class	**Mammalia**
order	**Rodentia**
family	**Dipodidae**
genera & species	***Allactaga sibirica*** ***Dipus sagitta*** *feather-footed jerboa* ***Jaculus jaculus*** *desert jerboa* *others*

Nose to the ground, hindlegs splayed and tail trailing—the desert jerboa forages for food.

JL Dubois: Jacana

Jewel fish

This is one of the most beautiful of African cichlids and a favourite with aquarists as well as with those studying fish behaviour. The adults are gorgeously coloured and seem to be spangled with jewels. They are up to 4 in. long and the colouration is similar in both male and female although at times the female is the more brilliant. The male has, however, more 'jewels' especially on the gill-covers and a more pronounced crescent on the tail fin. The general colouring is dark olive to grey brown with a greenish sheen and there are 6–7 rows of sky-blue spots along each side of the body.

Little savages

The colours of the beautifully patterned jewel fish play an important part in its life. They help it find a mate and protect it as a baby. As the time for egg laying approaches the red on the body becomes more intense and covers a larger part of the body. Male and female spend much time lying side by side on the sandy bottom during a period of 2–3 days then they begin to clean a hard surface for the eggs. These, $\frac{1}{20}$ in. long, are laid in rows, looking like small strings of tiny pearls, the male following to fertilise each row, until a rounded patch of eggs covers the surface, 500–700 in all. The female fans the eggs with her pectoral fins to aerate them, the male taking over when she leaves to feed. When the baby fishes are about 7 days old they begin to feed, first on babies will soon be eaten, so the parents must have some way of calling their broods to them when danger threatens, and the babies must have some way of recognizing when their parents are calling them.

In some of the earliest of the experiments three glass aquaria were placed side by side with their long sides touching. Some baby jewel fish were put in the middle tank and in each of the end tanks was put a disc on a long rod, the rods being fixed above on a converted windscreen wiper. When this was set going the disc in each of the end aquaria moved back and forth in sight of the baby fishes. One disc was painted scarlet, the other was painted black. As soon as the discs started moving the young jewel fish moved over to the side of their aquarium nearest the scarlet disc.

Barry Pengilley

This jewel-spangled African cichlid is a favourite among aquarists. Although it is only 4 in. long when fully grown it will bully other fishes in a tank and so for this reason is best kept in a separate aquarium. Even so a group of jewel fish makes a beautiful display.

There are also 3 larger dark spots on each side, one on the gill-cover, one in the centre of the flank and one at the base of the tail fin. These are more pronounced in the male than the female. There are scarlet edges to the fins, and the body more especially of the female is tinged with red or scarlet over the head, shoulders and belly. These remarks on colour can only be general because there is so much change, with the breeding season and with the mood of the fish, and it can happen sometimes that the male is the brighter of the two.

The jewel fish is found in rivers over most of tropical Africa, from the Niger and Congo to the Nile.

protistans, then on rotifers and small crustaceans. After a month they look like the parents and although small they start to fight, their pugnacious character coming out at an early age. They grow $\frac{3}{4}$ in. a month.

A colour-key for mothers

The behaviour of the jewel fish is very like that of the Jack Dempsey, which has also been much studied in aquaria. Attention will be given therefore to other features of the behaviour, notably to the part colour plays in keeping the baby fishes with their parents. It will be of interest to describe how the experiments are carried out.

The parent jewel fishes, like the parent Jack Dempseys, herd their brood when they are able to swim. This is a necessary protection because if left on their own the

When young fishes leave home

Having done this the experimenters then used different sizes of discs, 1–3 in. diameter. They also used different coloured discs and they tried the effect of having the discs merely hanging in the end tanks or having them move quickly or slowly. They also experimented with broods of different ages. This meant hundreds of tests and the results show the following. Baby jewel fishes are born with a preference for scarlet over all other colours. Some colours, such as yellow or dark blue, did not attract them in the slightest. Their preference for scarlet becomes even stronger as they get older, so besides having the built-in preference for the main colour on the mother's body, this grows stronger as the young fish grows in size. There comes a time, however,

Jane Burton: Photo Res

△ *The eggs are laid in rows on a clean rock. Once fertilised both parents take it in turns to fan the eggs with their pectoral fins.*

▽ *An attentive parent spits tiny straying baby jewel fish back onto the nursery stone. If allowed to stray they would soon be eaten.*

Jane Burton: Photo Res

when the baby fish's liking for red declines. This is when it is several weeks old, and when it is time for the young fish to leave its parents' care. The waning effect of red makes it stray farther from its parents. As this is happening to all members of the brood the family eventually breaks up.

Size is important

The results of the experiments also show that size is important. A baby jewel fish will swim over to any disc coloured red but will swim over more slowly to one that is only 1 in. diameter than it will to one that is 2 or 3 in. diameter. Parent jewel fishes are about 2–3 in. long. Movement also makes a difference. A scarlet disc that is not moving will not attract the baby jewel fishes, or will not attract them strongly. In the same way a sluggish parent will not be able to call its brood together effectively. An active parent, sensing danger, moves more quickly and so imparts a sense of urgency to its brood. Moreover, at such times, the mother jewel fish raises and lowers her unpaired fins several times in succession and this fin flicking acts as a signal to bring her babies rapidly towards the red on her body.

In other species of cichlids which herd their broods as the jewel fish do the same results have been obtained except that the babies respond most to discs coloured like their parents, to black discs if the parents have black blotches or large black spots, and so on. Similar tests made on courting fishes show similar results. For example, a jewel fish is more attracted to a partner which not only shows red but moves quickly than to one that shows even more red but moves sluggishly. It is an advantage for a female jewel fish to choose a mate that moves quickly. He will be much more likely to protect her eggs after they are laid.

No two alike

The detailed colour pattern of the jewel fish has its value as well as the general colour. Once two fishes have paired they recognize each other even when among a crowd of their own kind which to our eyes all look alike. A male jewel fish will know his own mate when there are several females in his territory. He will drive the others away but will not molest her, and tests have shown that he recognizes her by small differences in the pattern of her colours. When the male of a pair is taken out of an aquarium and one or more strange males put in the female will attack these and try to drive them out but will welcome her mate when he is put back into the aquarium. There have been instances in which a female fish, after mating with a male, sees him the following year in a nearby aquarium and tries to get to him although another male has been put into her aquarium. So while the jewels of ornate fishes may be a joy to the human eye they play an important part in the life of a fish.

class	**Pisces**
order	**Perciformes**
family	**Cichlidae**
genus & species	***Hemichromis bimaculatus***

John Dory

This fish, of curious shape and habits, is included in an order known formerly as the Zeomorphi but now called Zeiformes. The non-classical scholar may be forgiven for translating these two names as god-like or god-shaped.

The John Dory has a very high and narrow body, flattened from side to side and rounded in outline, it is shaped like a plate. The large head has a mournful expression due to the drooping mouth and the jawbones are such that the mouth can be shot forward when seizing prey. The dorsal fin is in two parts, the front portion being high with the spines strong and, in older individuals, long and carried backwards to end in a line with the tail. The rear part of the dorsal fin and the anal fin that lies opposite it are soft and flexible. Along the bases of the dorsal and anal fins are spines, but the scales on the body are small and spineless, and the skin is smooth. There are also 8–9 spiny plates along the belly. The John Dory is grey to fawn or golden yellow with long blotches of reddish-purple, and on each flank just behind the gill covers is a large black spot with a yellow margin. The maximum length is 22½ in. and it can weigh up to 18 lb.

It lives in the Mediterranean and eastern Atlantic as far north as the southern and southwestern waters of the British Isles and only occasionally wanders as far north as Norway.

Cat-like stalking

The John Dory with its high plate-like body cannot chase its prey. Instead, it stalks its food, keeping its body rigid, swimming by waving its second dorsal and its anal fin, using the tail fin as a rudder. Its plate-like shape means it can slip easily through the water for short distances. Keeping its eyes on its prey, it gradually draws nearer and nearer to it, finally seizing it by shooting out its protrusible toothless mouth. While stalking it shows signs of excitement. It holds its dorsal fin erect and quivers its fins, its colours blushing and fading all the time. These signs of supposed excitement may have an added value. Seen from head-on the high and very narrow body looks like a thin vertical stripe. The colours coming and going and the quivering of the fins tend to blur even this, so the small fish being stalked is oblivious of impending danger and makes absolutely no attempt to swim away.

The John Dory lives at depths down to 300 ft and little is known about its way of life apart from what has been seen of occasional individuals kept in aquaria. It feeds almost exclusively on small fishes, especially young herring, pilchard and sand eels, although it has been seen to take shrimps in captivity. It takes only live food; a John Dory in an aquarium was seen to spit out a dead fish it had seized. Nevertheless, Dr Douglas Wilson at the Plymouth Aquarium was able, in due course, to persuade a captive John Dory to take strips of squid which looked like fish when dropped into water and slowly floated down.

Sexing the John Dory

There is no outward difference between the sexes. Only by dissection and by examining the roes is it possible to distinguish female from male. In the same way we learn that the eggs are $\frac{1}{10}$ in. diameter. It is likely that they are laid on sand, like the eggs of sand eels, in June to August.

Dual personality

The John Dory is used as a food-fish but people are divided on the quality of its flesh. There is also a division of opinion so far as its name is concerned. It seems to have a romantic ring, almost reminding one of the tang of the sea, so one suspects the fish might have been named after some swash-buckling buccaneer or other adventurous seadog. Then there is the story that the black marks on its flank are where the finger and thumb of St Peter pressed when he took the coin from the fish's mouth, so getting the name *Peterfisch* in Germany. But there is the same legend about the haddock, and also about a species of *Tilapia,* but since the John Dory and the haddock are both marine, the *Tilapia,* being a freshwater fish, should take the credit.

Two other suggestions rob it of any glamour it might have. One is that its name is a corruption of the Italian word *janitore,* for a doorkeeper, the other that it is from the French *jaune dorée*, because of its golden yellow colour. The scientific name is *Zeus faber,* the first name being that of the overlord of the Greek gods; the second is Latin for a blacksmith.

Kendall McDonald

J Vasserot: Jacana

class	**Pisces**
order	**Zeiformes**
family	**Zeidae**
genus & species	***Zeus faber***

△ *Never seeing the bright side of life the John Dory swims around with a permanent gloomy expression on its face. Apart from the unfortunate pout this fish has exquisite dorsal fin spines which grow trailing filaments and the large black flank spots. The legend goes that St Peter made these marks with his finger and thumb.*
◁ *Because of its high plate-like body the John Dory cannot chase its prey. Instead it stalks its food and seizes it by rapidly shooting out its toothless mouth.*
▽ *Head of John Dory with the mouth retracted (left) and protruded (right).*

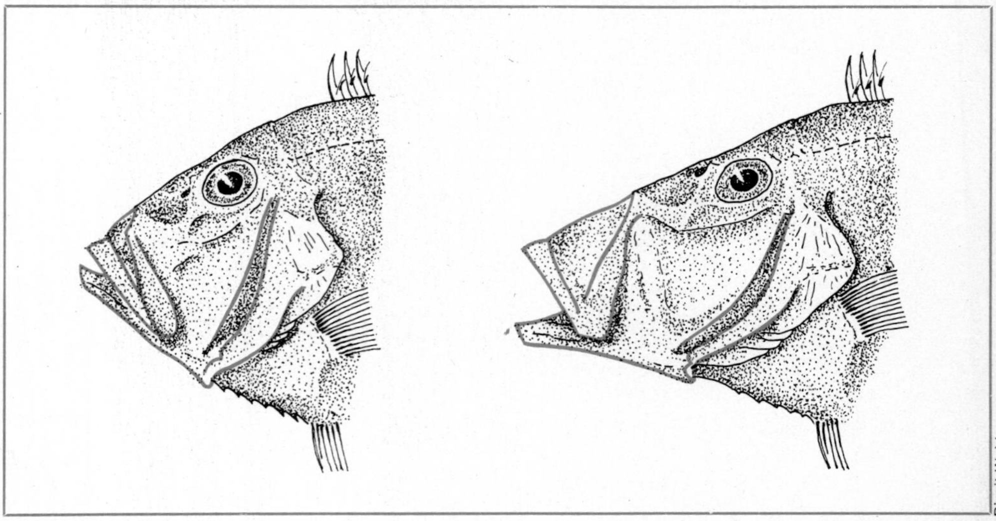

Birgit Webb

The stately male red jungle fowl takes a rest. This is the best known of the four species of jungle fowl. It has magnificent red plumage with an iridescent sheen. The cock has fleshy appendages, comb and lappets on his head, which mark them off from most of the pheasant family.

Jungle fowl

The four species of jungle fowl are not very closely related to the rest of the pheasant family. The cocks have the characteristic fleshy appendages on their heads: a comb rises from the top of the head and lappets hang under the chin, while most of the face is naked. In the females the appendages are vestigial and the plumage is duller. The best known is the red jungle fowl from which the domestic chicken was derived. The plumage is mainly red and black with an iridescent greenish sheen. The red jungle fowl is found in the warmer parts of Asia from the Indian sub-continent to southern China and the Indonesian islands, but it is absent from Borneo. The populations on various Pacific Islands such as the Philippines were probably introduced by man. The red jungle fowl has also been established in Natal, South Africa, and there are free-living populations in several parts of the world, for jungle fowl are popular with bird fanciers. The grey jungle fowl lives in the southern and western parts of the Indian peninsula, the green jungle fowl in Java and the fourth species is confined to Ceylon. The comb of the cock Ceylon jungle fowl is yellow with a red border. Its plumage is red and brown with greenish-black iridescent wings and tail and a purple rump.

In Australia some of the megapodes or brush-turkeys are known as jungle fowl.

Keeping out of the way

Jungle fowl live in forests and so their range is shrinking as forests are cut down and the country opened up for agriculture. They probably survive because they are extremely wary. Jungle fowl come out into clearings, roadsides and fields to feed, especially in early morning or after rain, but run for cover at the first alarm.

Even when undisturbed they are still wary. Some jungle fowl have been watched in the bamboo jungle of Thailand. They live in small flocks of one cock with 2–5 hens. In the morning the flock leave their roosts 15–20 ft up in the bamboos and are led down by the cock to drink at a stream. While the hens are drinking the cock keeps watch from a nearby perch. When the hens have finished the cock drinks hurriedly, then quickly leads his flock back to cover.

Scratching for food

The food of jungle fowl consists of virtually anything they can find in the leaf litter and soil of the forest floor, including green plants, seeds, berries, earthworms, insects and other small animals. They feed like domestic chickens, scratching violently with their strong toes and stepping back to search for anything brought to light.

In Ceylon the nellu plants form a great part of the undergrowth in the forests. They flower at intervals of several years and large numbers of jungle fowl and other birds gather to feast on the seeds.

Fighting cocks

Jungle fowl breed during most of the year but more often during the rainy season. The cocks are more aggressive than most of the pheasant family. Normally the unmated males hang about the territories of the mated cocks and are extremely secretive, but during the main part of the breeding season they challenge the established cocks by crowing and clapping their wings over their backs. This is a definite challenge and cocks can be lured by imitating the clapping. When fights break out they are fierce and one of the combatants may be severely wounded by the sharp, 1 in. spurs of its adversary.

The cock courts the hen by waltzing around her with one wing lowered to the ground, rubbing the primary feathers of that wing with the nearest foot to produce a rasping sound. The hen makes her nest by scraping a hollow in the ground but sometimes uses the top of a tree stump or takes over the abandoned nest of a large bird. The eggs, usually 2–4, are speckled and are incubated for 19–21 days. The chicks can walk and feed themselves almost as soon as they are hatched. They can fly when a week old, when they begin to roost in the trees.

Safe perch

Jungle fowl fall prey to all manner of flesh-eating animals. Their only defence is to be extremely wary and to take flight at the first alarm. The exception is the incubating hen who will not leave the nest until the last moment. The roosts where the jungle fowl spend the night are chosen with care. Foliage shelters the sleeping jungle fowl from owls and by choosing a perch well out on the most slender branches they reduce the chance of being surprised by such nimble creatures as the palm civet.

Philip Wayre: NHPA

Rapid turnover

The jungle fowl's behaviour is very difficult to study in the dense vegetation of its natural home, but it has been studied in detail in semi-wild populations, such as there are at the San Diego zoo. About 150 jungle fowl roam about the zoo grounds in several flocks which have provided a great opportunity for studying their social behaviour. During the course of the study the surprising fact emerged that only 6 out of every 100 chicks survived their first year of life. Threequarters of the chicks never survived to independence and jungle fowl that did survive to maturity never lived more than 3 years.

There were probably very few predators in the zoo. The most obvious ones were behind bars. Foxes and cats, however, were known to hunt in the grounds. So it seems that the life of a jungle fowl is precarious and its wariness and care in selecting a roost are hardly sufficient protection. Yet a rapid turnover of population is found in many species, and if it were not so and each jungle fowl lived to a ripe old age, life would be hard for flesh-eating animals.

Many animals—songbirds and fishes, for instance—produce large numbers of young; but very few of these survive to reproduce. If they did, the population would rise enormously and food would run short. Instead, the surplus provide food for flesh-eating animals.

class	**Aves**
order	**Galliformes**
family	**Phasianidae**
genus & species	***Gallus gallus*** *red jungle fowl* ***G. lafayetii*** *Ceylon jungle fowl* ***G. sonnerati*** *grey jungle fowl* ***G. varius*** *green jungle fowl*

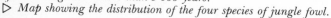

Joe Van Wormer

When did the fowl become a chicken?

◁ *An alarmed grey jungle fowl making a hurried retreat. Jungle fowl live in forests in the warmer parts of Asia. As more and more forests are being cut down to make way for agriculture so their range is slowly shrinking. They are managing to survive simply because they are wary birds. Their only defence is to take flight once disturbed.*
△ *Cock and hen red jungle fowl. The scientific name,* ***Gallus gallus****, of this jungle fowl is also the name of the domestic chicken (see page 423), and it is thought that the chicken has been bred from this wild species. This is easy to see from the female which looks quite drab beside her mate. There are other views that the domestic chicken is descended from any one or more of the four species of* ***Gallus*** *living in southeastern Asia and for this reason some scientists prefer to call it* ***Gallus domesticus****. The time of domestication is unknown although there are Asiatic records of it which go back more than 3 000 years.*
▷ *Map showing the distribution of the four species of jungle fowl.*

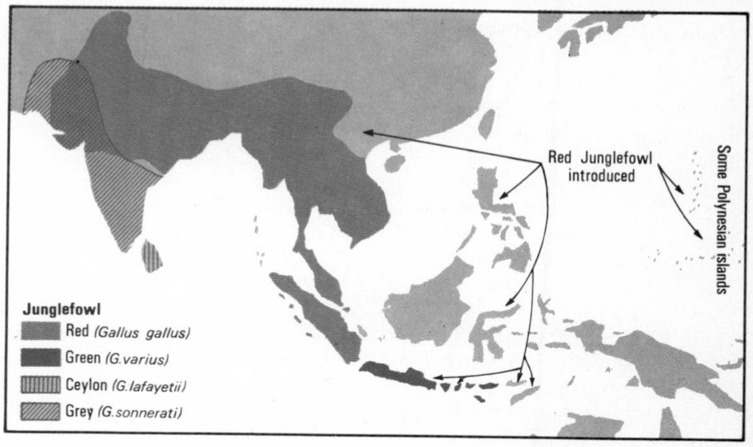

Constance P Warner

The kagu is found only on the island of New Caledonia. Only a century after it was discovered it is on the verge of extinction. Zoo birds could be the nucleus of a breeding flock to save the species.

C Zuber: WWF

The large head has a long shaggy crest which is raised like a fan in anger or display.

Kagu

This is an unusual, probably primitive bird, that leads a precarious life in the forested highlands of New Caledonia. The fear is that it may not be many years before it is only surviving in zoos. There is only one species of kagu in a family on its own. It has no very close relatives, the nearest being the cranes and rails.

The kagu is somewhat larger than the domestic fowl and has longer legs. The legs and the strong, slightly curved bill are a striking red. The plumage is pale slate grey with slightly darker wings and there is a loose crest that is like the crest of the secretary bird, recalling the clerk of long ago with a bunch of quill pens in his wig. The eye is large and dark red. The wings are rounded and when spread they show a conspicuous pattern of white, red and black markings.

Coming out at twilight

The kagu was probably once widespread over New Caledonia where it had no natural enemies and although the aboriginals hunted it with slings its numbers were little affected. The island was occupied by Europeans in 1853. Dogs, cats and pigs were taken to the island and rats found their way there. Forest fires played havoc. The birds were hunted with dogs, their carcases sold in the markets as poultry, their feathers were sold for household ornaments and their skins were sent back to museums in Europe. The birds survived nevertheless in thick mountain forests with dense undergrowth. They come out at twilight, in small groups, walking slowly about inspecting the ground for large land snails, earthworms, insects and other small invertebrates. They can drive their bills 2–3 in. into the ground in search of worms or insect larvae and they have a tubular scroll-like horny sheath protecting the nostrils from becoming plugged with earth. When alarmed the kagu runs fast with its wings spread. It seldom flies, except, like the domestic chicken, as a last resort or to surmount an obstacle.

Crazy displays

The cry of the kagu is a penetrating yelp somewhat like that of a puppy. This yelp can grow into a two-syllable scream resembling the name, kagu, which was given to it by the Melanesian inhabitants of New Caledonia. The scream can be heard a mile away. This bird has a number of curious habits. For instance it will run rapidly then suddenly stop to stand motionless. In the courtship display it may whirl around in a running skipping dance holding the tip of its tail or its wing in its bill. In these displays the wings are spread and brought somewhat forward, and a loud rattling call is uttered.

One egg at a time

The kagu makes a nest of leaves and sticks on the ground under thick bushes. A single egg is laid, pale brown, streaked and spotted with reddish brown. Male and female share the incubation for 35–40 days, the male sitting by day, the female by night. Both parents feed the chick which leaves the nest after a few days and becomes independent when 4 weeks old. It is dark brown with a downy plumage which is replaced at 30–45 days old by the first juvenile plumage of brownish-black with darker bands. This changes over several years becoming lighter until the adult plumage is reached. In zoos kagu have lived up to 30 years.

Holding their own

The enemies of the kagu today are dogs, cats, pigs, rats, animal collectors, aboriginal hunters and bush fires. Both the single egg laid at each nesting, and the chick, are sitting targets especially to the introduced animals. Although each pair produce one egg several times in the year they are, nevertheless, relatively slow breeders, which is another reason why fears are expressed for the continued survival of the species. It is, however, of interest to recall that in 1913 Fritz Sarasin, the Swiss naturalist, wrote that the end of the kagu is certain unless energetic measures for its protection are taken. It is now protected but despite Sarasin's pessimism which is being constantly reiterated today, half a century later, the demise of the kagu still seems far off unless the island of New Caledonia becomes more heavily settled. There are also many kagus in zoos but although these have laid eggs there has been a notable lack of success in rearing the chicks, apparently because the chicks have difficulty in getting out of the shell. One important factor in its survival in the wild is that it is long-lived. A pair may produce only one egg at a time, but they do this several times a year, and since each pair surviving 20 or 30 years produce 60 to 100 eggs in a lifetime they can afford the loss of all but two of their offspring to ensure a steady level of population.

class	**Aves**
order	**Gruiformes**
family	**Rhynochetidae**
genus & species	***Rhynochetos jubatus***

Kakapo

This is a flightless owl-like parrot with most unusual habits, living in the rain forests in parts of New Zealand. Once plentiful, it is now rare and may soon be extinct. Information about it is scarce because today the survivors live in forests where the branches of the trees are heavily draped with vines and festooned with lichens and the ground is a jumble of rotten tree trunks, large boulders and ferns. To see a well-camouflaged nocturnal bird in these circumstances is not easy.

The kakapo is 20 in. long, greenish on the upper parts and pale yellow underneath, its plumage is streaked with black, brown and grey, so it blends with the foliage in the dim light of the forests. The first settlers from Britain called it the owl-parrot, although its booming call-notes are more like those of the bittern and can be heard a mile away. The kakapo's eyes are surrounded by a facial disc of slender feathers and its plumage is soft and noiseless in flight, like that of owls. Another feature shared with owls is that the base of its bill is hidden under feathers.

MF Soper

Too easy to catch: both man and introduced predators have reduced kakapo numbers to less than 100.

Parrot with owl's habits

During the day the kakapo probably rests in cavities in hollow trees, between rocks and boulders or under the buttress roots of large trees. At night it comes out to feed, running quickly along the ground. Sometimes it spreads its short rounded wings as it runs, presumably using them for balance. It makes trails through the vegetation on the forest floor, about a foot wide, as small mammals do elsewhere. Early settlers who first saw these trails thought they must be human paths through the forest and expected to find the aboriginal people who made them. These trails are further marked because of the bird's unusual way of feeding. It takes a blade of grass in its beak and chews it without biting it off. After it has taken all the juices from it the grass blade is left as a ball of tangled fibres which dry out white and show up, so marking the trail. Tough or hard leaves are said to be chewed again, as a cow chews the cud'.

Sometimes the kakapo climbs tall trees to eat fruit or to find nectar. It uses its hooked bill as any other parrot would for climbing but glides down to the ground on its small wings, some glides being up to 90 ft long.

The kakapo makes its nest among rocks or under large roots of trees. It is little more than a layer of soft rotten wood with a few feathers on which 3 or 4 white eggs are laid. It seems that each bird breeds every 2 years.

Everything against them

When Europeans first settled in New Zealand and began to explore the country, the kakapo was so numerous and so easily caught that it was often killed for the pot by those who had to live off the land. By 1900 it had become rare and by 1910 there were already fears that it might soon become extinct, not because it was being killed for food but because of introduced domestic cats preying on it. Stoats also have been introduced as well as rats and, near farmsteads, dogs must have accounted for a fair number of kakapos. Then deer were introduced and went wild. Wherever the deer went the kakapo disappeared, possibly because they eat the same plants as the bird. Today the owl-parrot lives in a few wooded valleys in the extreme southwest of New Zealand. It may be more numerous than is supposed, but New Zealand zoologists argue that this is unlikely, its traces are too obvious to be overlooked even if the birds themselves are not seen. These are their 'paths', their droppings (which are described as like a meringue), their booming calls and also their 'dust-bowls'; these are like those made by domestic chickens for dust-bathing but are believed to be made by kakapos when displaying in the breeding season. Above all, the most obvious traces are the white, bleached blades of grass.

class	**Aves**
order	**Psittaciformes**
family	**Psittacidae**
genus & species	***Strigops habroptilus***

Kallima

This, from a Greek word meaning beautiful, is the generic name of certain butterflies belonging to the family Nymphalidae which are also called leaf butterflies or, more commonly, dead-leaf butterflies. This same family includes the fritillaries, purple emperor, white admiral, and the vanessid butterflies such as peacock, red admiral, tortoiseshell and Camberwell beauty, all brilliantly marked and powerful in flight. The dead-leaf butterflies share these qualities but with the exception that when they close their wings they are transformed. The several species of ***Kallima*** *range from New Guinea through southeast and south Asia to India and Ceylon, with species in Madagascar, the Gold Coast and Ashanti.*

The Indian and far eastern species ***Kallima inachus*** *and* ***K. paralekta*** *are $3\frac{1}{2}$ in. across the spread wings. The upperside of the wings is patterned with dark brown, blue and bright orange but in the Ceylon species* ***K. philarchus*** *the orange is replaced with white. The other species are variously coloured but all have this kind of colour combination.*

Bogus foliage

The shape of the wings of kallima butterflies when closed over the back, together with the colours and patterns of their undersides, give the appearance of a dead leaf. Many members of their family have 'tails' on the rear margins of the wings. These are short and blunt-ended. The dead-leaf butterflies have one such tail and when the butterfly comes to rest on a twig this touches the twig and looks like a leaf stalk. The tip of the leaf is represented by the pointed and curved tips of the forewings as they lie together. Between this tip and the bogus leaf stalk runs a dark line, across both fore- and hindwings, which looks just like the midrib of a leaf.

Trembling like a leaf

Less distinct dark lines run obliquely upwards from this central line to the margins of the wings, and these look exactly like the veins of a leaf. To complete the illusion, and this is especially true of *K. inachus,* the species most often seen in museums or books, there are patches on the wings just like the holes and tears, the fungal growths and other blemishes found on dead leaves. The body, head and antennae are tucked away between the wings when the butterfly is resting and the whole effect is such that once the butterfly has settled it is almost impossible to see it against the background of leaves and branches. No two butterflies of the same species are patterned alike on their underwings, just as no two dead leaves are exactly alike. And immediately the butterfly settles it turns and faces down the stem, as a dead leaf would hang, and it starts to sway gently as if in a breeze.

The celebrated British naturalist AR Wallace met *K. paralekta* in Sumatra in 1861 and he describes in his book, *The Malay Archi-*

pelago, how he had the greatest difficulty in finding the butterfly, once it had settled, even when he had watched it fly in and marked the spot with his eye.

Only flies when it must

Dead-leaf butterflies live in regions of heavy rainfall, in thick forests in hilly and mountainous districts. They are seldom seen in the open and never fly far, spending most of their time resting on bushes. When they do fly, as when they are disturbed, they fly off rapidly on an erratic course, the bright colours on the uppersides of their wings making them very conspicuous. The result is they are often chased by birds, but once the butterfly settles and closes its wings the bird chasing it is baffled. The butterfly has done the perfect disappearing act.

Flaunting its colours

The butterflies often settle on sweet sap exuding from trees or on over-ripe fruit or on damp patches on the ground to drink. At such times they hold their wings partly open and move them up and down, with no attempt at concealment.

The disappearing trick

The orange oakleaf, as *K. inachus* is sometimes called, is double brooded. One breeding season is from April to June and the other is after the rains. Its caterpillar feeds on flowering trees and shrubs *Strobilanthus* and *Pseuderantheum.* It is golden brown with nine longitudinal rows of fine spines. Its head and legs are black and on the head are two long red 'horns' set with minute branched spines.

The remarkable resemblance the settled orange oakleaf butterfly bears to a dead leaf has led to this species being used as the last word in perfect protective resemblance. A few entomologists have questioned whether this may not be a mistaken idea because the butterfly usually settles among green foliage, not among dead leaves. On the other hand we have the testimony of Wallace and others that the insect is surprisingly hard to find once it settles. We are on more certain ground in using *Kallima* to illustrate two other principles. The first is that known as *coincident disruptive pattern.* The line which represents the midrib of the leaf runs across the fore- and hindwings, and only forms the unbroken line required for its camouflage effect when the wings are held in the natural position of rest, and this is also true of the leaf-like outline formed by the wings. Any alteration in the relative position of the wings largely destroys the illusion. The other principle is that of *flash coloration.* The upper surface of the wings of *Kallima* are brilliantly coloured orange and blue. When the butterfly suddenly flies there is a startling explosion of bright colour, and when it alights a large blue and orange butterfly apparently disappears, the detailed camouflage of the undersides of its wings seeming to transform it into a dead leaf. Both effects are puzzling and confusing to a predator (or collector) searching for the butterfly, more so than if it had inconspicuous coloration on both upper- and undersides of the wings.

Carlo Bevilacqua

◁△ *Museum specimen of* ***Kallima inachus,*** *uppersides of its wings flaunting the beauty that gave it its name.*

◁ *The underside of the same butterfly—each wing a perfect imitation dead leaf, even to the 'veins' and 'fungus holes' all over it.*

△ *Now you see it: few predators drawn to the bright, flashes of* ***Kallima inachus*** *in erratic flight can distinguish between butterfly and dead leaf once it has landed.*

▷ *Photographer's reconstruction of* ***Kallima inachus*** *in typical pose, showing the peak of perfection reached by this insect's camouflage.*

phylum	**Arthropoda**
class	**Insecta**
order	**Lepidoptera**
family	**Nymphalidae**
genus & species	***Kallima inachus, K. paralekta, K. philarchus***

Stephen Dalton: NHPA

Kangaroo

The best-known of the five kangaroos are the great grey and the red. The great grey or forester is up to 6 ft high, exceptionally 7 ft, with a weight of up to 200 lb. Its head is small with large ears, its forelimbs are very small by comparison with the powerful hindlimbs and the strong tail is 4 ft long. The colour is variable but is mainly grey with whitish underparts and white on the legs and underside of the tail. The muzzle is hairy between the nostrils. The male is known as a boomer, the female as a flyer and the young as a Joey. The great grey lives in open forest browsing the vegetation. The red kangaroo is similar to the great grey in size and build but the male has a reddish coat, the adult female is smoky blue, and the muzzle is less hairy. Unlike the great grey kangaroo it lives on open plains, is more a grazer than a browser, and lives more in herds or mobs, usually of a dozen animals.

*The 55 species of kangaroo, wallaby and wallaroo make up the family Macropodidae (**macropus** = big foot). Only two are called kangaroos but there are 10 rat kangaroos and two tree kangaroos which, with the wallabies, will be dealt with later. A third species is known as the rock kangaroo or wallaroo. There is no brief way of describing the difference between a kangaroo and a wallaby except to say that the first is larger than the second. An arbitrary rule is that a kangaroo has hindfeet more than 10 in. long.*

The red is found all over Australia. The great grey lives mainly in eastern Australia but there are three races of it, formerly regarded as species: the grey kangaroo or western forester of the southwest; that on Kangaroo Island off Yorke Peninsula, South Australia; and the Tasmanian kangaroo or forester. The wallaroo or euro lives among rocks especially in coastal areas. It has shorter and more stockily built hindlegs than the red or the great grey.

Leaps and bounds

When feeding, and so moving slowly, kangaroos balance themselves on their small forelegs and strong tail and swing the large hindlegs forward. They then bring their arms and tail up to complete the second stage of the movement. When travelling fast, only the two hindfeet are used with the tail held almost horizontally as a balancer. They clear obstacles in the same way, with leaps of up to 26 ft long. Usually the leap does not carry them more than 5 ft off the ground but there are reports of these large kangaroos clearing fences up to 9 ft. Their top speed is always a matter for dispute. They seem to be capable of 25 mph over a 300yd stretch but some people claim a higher speed for them.

Eating down the grass

Kangaroos feed mainly by night resting during the heat of the day. The red kangaroo, because it eats grass, has become a serious competitor with sheep, important in Australia's economy. By creating grasslands man has helped the kangaroo increase in numbers. In turn the kangaroo tends to outgraze the sheep, for which the pastures were grown, not only through its increased numbers but by its manner of feeding. Sheep have lower teeth in only the front of the mouth, with a dental pad in the upper jaw. Kangaroos have front teeth in both lower and upper jaw which means they crop grass more closely than sheep. At times, it is reported, they also dig out the grass roots. They can go without water for long periods, which suggests they were originally animals of desert or semi-desert, but where water is supplied for sheep kangaroos will, if not kept out, take the greater share.

Kangaroos set a problem

Enemies of the larger kangaroos are few now that the Tasmanian wolf has been banished. The introduced dingo still claims its victims but that is shot at sight. The loss of natural enemies, the creation of wide areas of grassland and the kangaroo being

◁ *Dusk falls on a kangaroo couple.*

▽ *The despair of Australian graziers, kangaroos let no fence stand between them and their drink.*

Ederic Slater

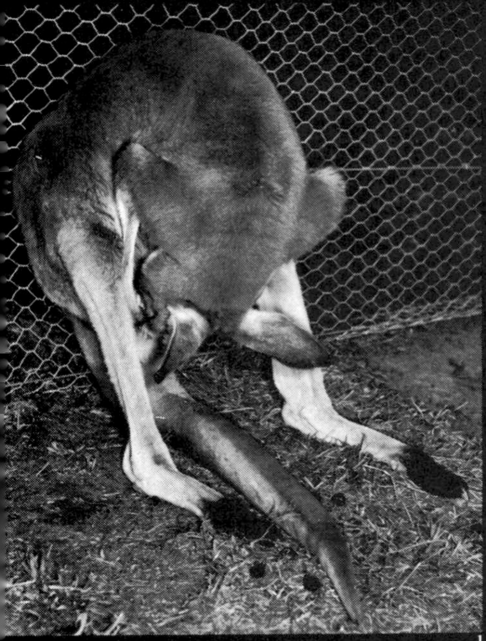

1

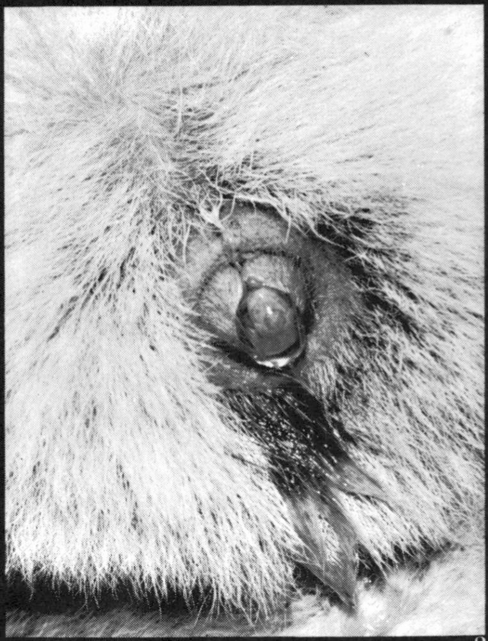

2

3

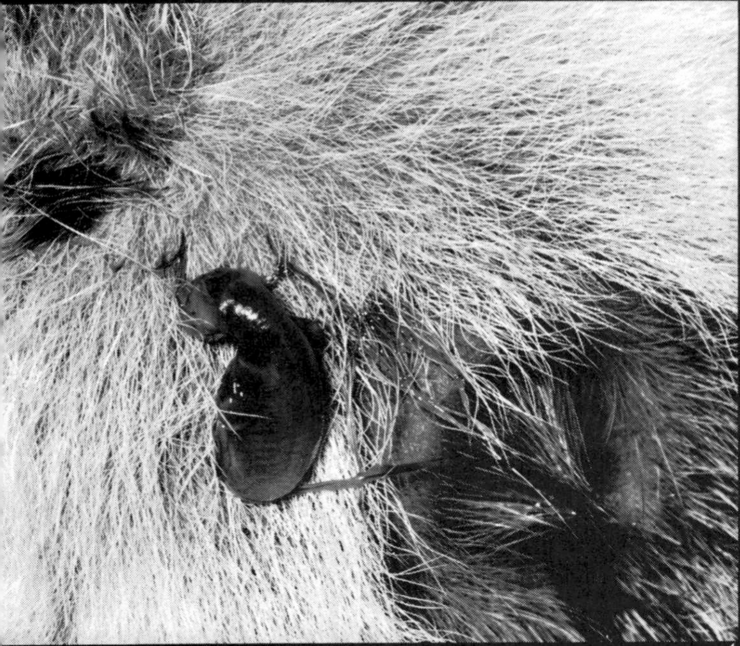

4

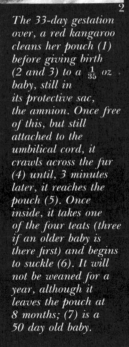

The 33-day gestation over, a red kangaroo cleans her pouch (1) before giving birth (2 and 3) to a $\frac{1}{35}$ *oz baby, still in its protective sac, the amnion. Once free of this, but still attached to the umbilical cord, it crawls across the fur (4) until, 3 minutes later, it reaches the pouch (5). Once inside, it takes one of the four teats (three if an older baby is there first) and begins to suckle (6). It will not be weaned for a year, although it leaves the pouch at 8 months; (7) is a 50 day old baby.*

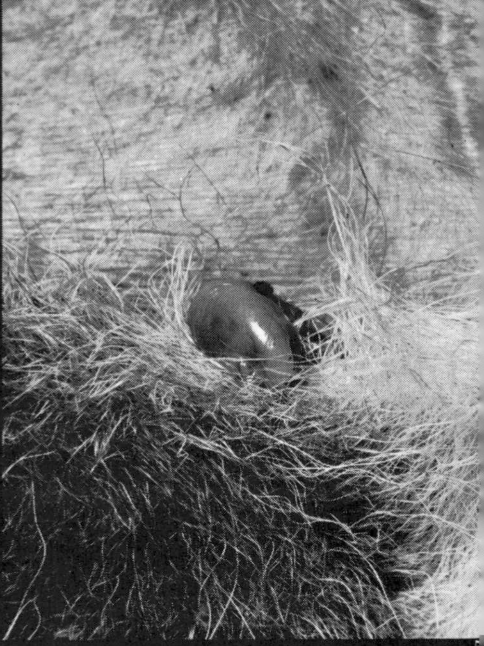

5

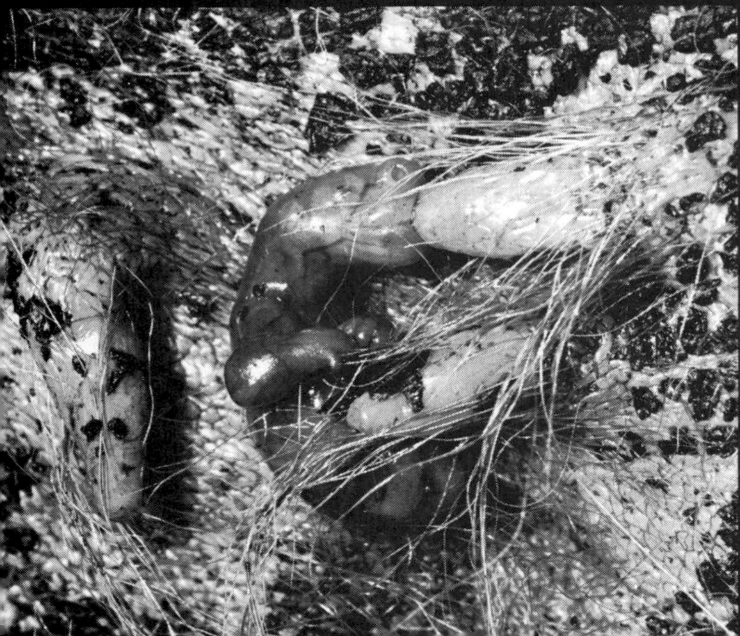

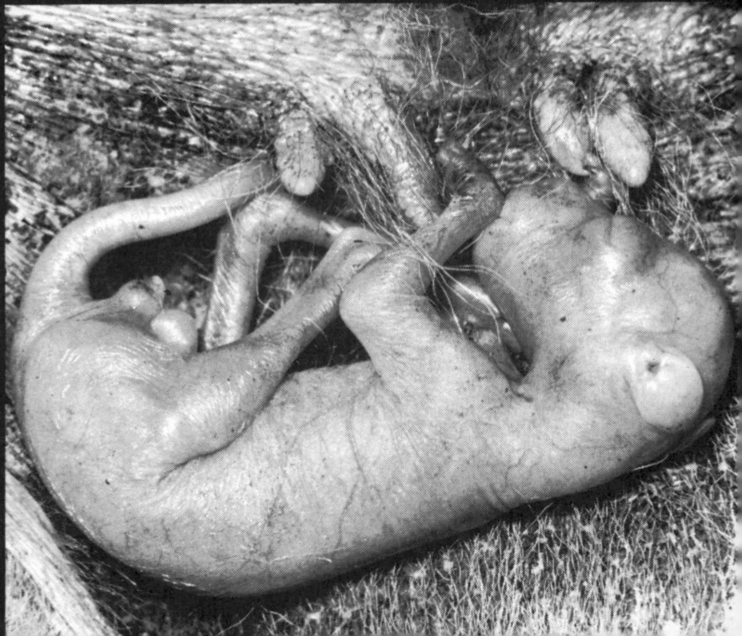

able to breed throughout most of the year, has created a problem, especially for sheep graziers, in Australia. Fencing in the pastures, often thousands of acres in extent, is costly – about £200 a mile – and kangaroos have a trick of squeezing under the fence at any weak spot. So kangaroos are shot. In one year, on nine sheep properties totalling 1 540 000 acres, 140 000 kangaroos were shot and it would have needed double this number of kills to keep the properties clear of them. Another problem is that kangaroos often bound across roads at night and collide with cars causing costly damage and endangering those in the cars.

Bean-sized baby

The manner in which baby kangaroos are born and reach the pouch had been in dispute for well over a century. In 1959-60 all doubts were set at rest when the birth process of the red kangaroo was filmed at Adelaide University. About 33 days after mating the female red kangaroo begins to clean her pouch, holding it open with the forepaws and licking the inside. She then takes up the 'birth position' sitting on the base of her tail with the hindlegs extended forwards and her tail passed forward between them. She then licks the opening of her birth canal or cloaca. The newborn kangaroo, $\frac{3}{4}$in. long, appears headfirst and grasps its mother's fur with the claws on its forefeet. Its hindlegs are at this time very small. In 3 minutes it has dragged itself to the pouch, entered it and seized one of the four teats in its mouth. The birth is the same for the great grey except that the female stands, with her tail straight out behind her. The baby kangaroo, born at an early stage of development, weighs $\frac{1}{35}$ oz at birth. It remains in the pouch for 8 months, by which time it weighs nearly 10 lb. It continues to be suckled for nearly 6 months after it has left the pouch and can run about, putting its head in to grasp a teat. Meanwhile, another baby has probably been born and is in the pouch. The red kangaroo has lived for 16 years in captivity.

Overlooking the obvious

The truth about kangaroo birth took a long time to be established. In 1629 Francois Pelsaert, a Dutch sea captain, wrecked on the Abrolhos Islands off southwest Australia, was the first to discover the baby in the pouch of a female wallaby. He thought it was born in the pouch. This is what the Aborigines also believed. In 1830 Alexander Collie, a ship's surgeon on a sloop lying in Cockburn Sound, Western Australia, investigated the birth and showed that the baby was born in the usual manner and made its way unaided into the pouch. From then on various suggestions were put forward: that the mother lifted the newborn baby with her forepaws or her lips and placed it in the pouch, or that the baby was budded off from the teat. In 1883 Sir Richard Owen, distinguished anatomist, came down heavily on the side of those who said the mother placed the baby in her pouch holding it in her lips, yet in 1882 the Hon L Hope had shown Collie to be correct. In 1913 Mr A Goerling wrote a letter to the Perth *Western Mail* describing how he had watched the baby make its way to the pouch with no help from the mother. It was not until 1923, however, that this view was generally accepted, when Dr WT Hornaday, Director of the New York Zoological Gardens, watched and described the birth. Finally, in 1959-60, the whole process of birth was filmed by GB Sharman, JC Merchant, Phyllis Pilton and Meredith Clark, at Adelaide University, setting the matter at rest for all time. It seems so obvious to us now!

class	**Mammalia**
order	**Marsupialia**
family	**Macropodidae**
genus & species	***Macropus giganteus*** *great grey kangaroo* ***M. robustus*** *rock kangaroo or wallaroo* ***M. rufus*** *red kangaroo*

Full steam ahead: a shallow water sprint shows the versatility of bounding movement.

HAE Lucas

Douglass Baglin

△ *Support from the rear: a red kangaroo resting on his powerful hindlegs and long tail.*

◁ *A place in the sun: a red kangaroo group whiles away a lazy sociable afternoon.*

▷ *Sticking his neck out: Joey investigates the grazing from the warmth of his mother's pouch.*

▽ *Bouncing retreat: great grey kangaroos leaping along on their hindlegs, up to 26 ft at a bound, using their tails as balancers. They can be identified by the black tips to their tails as well as by their large size.*

EO Hoppe

Photo Researchers

Kangaroo mouse

There are many species of mice and a fair proportion of these hop or progress in leaps. So it is not surprising that several different species that have specialized in progressing by leaps should have been called kangaroo mice even when they live far from Australia. In Australia itself there are species of mice which some Australian zoologists call hopping mice but the standard textbooks call kangaroo mice. There are also, in this same continent, mice that are not true mice but related to kangaroos. These are sometimes called kangaroo mice and there are 15 of them. These are better called marsupial mice and will be dealt with under that title.

Australia's hopping mice

The kangaroo mice of Australia burrow into sandy soil and are very difficult to dig out because of the speed with which they burrow, and once on the surface they are hard to catch because they hop along so quickly. They are vegetarians, feeding on seeds, leaves and berries. Because they do not compete for food the carnivorous marsupial mice often live in the same burrows as the hopping mice. There are 76 species of true rodents in Australia, not including the introduced ship rat and common rat, and nine of these are variously known as kangaroo mice or hopping mice. They have even been called jerboa mice. They are much the same size, colouring and shape as house mice but their hindlegs are longer in proportion, so the hopping mice look more like jerboas (p 1196). There are 2–5 young in a litter and their life-span is believed to exceed 3 years.

New Guinea's kangaroo mouse . . .

In New Guinea lives another true rodent, a mouse very like the Australian pouched mice. Little is known about its way of life; it is like the Australian hopping mice in size, colour and shape but too little is known of its habits to say whether these compare also with those of the hopping mice.

. . . and more in America

To add to the confusion, there are species in America which are also called pygmy kangaroo rats. They are a lighter colour than the Australian forms but much the same size and they have long hindlegs, a long tail and large ears, and their head is larger in proportion to the body. Another difference is that the soles of the feet are furred, which enables them to hop easily over loose sand. They stay in their burrows by day and come out at night to feed on seeds. In habits they are very like the kangaroo rat, which is discussed separately, especially in their ability to go without water indefinitely, getting the moisture they need from dry seeds. No doubt at times they drink dew or get moisture by eating succulents, but they can do without even these.

The young of both species are born in May or June, in burrows. There are usually 3 or 4 in a litter but there may be as many as 7, and there may be 2 litters a year.

Looking like each other

Although it is highly confusing to have a number of animals known by the same name there is a particular point in bringing them together here, even if each can be discussed but briefly. They illustrate probably better than any other collection of animal species what is known as convergent evolution. By this is meant the principle that animals having the same way of life come to look like each other. All, with perhaps one exception, the New Guinea kangaroo mouse, live under desert or semi-desert conditions in which a hopping or kangaroo-like way of moving over the ground has great advantages. Firstly, in deserts food is scarce and hopping enables an animal to cover ground quickly in search of scanty food. Secondly, hopping is the best way of moving over shifting soil. The jerboas are like them and it is only accidental that they have not been called kangaroo mice—or kangaroo rats, since they are bigger.

There need be little surprise that so many mice should have specialized in leaping. Many animals show a tendency to do so, especially when young. Baby hedgehogs leap into the air when touched. They only leap up a few inches, but then their legs are not strong nor are they built for jumping. When we come to deal with lungless salamanders we shall find there is at least one species that leaps about and a salamander is the last animal we should expect to do this. Rats and mice are almost pre-adapted for this habit. Baby house mice of the wild strain leap about, and so do rats. Some go farther and progress in leaps when adult. It only needs a slight change in their structure, a slight lengthening of the hindlegs and they are already on their way to joining the company of kangaroo mice.

class	**Mammalia**
order	**Rodentia**
family	**Heteromyidae**
genus & species	***Microdipodops megacephalus*** *American*
family	**Muridae**
genera & species	***Lorentzimys nouhuysii*** *New Guinea* ***Notomys filmeri*** *Australian*

▽ *All ears, an apprehensive **Notomys cervinus** backs away from a strange sound.*

Queensland Museum

▽ *Hop-scotch in the sand: kangaroo mice **Notomys fuscus** caught by the flashlight. They spend the day scurrying about in their burrows, coming out at night to feed on berries and fruit.*

Defenceless but for its leaping power, ***Dipodomys ordii*** *waits for a sound to confirm its suspicions.*

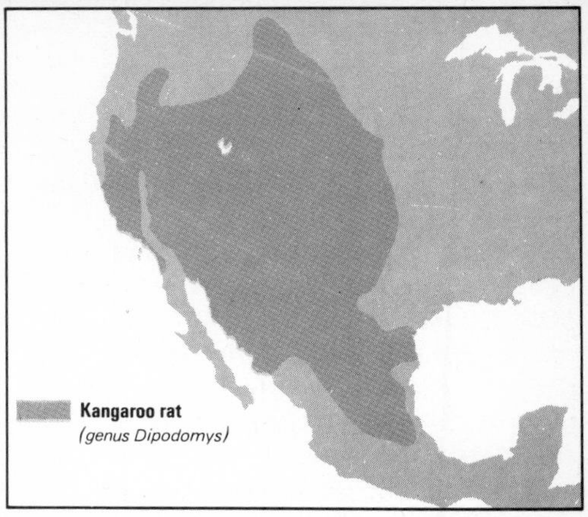

△ *The desert range of the kangaroo rat.*

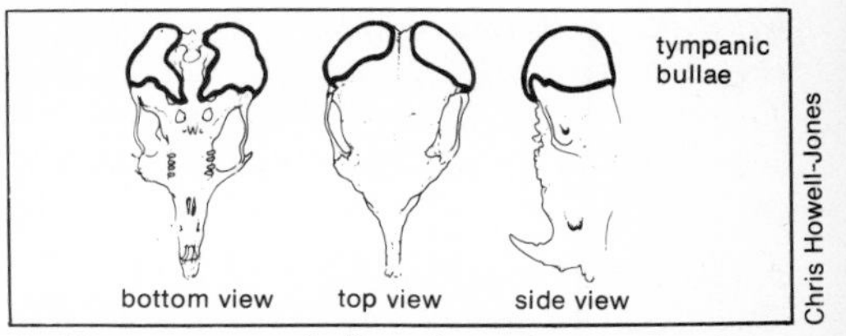

△ *Kangaroo rat skull—adaptation for hearing.*

Kangaroo rat

Kangaroo rats are rodents, named for their long hindlegs and tail, short forelegs and leaping gait. They are similar in these respects to jerboas and kangaroo mice, and like these animals they live in deserts. There are 24 species. Their head and body lengths range from 4 to 8 in. with a tail longer than the head and body combined. The fur is pale to dark brown above and white underneath. There is a dark stripe running along the top of the tail, which ends in a tuft of hair.

Kangaroo rats live in North America west of the Missouri, from southwestern California to central Mexico.

Dust bathing for health

Kangaroo rats live in dry or semi-dry country, preferably with sandy soil that they can easily dig and sparse vegetation which favours their bounding method of locomotion. They are nocturnal and will not come out even in moonlight. Wet weather also stops them from coming out.

Dust bathing is apparently very necessary for these animals. Without it they develop sores and their fur becomes matted. Their habits are similar to those of jerboas, as might be expected from their similar form and habitat.

Dry stores

Kangaroo rats can survive long periods without drinking. They obtain their water from dew-soaked and succulent plants but they can also live on dry food like jerboas, getting water from the breakdown of fats and carbohydrates. Their kidneys are very efficient and little water is needed to remove the body wastes.

They eat a variety of plants, including the seeds, leaves, stems and fruits. A few insects are also taken. They collect food in caches for use in times of drought when the sparse vegetation withers up. The kangaroo rats carry the food in their cheek pouches to caches and empty it out, the animal using both forepaws to squeeze the cheeks simultaneously. The pouches are formed from folds of skin and are lined with fur, and stretch back as far as the neck. The kangaroo rats do not merely store their food, they process it first to prevent it going bad. Investigations showed that just after the rainy season the giant kangaroo rat stored seed pods in small pits around its burrow. One kangaroo rat had 875 pits each covered with soil and pressed down. A few months later the pits were empty but the kangaroo rat's burrow contained several large caches of seed pods. It appeared that it was storing its food in shallow pits until it dried out and then transferring it to permanent and more convenient stores. Moreover it was seen to take seed pods that had dried naturally straight to the caches instead of first storing them in pits. Kangaroo rats near grain fields may steal enough grain to be pests.

Breeding by the climate

Kangaroo rats breed at any time of the year providing the climate is suitable. Some breed all the year round, but with few births during the winter months. Gestation lasts 4–5 weeks and the litters consist of 1–5 babies which stay in their mother's burrow for 6 weeks. Each female may bear up to three litters in a year.

Listening for trouble

A feature of any desert-living animals such as elephant shrews, gerbils and jerboas is extremely sensitive hearing. These animals also have very large tympanic bullae, the domed-shaped bones that lie under the base of the skull just beneath the ears. At one time it was thought they acted as resonators that amplified the sounds being transmitted to the inner ears, so allowing these animals to hear very faint sounds.

The function of these bullae and the important role they play in the life of these animals was demonstrated by a series of experiments carried out by Douglas Webster. First he showed that kangaroo rats are extremely sensitive to sounds of frequencies between 1 000 and 3 000 cycles per second. Two mechanisms are involved. Sound waves are transmitted from the eardrum to the sense organs of the inner ear by three small bones in the inner ear. They also amplify the sound, and those of kangaroo rats amplify sound five times more than those in human ears. The large space contained in the auditory bullae was also found to increase the sensitivity of the ear. The enlarged bullae do not act as resonators, but allow the eardrum to vibrate more freely. The eardrum in a normal ear is damped because air pressure builds up behind it in the middle ear, resisting its movements. In the kangaroo rat and other desert animals, the large space inside the bullae easily absorbs any increase in pressure and the eardrum is able to vibrate in response to much weaker vibrations.

Kangaroo rats are preyed on by owls and rattlesnakes and Webster was able to show that the rats can hear their enemies coming and so escape. He placed barn owls or rattlesnakes in a darkened cage and released kangaroo rats onto the floor. As the predator struck the kangaroo rat leaped out of the way. Using sensitive recording equipment Webster was able to detect incredibly faint rustlings from the predators as they pounced, and the rustling sounds were of the frequencies to which kangaroo rats are particularly sensitive. Without these highly sensitive ears the kangaroo rats would be sitting targets. As it is, only a minimal percentage of them are lost to predators.

class	**Mammalia**
order	**Rodentia**
family	**Heteromyidae**
genus & species	***Dipodomys ingens*** *giant* ***D. merriami*** *Merriam's* *others*

Katydid

The name of this American group of bush crickets is at least as well known because of the popularity of a series of girls' books on the theme of What Katy Did . . . *as it is for being the loudest of the grasshoppers. Not only do the katydids make the most strident calls but these have been intensively studied, so shedding valuable light on the whole subject of insect stridulation. These particular American longhorned grasshoppers or bush crickets seem to be calling 'Katy did, she did', hence their name, but this is an over-simplification.*

Two of the better known katydids are ***Pterophylla camellifolia,*** *common in the eastern states, and* ***Microcentrum retinerve***, *common in the southern and western states. Katydids feed mainly on leaves, as other bush crickets and grasshoppers do, and their chief enemies are birds. In autumn they lay flattened, slate-coloured eggs laid in two rows along a twig. These hatch the following spring and the nymphs grow by moulting in the usual way* *(see p 683)**. The main interest here is in their song and one species in which this has been closely studied is* ***Scudderia texensis***, *the Texas bush katydid. This is common on waste lands and fallow fields, on the verges of highways and railway embankments, and wherever weeds and grasses abound. Its range covers the eastern United States. In Florida and southern Georgia it has two generations a year, adults appearing in June and September. In more northerly parts of its range there is probably only one generation a year in early July.*

Songs for separate occasions

Katydids are famed for their sounds, of which there are several different kinds, making up an insect language. The males of the various species of katydids produce two or more different sounds even when on their own and they produce others in response to other males of their own species. The females also make their own sounds. The male Texas bush katydid makes four different sounds, but each of these can be altered according to circumstances. This can be best appreciated by following a day in the life of this katydid.

Tuning up after noon

In the morning and middle of the day the katydid makes no sounds. In the late afternoon and evening he makes short lispy sounds called the fast-pulsed song. This normally lasts less than a minute. At twilight he begins to make a soft ticking sound which can be heard only a few feet away, interspersed with occasional fast-pulses. As darkness sets in a slow-pulsed song is added. Each slow-pulse is followed by a fast-pulse and then a pause, and as the night wears on the fast-pulse gets longer and longer until late at night the fast-pulse may last

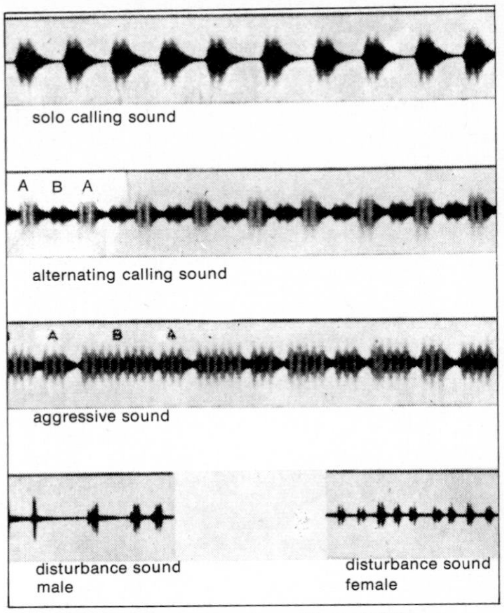

△ *The chirping repertoire of katydid* ***Pterophylla camellifolia***, *recorded as patterns. Alone, it sings calmly (top); at another's approach, it quickens, and the insect's songs (A and B) alternate. In the alternating and aggressive sounds, chirps from two different individuals are designated A and B.*

▷ *Fork-tailed katydid* ***Scudderia tureata***.

half an hour or more before the slow-pulse is produced. So it is not a simple case of the katydid singing a monotonously produced song, but of a changing song as the light fades at dusk.

Dim lights and soft music

To a large extent the songs of katydids, and presumably of all bush crickets, grasshoppers and true crickets, are influenced by the intensity of light. In many species a low light intensity is needed for them to sing. In others, of which the Texas bush katydid is one, certain sounds are produced principally by day, others in twilight and others in full daylight. In a few species the same sounds are produced by day and by night. The link between different intensities of light is well brought out when a katydid singing in the afternoon in sunlight changes to his twilight song when a cloud passes overhead. Even so, a male of any of these may change his song for a while without any change in the intensity of light. Then, we may presume, it is some change within the insect itself that causes the alteration in the song. Another change comes when one male answers another. Then one calls, waits for the other to answer, then replies, the second one becoming silent to listen for this.

Singing man to man

Generally, bush crickets and grasshoppers that live in dense numbers produce low-intensity songs, that are audible to man at a few feet only. Those well spaced out use louder songs, audible at 200–300 yd. This is reasonable, for where they are close together only a 'whisper' is needed as compared with the 'shout' needed when they are widely separated. In the Texas katydid the male's song changes when another male is moving closer to him. Putting this briefly and in simple terms, the male is first of all singing to himself. Then as another male moves towards him he advertises the fact he is there and is in effect saying 'Go away'. Finally, if the second male moves in much closer the song becomes a threat.

Talking him in

The last use to which the song is put is to bring male and female together for breeding. In some katydids the male calls and the female who is ready for mating answers him with a ticking call—sometimes it is said that she lisps at him—but stays where she is, he having to go all the way to her. In other species the male sings and the female comes towards him, part of the way, then she begins to tick in answer to his song and he moves over to her, homing on her ticks. There is a third group of species in which when a male calls the female ticks back at him 'come on, then'—and he moves towards her. Having gone so far he changes his tune and stands still. The female now goes the rest of the way to meet him. This is all very different from what we find in other bush crickets and grasshoppers. In these the male sings and the female, who is mute, goes all the way to him.

There may be species of katydid in which both male and female move towards each other at the same time. This is suspected in one species at least, but there is an obvious disadvantage: it is not easy to keep track of a moving sound. We see this principle in operation in the Texas katydid. The male calls and the female ticks her answer and the way she responds, with one, two or three ticks, tells him whether she is fully ready for mating or not. When he receives the maximum response he moves over the bush or plant on which he is perched in her direction. Then he takes wing. If he lands on a bush or plant near her, he calls and she answers, so he takes off again. Once he lands on the same plant as she is on there is silence because she, seeing or feeling him land, sways gently and shakes the plant, so he can find her.

Katydid's hearing aid

Most insects find their mates by seeing each other, as in butterflies, by scent, as in moths, or by being attracted to the same kind of food so they meet there. Few use sounds to bring the sexes together, and of those few the katydids have the most complicated techniques for using sound. We even find that a male katydid will sometimes lean to one side to lift a foreleg and hold it in the air. His ears are on his forelegs, and this action seems to be a definite 'straining to listen'.

phylum	**Arthropoda**
order	**Insecta**
class	**Orthoptera**
family	**Tettigoniidae**
subfamily	**Phaneropterinae**

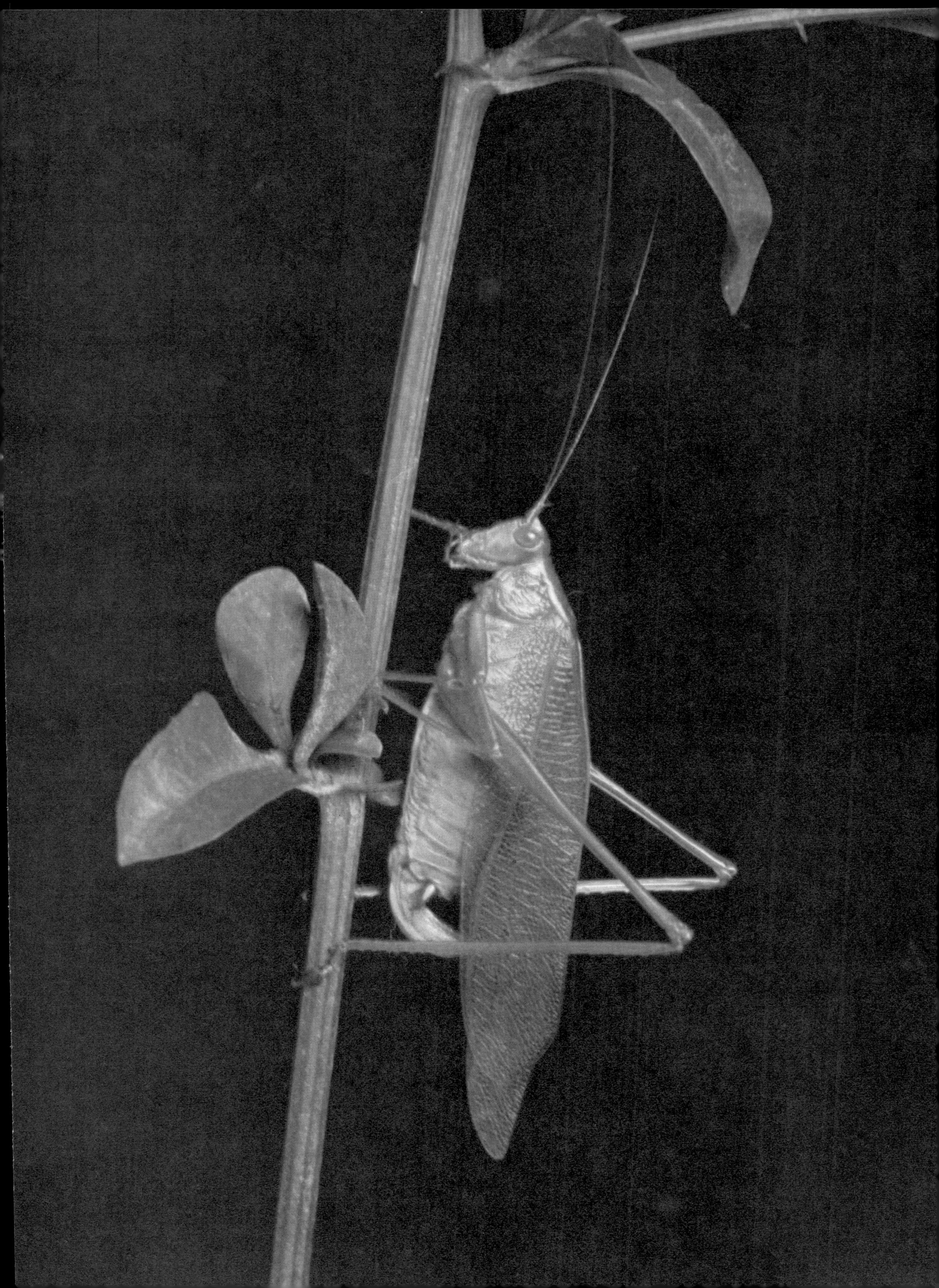

Kea

The kea is an unusual parrot that is found only in South Island, New Zealand. It is the size of a raven and its plumage has a scaly appearance. In general, keas are olive green with streaks of orange and red on the underparts. The legs are yellow brown and the eyes have yellow pupils that give the kea a beady-eyed look. The bill is nearly 2 in. long and very sharp, but not so curved as in other parrots. It is very strong and the kea is reputed to be able to rip open corrugated iron roofs.

Closely related to the kea is the kaka, which is similar in both habits and appearance. The South Island variety of kaka is larger than that found on the North Island and has a white crown and greenish back instead of a grey crown and predominantly brown plumage with red under the wings. The kaka lives in dense forests and on Kapiti Island there is a kaka sanctuary where they are becoming tame.

In common with all parrots the kea and kaka are very noisy and their names are derived from their harsh calls.

Tin-opener beak

Keas are the hardiest of parrots, sometimes being found in the snow above the treeline. In winter they retreat down the mountainsides and live in the forests. The kakas live permanently in the forests, lower down. Both live in flocks outside the breeding season. Keas are strong fliers, soaring and gliding gracefully from rock to rock or tree to tree. On the ground they are less agile and move by hopping.

The kea's favourite food is the young leaves and buds of trees but it also walks along the branches tearing off moss, lichen and bark. Feeding is slow and deliberate, the upper half of the powerful bill being used as a lever while the lower half is used as a gouge. When in season, nectar and berries are also eaten. The tongue has a fringe of hairs reminiscent of that on the tongues of honeyeaters (p 1095) and is used to lick nectar from flowers or juice from succulent fruit. Unlike the honeyeater and many other nectar-drinking birds, the keas do not pollinate the flowers they feed upon. Indeed, they destroy the flowers, often chewing them to extract the juices and spitting out the remains.

Grubs and beetles are extracted from the ground and keas also eat flesh. This latter habit is presumed to have developed since sheep were brought to New Zealand. Keas

▽ Scruffy junior: this gawky bundle of adolescent plumage will grow into an adult, swift and powerful in flight, if a little clumsy on the ground.

▷▽ Not-so-pretty Polly: with a wicked glint in its eye, a kea parrot surveys its territory.

John Tashjian at San Diego Zoo

have formed the habit of feeding on carrion and also of tearing open the flesh of living sheep to eat the fat around the kidneys. Tame keas have also been known to eat mice.

Kakas feed on nectar taken up with their brush-tipped tongues, and on berries and other fruits, insects and their larvae.

Nesting under rocks

Keas have very loose territories centred around the nest and roost. Flocks of keas can enter a territory with impunity and the home pair will join them to feed but retire to their own roost at night. Strange keas which are apparently attracted by the calls of the young are tolerated until they come within 25 yd of the nest. The pair then challenge with a cry of 'kua-ua-ua-ua', a call that is also used to challenge man and even vehicles.

Breeding takes place all the year round but mainly in the summer months. The nest of lichens, moss, leaves, ferns and chips of rotten wood is made on the ground, under a boulder, in a crevice, hollow log or among the roots of a tree. There may be an entrance tunnel up to 20 ft long and a well-worn runway and accumulated droppings indicate that the same nests are used year after year. Two to four eggs are incubated for 3–4 weeks. The male kea roosts on a boulder outside the nest and the female joins him there when the chicks are 8 weeks old and filling most of the nest. At first these are helpless and the female feeds them by pushing food into their mouths. After a short time the female loses interest in the chicks and the male has to do all the feeding. The young males become independent 4 weeks after fledging but, for some unknown reason, the adult male continues feeding the young females for another few weeks.

Kakas nest in hollow trees, the female laying four eggs on a layer of powdered wood in a cavity in a tree.

Sheep slaughterers?

Keas have a very bad reputation as sheep killers, perching on the sheep's backs and tearing open their skin to eat the fat and flesh. The wounds themselves may not be severe but poisoning often sets in and leads to death. It is sometimes said that sheep farmers have been put out of business by keas and their reputation has been bad enough for them to be slaughtered by the thousand. In 1886 the Government paid a generous bounty for each beak. The slaughter is still continuing and keas are becoming rare in many places.

Recent researches have, however, suggested that damage by keas is greatly exaggerated and that attacks are mainly made by a few birds that have formed the habit. In some places the burying of offal after slaughtering has reduced the attacks on live sheep as the keas are no longer attracted to the vicinity of the farm. The point has also been made that keas are not very efficient as predators and will wound more sheep than they kill. This means that if keas cause as much damage as they are said to, there must be very large numbers of wounded sheep. Yet one grader who inspected 20–40 thousand fleeces in 10 years never found a single scar from a kea wound.
Keas will sometimes settle on humans who encourage them for the fun of it. Very soon the birds begin to peck through their clothes, but as soon as they peck flesh and the victim flinches, the keas fly off. Presumably the same must happen with sheep and the keas are only able to persevere with sick or trapped sheep.

class	**Aves**
order	**Psittaciformes**
family	**Psittacidae**
genus & species	***Nestor meridionalis*** *kaka* ***N. notabilis*** *kea*

John Warham

Kestrel

The kestrels are small falcons, distributed over all the continents except Antarctica, noted for hovering on gently fanning wings while searching the ground below for prey. In all kestrels the plumage is chestnut and grey with black spots in the male and pale reddish-brown with black streaks and bars in the female.

The common kestrel has numerous races all over Europe, including the British Isles, as well as Asia and Africa. Male and female are about the same size, 13–14 in. long, but the mature male has a grey head while the female and young have brown heads, the young male getting his grey head at 2 years. The American species, called a sparrow-hawk, is very like it. The lesser kestrel, about a foot long, is now regarded as more nearly related to the red-footed falcons. There are several species on the islands of the Indian and western Pacific Oceans, and the Mauritius kestrel is the rarest of all falcons, down to less than 10 pairs. The largest kestrels are two African species, the greater kestrel and the fox kestrel. Neither of these hovers or they do so very rarely. They catch insects, reptiles and small mammals on the ground.

Hovering for a living

The common kestrel nests and roosts in open woodland but hunts over open country. It also takes up residence in the towers of tall buildings in cities, for example, in the heart of London, feeding mainly on house sparrows and starlings. Besides hovering it takes up position on a perch, on the top of a bush, on a wall or building, on a post or on telegraph wires and from these vantage points drops to the ground to take prey. When hovering, with head into the wind and tail bent down and fanned, it may glide on the slant to take up a new hovering station, or it may drop to the ground then fly up again to a new position. In straight flight it alternates glides with a few quick wingbeats. The call is a loud 'kee-kee-kee'.

It feeds on mice and voles, small birds, insects and earthworms, and this is typical of all kestrels except the two large African species. Insects taken are mainly large beetles, moths and grasshoppers. The proportion of these foods taken depends much on the season and on local abundance. For example, it is not unusual for a kestrel to spend an hour or more hovering over one field, dropping to earth every now and then, eating nothing but butterflies and moths. At another time a kestrel may spend long periods dropping from a post and back again taking nothing but earthworms.

Andrew Anderson: NHPA

◁ 'Mantling': disturbed just before a meal, an irate kestrel threatens the intruder.

△ Clumsy homecoming: wings and legs akimbo, a kestrel makes an awkward arrival at its nest.

▽ Kestrel about to feed a large rodent to a hungry family. The chicks fledge in a month.

Roebild

Fritz Siedel

Joseph van Wormer

James Hancock

James Hancock

◁△ *In its element: riding wind and rising air, a kestrel patrols late summer fields.*

△△ *An American sparrowhawk awaits the tiny movement which will betray its next victim.*

△ *Slumming: kestrel and nest in Central London. With the mice and sparrows of Regent's Park only a minute's flying time away, the chick (right) is well fed in its avian hovel.*

Kestrels also take carrion, such as large bird carcases, and both the European and the American kestrels have been seen taking meat scraps and bread from bird tables. They will also rob other birds of prey: one kestrel flew to a barn owl carrying a vole, turned on its back under the owl, seized the vole in its talons and then flew away.

Aerial courtship

Courtship, in late March or early April, consists of aerial displays by the male flying in circles over the perched female. Throughout his displays he flies with 3 or 4 wingbeats followed by a glide, repeated as if part of a ritual, and calling 'kee-kee-kee', all the time. Every so often he flies at the female, not stooping at her but buzzing her, pulling out of his dive at the last moment to fly up and circle her again. Sometimes she flies up and he continues these same manoeuvres over and around her. Kestrels make no nest so the 4–6 eggs, white with blotches of dark red-brown, are laid at intervals of 2 days in the abandoned nest of a large bird such as a crow, in a crevice in a building or on a ledge on a cliff or in a hollow tree. Incubation is mainly by the female, the male bringing her food, but he does sit sometimes. The eggs hatch in a month, the nestlings being brooded by the hen while her mate continues to bring food. The babies fledge at $4-4\frac{1}{2}$ weeks, but are fed for a further period after fledging. When they finally go the nest is littered with pellets regurgitated by the young birds.

Lashing out at intruders

The defence reaction of young kestrels is to throw themselves on their backs, presenting two sets of talons to an intruder. When the intrusion is a human hand the talons take firm hold of it and the bird will continue to cling even when lifted up. Then the beak is brought into action as well. Little is known of the enemies of kestrels but this defence reaction of the young, shared by other birds of prey including owls, is probably sufficient to keep most predators at bay. Deaths are mainly accidental, like the kestrel that flew down to seize a vole just as a weasel was about to do the same. The weasel killed the kestrel. Sometimes a kestrel will seize a weasel in its talons, and be bitten fatally by its intended victim.

Kestrel's keen sight

The kestrel, or windhover as it is sometimes called, may hover at heights of a few to 100 ft or more, moving its head from side to side scanning the ground beneath. At the same time it is not unaware of movement to the side as shown by a simple instance which also brings out the keen eyesight of falcons. A kestrel was hovering over a field when it suddenly glided to its right to the top of a tall oak 200 yd away. A human observer watching the kestrel, a similar distance from the oak, could see nothing, with his naked eye, on the foliage of the oak to attract the kestrel. When he brought his binoculars up, however, he could see that the kestrel had taken a small white butterfly in his beak.

class	**Aves**
order	**Falconiformes**
family	**Falconidae**
genus & species	***Falco alopex*** *fox kestrel* ***F. naumanni*** *lesser kestrel* ***F. punctatus*** *Mauritius kestrel* ***F. rupicoloides*** *greater kestrel* ***F. sparverius*** *American sparrowhawk* ***F. tinnunculus*** *common kestrel* *others*

Killdeer

A common plover of America, the killdeer, named after its call, breeds on inland pastures and meadows. It is 10 in. long, rather larger than the related ringed plovers but similar in plumage. The upperparts are bright chestnut and the underparts white. The forehead and breast have conspicuous white bands. There are two bands on the breast compared with the single band on the ringed plover and the semipalmated plover. The long legs are straw-coloured and the bill black.

The killdeer breeds from Canada to Chile, including the West Indies. The northern population migrates south for the winter and occasional stragglers find their way across the Atlantic, although less than two dozen have been recorded in the British Isles.

Joe van Wormer: Photo Res

△ *Alone with its reflection, a killdeer scours the shallows for anything unfortunate enough to move.*

Hard to see, easy to hear
Outside the breeding season killdeer live in flocks, inland or along the shore. Despite their apparently striking plumage with the black bands contrasting with the white background, the flocks of killdeer are difficult to see, and because they are quite tame one can sometimes walk almost up to a flock before noticing them. The black bands are an example of a 'disruptive pattern', breaking up the outline of the body and making it difficult to see. By contrast killdeer are very noisy, as indicated by the scientific name *Charadrius vociferus*. Its English name is derived from its call note 'kill-dee', with a final 'r' added. When disturbed killdeer fly very rapidly, not far off the ground, and they can also run very rapidly.

Beneficial bird
The flocks of killdeer feed scattered over the ground rather than in a compact bunch, eating insects and other small animals. They follow the plough to catch the animals thrown to the surface or search among grass or low plants. In one study, two-thirds of the animals found in killdeers' stomachs were insects, of which one-third were beetles. There were also grasshoppers, caterpillars, flies, ants, weevils and bugs among the other insects found, and there were also centipedes, ticks, earthworms and snails. Many of the insects taken are pests, such as weevils, wireworms and caterpillars. Killdeer are one of the most important predators of the cotton boll weevil, one killdeer being found with 380 weevils in its stomach. Grasshoppers are also eaten in large numbers and killdeer have earned a good name through eating mosquito larvae and cattle ticks.

Nesting on pebbles
Male killdeer have a spectacular aerial display. They fly back and forth or climb in spirals, sometimes hovering, for up to an hour at a time. All the while they are in the air they give voice to a continuous musical trill. On the ground the female is courted with a display in which the male lowers his spread wings on the ground and fans his tail over his back.

The nest is no more than a depression in the ground lined with a few pebbles and other bits and pieces. Killdeer prefer to nest on stony ground, in meadows or cultivated fields, where the ground is bare and usually fairly near water. Unusual nesting places include the ballast between railway sleepers, a tar and gravel roof and a rubbish heap of old bottles and tins. The eggs are 3–5 in number, pale brown with brown or black irregular marks. Both parents incubate the eggs for 25–26 days and both guard the young birds which leave the nest shortly after they have hatched.

Feigning injury

The eggs and chicks of killdeer are extremely well-camouflaged, as is the rule among ground-nesting birds, but the adults make the nest or young even more difficult to find by luring predators away with distraction displays. Distraction displays are common among ground-nesting birds, especially waders. The most usual display is that known as 'injury feigning' where the parent gives a passable imitation of a bird with a broken wing and lures a predator, such as a fox, away from its brood then flies up just before it is attacked. A description of a curlew luring a coyote for half a mile is given on page 595.

It must not be thought that the bird is consciously trying to deceive its enemies. The display is probably caused by a conflict between an urge to defend the brood and an urge to fly away to safety, the result being a strange action that attracts the attention of the enemy. If anyone walks near the nest of a killdeer, one or other of the parents drops to the ground with one wing held over its back, the other beating against the ground and the tail fanned. The combination of movements and displaying the white on wings and tail make the killdeer very conspicuous. As it is approached, it runs normally a little way and repeats the performance. This is repeated until the intruder is about 100 yd from the nest when the killdeer flies off.

When confronted with grazing animals, such as cattle and sheep, that are dangerous only because they may trample the brood, the killdeer's reaction is different. They stand over the nest or young with wings outspread and quivering, calling vigorously. So effective is this that a flock of goats were once seen to part, each group running either side of the killdeer's nest.

class	**Aves**
order	**Charadriiformes**
family	**Charadriidae**
genus & species	***Charadrius vociferus***

Killer whale

The killer whale is closely related to the false killer whale (p 735) and the pilot whale. It has a very bad reputation for ferocity which is probably unjustified. Killer whales are small for whales, the females growing up to a maximum of about 15 ft, but an old male may be as long as 30 ft. They are one of the few whales in which there is a marked difference in size between the sexes, the sperm whale being another example. The colour is very striking and distinctive, both sexes having similar markings, which are black on the back and white on the underside. Occasionally the white is somewhat yellowish. The chin is white and there is a characteristic white oval patch just above and behind the eye. There is a small whitish patch just behind the dorsal fin which varies quite considerably in shape and hue in different animals. The white on the underside sweeps up towards the tail and the flanks are white between the dorsal fin and the tail. The flippers, which are broad and rounded, are black all over, but the underside of the tail flukes are white. The dorsal fin is very conspicuous, usually about 2 ft high, but in the old males it may be 6 ft.

The oldest males also have very long flippers, up to $\frac{1}{5}$ the animal's total length, the average length of the flipper in juvenile males and adult females being $\frac{1}{9}$ only.

Killer whales are found in all seas but are particularly numerous in the Arctic and Antarctic where there is abundant food to satisfy their voracious appetite. They are not uncommon around the British Isles, where a number have been stranded, mainly on the north and east coasts. These strandings take place in most months of the year. A larger number than usual were stranded on British coasts during the last war, mostly on the North Sea coast, probably due in part at least to anti-submarine activities.

Helmut Heinpel: Bavaria

△ *Running at the surface with blowhole open, a killer whale in relaxed mood.*

▽ *Affectionate play between a pair of killers. Sensory pits can be seen on the head.*

Kent Burgess

Living in packs

Killer whales hunt together in packs made up of both sexes. They are inquisitive and appear to take a close interest in anything likely to be edible. Nothing is known about their movements in the oceans or how much, if at all, the populations in different oceans mix. In the Antarctic they are often seen around whaling factory ships and probably they tend to follow the ships around as they offer an easy source of food. Otherwise very little is known about their habits.

Ruthless hunters

The killer whale is a voracious feeder and will take anything that swims in the sea. Included in its diet are whales, dolphins, seals, penguins, fish and squid. It will attack even the large blue whales and quite often killers will hunt in packs numbering from two or three up to as many as 40 or more. When attacking a large whale they are said to work as a team. First one or two will seize the tail flukes to stop the whale thrashing about and slow it down, then others will attack the head and try to bite the lips. Gradually the whale becomes exhausted and its tongue lolls from its mouth—to be immediately seized by the killers. At this point all is over for the whale: the tongue is rapidly removed and the killers take their fill, seeming to favour a meal from around the head of their monster victim.

Apart from attacking fully-grown and healthy whales, killers have earned the hate of whalers because they often take the tongues from whales that have been harpooned and are lying alongside the factory ship waiting to be processed. They will even take the tongue from whales being towed by the catcher boat, and in an effort to stop this looting a man may be posted with a rifle to deter the killers. If he should injure a killer all the others in the pack turn on it and it very soon becomes their next meal.

Killer whales also eat seals and porpoises, and there are a number of records of complete seals found in a killer's stomach. The greatest number recorded is the remains of 13 porpoises and 14 seals that were taken from the stomach of one killer whale, while another contained 32 full-grown seals. Off the Pribilof Islands in the Bering Sea, killer whales are often seen lying in wait for the young fur seal pups swimming out into the open sea for the first time. The number of seals actually taken by killers is not certain but it is likely that large numbers of pups must meet their end in this way before they reach the age of one year.

In the Antarctic, penguins form an important part of the killer whale diet. On many occasions killer whales have been seen swimming underneath ice floes, either singly or sometimes several at a time, and then coming up quickly under the floe either to tip it or break it up, thereby causing the penguins to fall into the water and into the waiting jaws of the killers.

Once killer whales were seen cruising close to an island where there was a colony of grey seals. As the killers came close in the seals hurried ashore in spite of a couple of people standing nearby. The certain danger from killer whales was more important to the seals than possible danger from man. It is said that when killer whales attack grey whales, these become so terrified that they just float on their backs unable to make any effort to escape.

Seven-footer calves

Very little is known about the breeding habits of the whale. They are thought to produce their young towards the end of the year, in November and December after a 16-month gestation. This is supported by examination of some of the stranded whales washed up on the beach and found to be pregnant. The calf at birth is about 7 ft long. The females suckle the young in the same way as other whales, but how long this lasts is not known.

No enemies

The killer whale probably has no real enemies. A few are killed by man, usually irate whalers. They are not a very valuable catch to a whaler although some Russian whaling fleets do catch a few, usually if there is nothing else worth shooting.

◁ *Flukes aloft, a killer sounds with a minimum of splash—a tribute to its streamlining.*

△ *A killer pack surges round the edges of encroaching ice.* ▽ *Killer curiosity.*

Photos: Brit Antarctic Survey

Chased by killers

The most famous story of killer whales is that told by Herbert Ponting who was the official photographer to the British *Terra Nova* Antarctic expedition led by Captain Scott in 1911. While the ship's cargo was being unloaded onto the ice some killer whales appeared nearby. Ponting went to take some photographs carrying the bulky photographic apparatus of those days over the floes. As he went across the ice the killers thrust up alongside and then followed him as he crossed the floes, tipping them from beneath. Ponting just managed to get to the safety of the fast ice in front of the killers—a lucky escape.

Ponting's experience must have been terrifying, yet it is often found that a reputation for ferocity is unfounded. Divers who have met killer whales have not been molested and several killer whales have been kept in oceanaria. All have been unaggressive or even hand-tame. One story goes of a fisherman of Long Island, New York, who threw a harpoon at a killer whale. The whale pulled free and followed the boat and its terrified occupants to shallow water, but it made no attempt to harm them despite such severe provocation.

class	**Mammalia**
order	**Cetacea**
family	**Delphinidae**
genus & species	***Orcinus orca***

L Lee Rue III: Photo Res

◁ *Female king crab blunders through the sand with two males in tow.*

▽ *Creature from the past, as its underside shows.*

AB Klots

King crab

The king crab, sometimes called horse-shoe crab, is not a crab but more nearly related to spiders. It hardly looks like a crab either. It looks more like something out of the past, which is what it is: a living fossil. Seen from above on a sandy shore, it appears to be made up of a rounded brown or dark olive-green dome hinged to a hard and roughly triangular abdomen, ending in a long, movable tail spike. The whole animal may be anything up to 2 ft long. When turned over to expose the underside, the dome, or carapace, is seen to have a horseshoe outline sheltering a series of pairs of jointed limbs. Behind the first short pair are four pairs of longer limbs, all alike. All these limbs end in little pincers except for the second pair (or second and third pairs, according to species) in the adult male. Next in the series is one more pair of legs with no pincers. Instead there are spines which spring from the last joint but one and help the animal in getting a grip on the sand. Finally, on this front part of the body is a pair of small structures of uncertain function, known as chilaria. The series is continued on the abdomen, first with a sort of cover or operculum with the paired genital openings on its under-surface, and then five pairs of flaps or 'gill books', so-called because each one is made of up to 200 thin leaflets. These are the gills.

Of the five species, ***Limulus polyphemus*** *lives on or near the shore in sounds, bays and estuaries down the Atlantic coast of North America from the Gulf of Maine to the Gulf of Mexico. It is especially common in Long Island Sound and the mouth of the Delaware river. In places it is so common it has been caught in large numbers, ground up and used either as a fertilizer or as chicken feed. The other four species live far distant, along the coasts of Asia from Japan and Korea south to the Philippines and the East Indies and the Bay of Bengal.*

Living sand plough

The tail-spike of the king crab, an innocuous and far from agile animal, is not the weapon it seems, but is used as a lever when its owner is ploughing through sand or mud. It is also used as a lever to right itself, on the rare occasions when it has been turned over by the waves. Much of the time a king crab rests partly or completely buried. There are two eyes to the side and a third eye in the middle further forward on top of the carapace. Digging and ploughing through sand is accomplished mainly by the last pair of legs, those in front serving more to lift the animal, while the last pair pushes backwards like a pair of ski sticks. The crab is also able to swim upside down in a leisurely manner by flapping its gill books, an action also important in circulating water amongst the leaflets.

Chewing with its legs

Although it may eat seaweed, the king crab eats mainly molluscs and worms and it is sometimes a serious predator on clam beds on the American coast. The mouth is on the underside, surrounded by the legs, and the basal joints of the legs have spiny protuberances used to chew food.

Coming ashore to breed

The American king crab breeds early in summer, when the moon is full and the tides deepest. The females, which are the larger, creep up the beach each with a male clinging to her abdomen. They scoop depressions in the sand near the limit of high tide and deposit in these 200–300 eggs, each $\frac{1}{5}$ in. diameter, and covered with a thick envelope. As they are laid the males fertilise them. The eggs are covered with sand and then the males and females go their separate ways. After about a month a short-tailed larva, about $\frac{1}{25}$ in. long, hatches.

It looks superficially like a tiny trilobite, the crustacean that flourished millions of years ago, and for that reason it is called a 'trilobite larva'. It is not until the third year, after the larva has shed its shell more than a dozen times, that sexual maturity is reached. On the other side of the world, when the king crabs come ashore to breed in July and August in the Gulf of Tonkin, they are caught and eaten by the local inhabitants. Europeans tend to find them sickening and it is said that the flesh can be poisonous under certain conditions.

A class of their own

Though called 'crabs', these animals are not only not true crabs, they are not even crustaceans. Like the crustaceans, insects, spiders and other animals with external skeletons and jointed limbs, they are classified as arthropods, but, within that phylum, few as they are, they belong in a class of their own. Their occurrence in two regions so far apart, separated by waters in which they are not suited to survive, suggests that they are relicts of a more widespread group, rather than that they are members of a group still in the process of extending its range. That this is so, is supported by the existence of fossils in Bavaria, in the Upper Jurassic. King crabs very like those living today have existed for practically two hundred million years. Animals looking, as adults, somewhat like the king crab larva inhabited the earth even before that. Another group of animals which they resemble in some ways but which they have long outlived, was the extinct eurypterids, scorpion-like aquatic animals that sometimes reached a length of 10 ft. Despite the resemblance of their larvae to them, king crabs are only distantly related to trilobites.

phylum	**Arthropoda**
class	**Merostoma**
order	**Xiphosura**

Kingfisher

There are over 80 species of kingfisher living mainly in the tropics. They are stockily built with long bills, quite short tails and often brilliant plumage, of which the common kingfisher of Europe and Asia is a good example. The well known kookaburra or 'laughing jackass' of Australia, another of the family, is treated under a separate heading. The common kingfisher is found throughout much of Europe and Asia, south into North Africa and east to the Solomon Islands and Japan. It is one of the most beautiful British birds, $6\frac{1}{2}$ in. long with a $1\frac{1}{2}$in. dagger-like bill, its upperparts a shining iridescent blue or green.

▷ *Psychedelic forest kingfisher of Malaya.*

▽ *A giant kingfisher* ***Megaceryle maxima*** *glares from a vantage point over a stream.*

FGH Allen

◁ ▽ *Malachite kingfisher* ***Corythornis cristata****, a very common African species. It feeds on fish, water invertebrates and flies.*

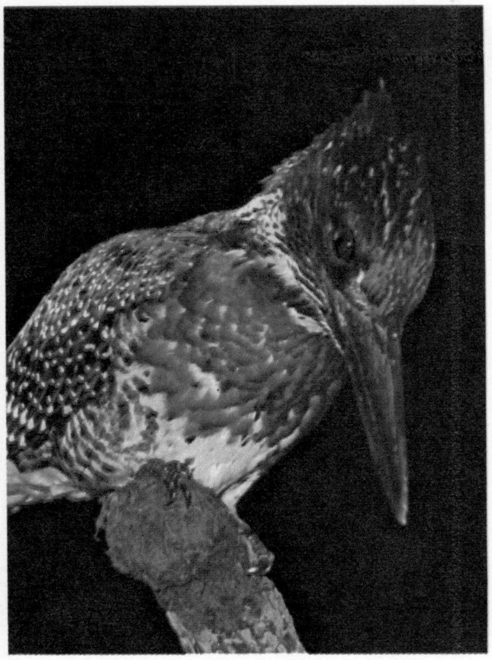

Peter Johnson

Peter Johnson

Keystone

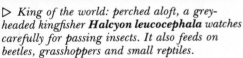

▷ *King of the world: perched aloft, a grey-headed kingfisher* ***Halcyon leucocephala*** *watches carefully for passing insects. It also feeds on beetles, grasshoppers and small reptiles.*

△ *Forest kingfisher* ***Halcyon macleyi*** *peers from its nesting hole in a termite nest on the side of a eucalyptus tree. This species is an insect-eater, living in Australia.*

The underparts are chestnut, the legs red and there are patches of white on the neck. The pied kingfisher of Africa south of the Sahara and southwest Asia is dull-coloured for a kingfisher but is nevertheless striking with its black and white plumage. Like many kingfishers it has a crest. The Amazon kingfisher, also crested, has brilliant green upperparts and white underparts, with a chestnut breast in the male. The Texas kingfisher, ranging into the southern USA, is very similar.
In some species where the sexes differ in plumage, the female is the more brilliant. On the other side of the Pacific the yellow sacred kingfisher is found in many parts of Australia and is the only kingfisher in New Zealand.

RT Peterson: Photo Res

A blur of colour

Kingfishers are usually seen as little more than a blur of colour as they fly low over the water on whirring wings to disappear into waterside undergrowth. If lucky one sees it perched on a branch, rock or post on the bank and its true colours can then be appreciated. Kingfishers are very much alike in habit as well as form; their feeding and breeding behaviour follow a pattern although some kingfishers rarely, if ever, go near water. Even the common kingfisher, associated so much with streams and rivers, sometimes nests some distance from water.

When thousands of exotic birds were being slaughtered and their carcases and feathers sent to Europe and North America as decorations and ornaments, it is not surprising that the dazzling kingfisher did not escape persecution. It was used for decorating hats and stuffed kingfishers in glass cases were a common household ornament. Later kingfishers were shot because they were alleged to eat enough trout fry to damage breeding stocks. The pollution of rivers and streams now threatens their wellbeing. Hard winters have a very severe effect on kingfisher populations.

Fishing over land and water

The method of catching prey is similar in nearly all species. The kingfisher waits on a perch, then darts out, catches its prey and carries it back to its perch. The common kingfisher flies out, hovers momentarily just over the water then dives in. Having caught a small fish or water insect it uses its wings to 'fly' through the water then up into the air without pausing. Larger prey are beaten against the perch to subdue them and may be tossed and caught again to get them into

2

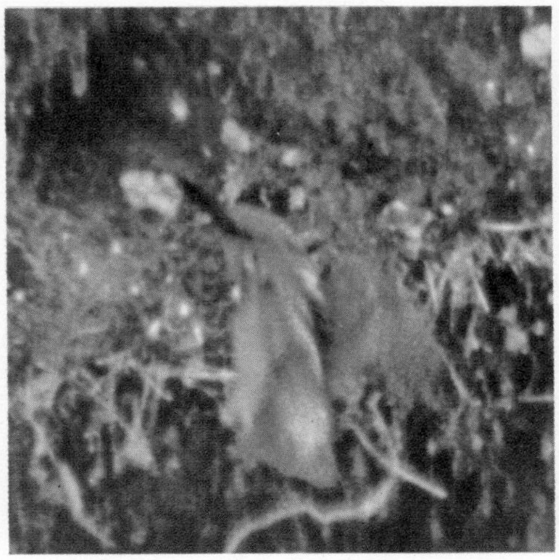

3

5

Flying piledriver
Kingfishers hollow out their nesting burrow in the side of a river bank by flying straight at it to chip away the earth.

1 Kingfisher flies straight at its burrow.

2 Nose up and into the vertical, the kingfisher positions itself for landing.

3 Into neutral as it folds its wings well back.

4 With all the feathers splayed, the last-minute air brakes are applied.

5 The kingfisher lands on the edge of the burrow to scoop out more earth from the inside.

The blue torpedo
From a post above the water the kingfisher dives and surfaces in one fell swoop. (Series of stills from 16mm ciné film by the Eastmans.)

6 On spotting a fish, a kingfisher plummets downwards through the water.

7 Using its wings as fins, it torpedoes towards its prey . . .

8 . . . surrounded by a mass of bubbles.

9 Right on target, it grabs its fish and, without a moment's pause . . .

10 . . . returns triumphantly.

◁*Common kingfisher with prospective meal.*

6

7

Series by Ron & Rose Eastman

9

10

Werner Curth

a suitable position for swallowing. Common kingfishers take mainly fish such as minnows, sticklebacks and gudgeon, also small perch and small trout. These last two are the reason for the persecution of kingfishers, but they also feed on water beetles, dragonfly larvae and waterboatmen which also kill small fish. Small frogs, tadpoles and pond snails are also taken.

The majority of kingfishers, however, take mainly land animals, although they hunt from a perch like the common kingfisher. They dart down from their perches like shrikes or they hawk passing insects like flycatchers. The racquet-tailed kingfisher, living in the area from the Moluccas to northeast Australia, hunts for lizards, centipedes and insects in the leaf litter of humid forests, swooping on them and sometimes driving its bill into the soft earth. The stork-billed kingfisher of India, 14 in. long with a large scarlet bill, catches fish as well as frogs, lizards, crabs and insects. It also robs other birds' nests, taking nestlings even from nests in holes in trees, but, true to its kind, it returns to its perch to swallow its prey. An exception to this is the shoe-billed kingfisher of the forests of New Guinea. It digs for earthworms with its flattened bill.

Hole nesting

Kingfishers nest in holes, those that hunt fish usually nesting in holes in banks near water while the more land-living kingfishers nest in holes in trees or abandoned termite nests. The striped kingfisher of Africa uses ready-made holes and may even dispossess swallows from their nests under eaves.

The nest hole is dug by the kingfishers repeatedly flying at one spot on the bank, loosening a bit of soil with their bills each time. When they have formed a ledge they can perch and dig more rapidly until the tunnel is $1\frac{1}{2}-3$ ft long. The 6 or 7 spherical white eggs are laid on the floor of the tunnel and incubated for 3 weeks. During this time a revolting pile of fish bones and droppings piles up around the eggs, a squalid contrast with the magnificent plumage of the adult birds. Until Ron and Rose Eastman made their prizewinning film 'The Private Life of a Kingfisher' in 1966 it was thought that pieces of fish were fed to the young. Their remarkable patience and technique, however, showed the young inside the nest burrow swallowing whole fish almost as big as themselves, the bones being later regurgitated. The chicks, which live in the tunnel for 3 – 4 weeks, are hatched naked but soon acquire a covering of bristle-like wax sheaths which are shed to reveal a plumage like that of the parents just before they leave the nest.

Halcyon days

The kingfisher has been the subject of many legends, some romantic and some prosaic. In the 12th century it was thought that not only did they not decay when dead but that the corpses, if hung up by the bill, moulted each year to reveal a fresh plumage. The odour of these miraculous corpses was said to be pleasant and to ward off moths. A dead kingfisher suspended from a string pointed north like a compass needle or, according to another version, towards the way of the wind. The habits of kingfishers, according to the Ancients, were most remarkable. Their Greek name was Halkyon, literally meaning 'conceiving at sea'. It was thought that the female fed and conceived at sea and laid her eggs at midwinter in a nest that was so hard that it could not be cut by iron. She was supposed to have incubated the eggs for 2 weeks and fed the chicks for another fortnight. Being in the favour of the gods the weather was kept calm for this period at midwinter, which has ever since been known as the 'halcyon days'.

class	**Aves**
order	**Coraciiformes**
family	**Alcedinidae**
genera & species	***Alcedo atthis*** *common kingfisher* ***Ceryle rudis*** *pied kingfisher* ***Chloroceryle amazona*** *Amazon kingfisher* ***C. americana*** *Texas kingfisher* ***Clytoceyx rex*** *shoe-billed kingfisher* ***Halcyon chelicuti*** *striped kingfisher* ***H. sancta*** *sacred kingfisher* ***Pelargopsis capensis*** *stork-billed kingfisher* ***Tanysiptera galatea*** *racquet-tailed kingfisher*

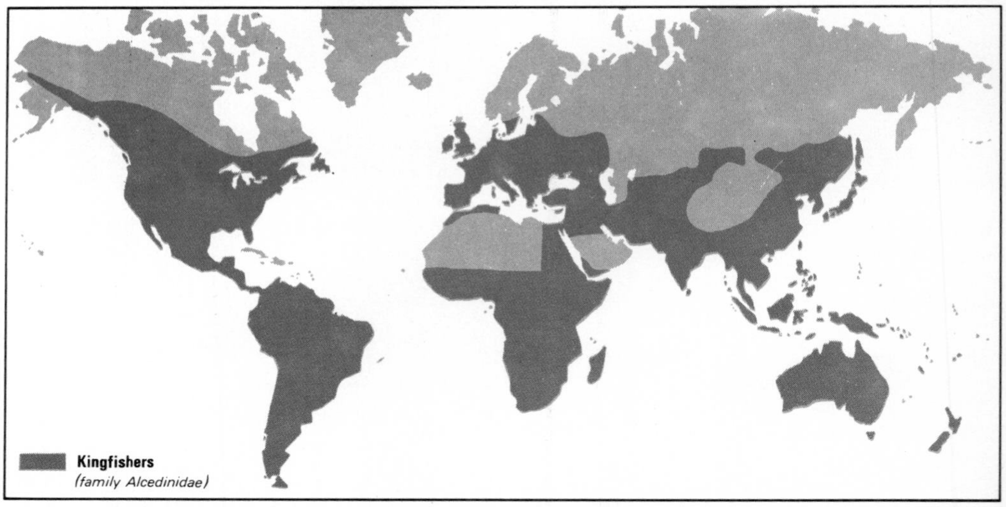

▽ *A squad of scruffy young belted kingfishers* ***Megaceryle alcyon*** *in a hungry line. They swallow small fish whole, regurgitating the bones.*

Photo Researchers

King penguin

King penguins look very much like emperor penguins, to which they are very closely related. They have the same stately walk as the emperors, with their long knife-shaped bills held up. King penguins are the smaller of the two, 3 ft long instead of 4 ft, but are otherwise similar in appearance. They both have blue-black backs and white fronts with yellow and orange patches around the neck, but in the king penguin the patches are separated into two comma-shapes on the side of the neck with a 'bib' of yellow on the breast.

King penguins live farther north than emperor penguins, in the ice-free sub-Antarctic seas between the Falkland Islands southwards to the South Sandwich Islands and Heard Island. There are very small colonies on Staten Island, near Cape Horn, and on the Falkland Islands. The largest colonies are found on islands such as South Georgia, Kerguelen, Macquarie and Marion.

Life on the Antarctic wave

▽ *The king penguins are quite at home in the sea, and when they are not breeding spend much of their time swimming and diving for food. They have streamlined bodies and sharp lethal bills which they use to catch squid and fish. The wings of these birds are modified for use as underwater flippers. The only remaining wing plumage is scale-like feathers which offer little resistance to water.*
▷ *King penguins do not make a nest but the single egg is incubated by the parents putting it on their feet and covering it with an abdominal fold of skin.*
▽▽ *Freshly moulted king penguins proudly displaying their magnificent new coats.*
▷▷ *A superb picture taken in South Georgia.*
▷▽ *A well-ordered colony of king penguins each with its own little territory.*

Jochen Köhler: Bavaria

Niall Rankin

RW Vaughan

John Warham

Niall Rankin

B Tollu: Jacana

*Yetis of the Antarctic! The little sheath bill **Chionis** is dwarfed by the big brown penguin chicks.*

Feeding at sea

Like other penguins, king penguins live at sea when they are not breeding and sometimes swim long distances, turning up on the fringes of the Antarctic pack ice. The latitudes in which the king penguins live are those of the roaring westerly gales, but these are unlikely to affect the penguins much except to drive them off course. Penguins are perfectly adapted to life at sea. Their bodies are streamlined and a layer of blubber under the skin insulates them from the cold water. The large king and emperor penguins can dive to considerable depths to hunt squid and fish which they catch in their sharp bills. The eyes of aquatic animals are designed to see underwater. Light is not bent so much as it passes from water into the eye as when it passes from air. To compensate, the lens is very strong. As a result aquatic animals are short-sighted out of water.

Prolonged childhood

The king penguin has the same problem of child care as the emperor penguin. Both are very large birds and their chicks take a long time to grow, yet the Antarctic summer is very short. The emperor penguin, as we have seen (p 723), has solved the problem by starting the 7-month nursery period in midwinter so the chicks become independent before the following winter. The king penguin has a different method. It lives farther north where the sea does not freeze and the adults are able to feed near the colony. So instead of laying their eggs in midwinter, the king penguins lay in spring or summer and when the chick hatches after $7\frac{1}{2}$ weeks it is fed throughout the following winter, becoming independent the next summer.

Just before they start breeding king penguins come ashore to moult. They spend a fortnight ashore shedding their old feathers to reveal the brilliant new coat, then retire to sea to feed and build up reserves of food before breeding. Returning to land, they make their way to the colony among the tussack grass and mud where each male takes up position and advertises for a mate. He stretches his neck, ruffs out his feathers and tilts his head back and calls, braying like a donkey. If an unmated female hears him, she wanders over and the two penguins introduce themselves by flagging their bills up and down. They then set off on an 'advertisement walk', strutting along on their toes, waving their heads from side to side, showing off their brilliant patches of colour. The colours are important—if they are covered with black paint a penguin stands no chance of getting a mate.

At first these partnerships do not last very long. The male displays at any female and keeps company with a succession of prospective mates. Gradually, however, he pays attention to one particular female and the bond between them strengthens and they perform another display; standing side by side they raise their beaks and stand on their toes as if stretching themselves.

The king penguin, like the emperor penguin, makes no nest but balances the single large egg on his feet, protected by a fold of skin. He does, however, defend a small territory rather than wander about with his egg. The first eggs are laid in November, and more are laid until April. After laying the female goes off to feed and make up the food reserves she lost forming the egg. The male is left guarding the egg until the female's return 2 weeks later. Thereafter, there is a shuttle service, each parent taking a turn in guarding the egg or chick.

As the chicks get older they spend more time on their own and eventually form crèches where they huddle together while parents go fishing. On its return a parent king penguin finds its chick by sound. It walks up to the crèche and calls, and one chick out of hundreds replies. They both walk towards each other, calling, and may even walk past, until another call brings them back to each other. Several pounds of food are transferred at each feed and the chicks put on weight rapidly, but as winter sets in feeding becomes very infrequent and the chicks huddle in their crèches, protected by their thick, woolly down but gradually losing weight. Then, in spring, when food becomes abundant again, the chicks put on weight, lose their down and the adult plumage emerges.

The chicks take to the sea 2 months later and learn to fish for themselves. This is well-timed because food is abundant at this season. The young king penguins stay at sea for most of their early life, spending more time ashore as they get older and begin to practise their courtship displays. At 6 years old, they come ashore and start courting in earnest.

Boiled for blubber

The enemies of king penguins are leopard seals. They lie in wait off the colonies, but the seals will find them difficult to catch as the penguins have an alarm system. When a king penguin sees a leopard seal, it panics and rushes towards the shore. Its flippers beat on the surface of the water and the clattering sound they make alerts other king penguins, and they all rush clattering to the shore. Not only are all the penguins alerted but the leopard seals are probably confused and will be able to catch only weak or unwary penguins.

At one time, man was a far greater enemy. As elephant and fur seals became scarce sealers killed king penguins for their blubber, which was used for tanning leather. Their eggs were taken and their skins sometimes used for fancy clothing. Some colonies were wiped out and others are only just beginning to recover their former numbers.

Slow breeding

It took only a few years for the sealers to reduce the numbers in a king penguin colony to such an extent that it was not worth their while to exploit them further. The reason for this is the extremely slow rate of breeding. After the egg has been laid, a pair of king penguins spends a year incubating, guarding or collecting food. By the time they are free of their offspring it is too late in the year to begin again and they leave the colony to feed during the winter and start breeding the following spring.

Therefore, king penguins, like the larger albatrosses (p 24) which also spend their first winter on the nest, cannot raise more than one young every two years. Furthermore, not all their offspring survive the first winter. If the egg is laid too late in the summer the chick will not have had time to accumulate enough fat with which to survive the winter. Without the attentions of the sealers, king penguins flourish; they are long-lived and generally survive to rear enough offspring to keep numbers constant.

class	**Aves**
order	**Sphenisciformes**
family	**Spheniscidae**
genus & species	***Aptenodytes patagonica***

John Tashjian at Arizona Sonara Desert Mus.

Lampropeltis getulus splendida, *Sonora king snake, has distinctive black marks along its back.*

King snake

These are North American snakes, harmless to man—as are most members of their large family, the Colubridae. A special feature of king snakes—and the reason why they are so named—is that they eat other snakes, including venomous species like rattlesnakes. Another feature is that they show many colour varieties.

The common king snake, also known as the chain snake or thunder snake, is up to 6 ft long. The typical form, along the east coast area of the United States, is shiny black, criss-crossed by bands of yellow or white forming a chain-like pattern on its sides. Its underside is black with white or yellow blotches. The head is narrow and there is a slightly marked neck. In the Mississippi Valley the king snake is greenish with white or yellow speckling. In Georgia, Alabama and Florida it is black or dark brown marked with yellow. The Californian subspecies is in two colour phases: one with yellow rings, the other with yellow stripes, the background colour of both being black or brown. These and other species and subspecies range over most of the United States northwards into southern Canada and southwards into Mexico. The milk snakes, up to 3½ ft long, are closely related to the king snakes. Their name is sometimes applied to king snakes in different localities.

Some king snakes are ringed red, yellow and black and look very like the venomous coral snakes. So they are sometimes called false coral snakes, a name also given to other colubrid snakes such as the rear-fanged ***Erythrolamprus*** *of South America, red with black rings.*

Terrorising the rattlers

King snakes, active especially in afternoon and evening, do not pursue other snakes. They eat small mammals, usually rodents, as well as lizards and frogs, caught in meadows and wooded areas. Should one of them meet another snake, however, it will eat it. It strikes it with its teeth and grasps the neck of its victim, at the same time throwing its body round the other snake, killing it by suffocation, just as pythons and boas kill their prey. King snakes are immune to snake venom, even that of rattlesnakes and copperheads, and the danger they represent to other snakes is shown by the behaviour of a rattlesnake in the presence of a king snake. Instead of coiling its body, raising its head to strike with its teeth, and raising its tail to shake its rattle, it keeps its head and neck on the ground and raises part of its body in a high loop, trying to beat off its attacker by blows from this loop.

The smaller milk snakes of North America take similar prey but the snakes they eat are younger and smaller. They are named for an alleged habit of taking milk from cows. This same story is current in parts of the world for other species of snakes. Not only is there no evidence to support it but the way a snake's teeth work make it virtually impossible to believe that any snake could take a cow's teat into its mouth without lacerating it badly.

Brighter babies

Mating takes place in spring, the female laying 10–30 white parchment-shelled eggs in summer. Sometimes these are laid on the ground, more usually they are under leaves and plant litter. In some species, she may coil her body around the eggs for the first day or so, but afterwards leaves them. They hatch in 4–6 weeks, the baby snakes being 7–8 in. long, coloured like the parents but with the colours brighter.

The long swallow

There are many stories, and photographs have appeared in the Press, of one snake swallowing another. This happens in zoos when two snakes seize the same food. Sooner or later their noses touch as they both try to swallow the same thing, and the one with the larger gape swallows the other. Doubtless this happens in the wild also, but rarely. There are, however, snakes like the European smooth snake *Coronella austriaca* which, besides eating frogs, lizards and mice, also eats snakes. One of the lizards it eats is the legless and snake-like slowworm,

Lampropeltis doliata amaura, *Louisiana milk snake or 'false coral snake' as it is sometimes called.*

John Tashjian at Fort Worth Zoo

AB Klots

◁ *A snake is a snake to a snake-eating snake and the common king snake does not think twice about eating one of his own kind when he is hungry. In one rapid movement the king snake strikes the black snake,* ***Coluber,*** *and ties himself in a tight knot around its victim killing it by suffocation.*
▽ *Map showing the distribution of two species of* ***Lampropeltis.***
▽▽ *Freak of nature, a two-headed snake.*

but smooth snakes, themselves only 18 in. long, will also eat young adders. Other snakes are snake-eaters to the extent of being famous for this habit, like the file snakes *Mehelya* of Africa. They behave like king snakes, in constricting their prey, and seem also to be immune to poison. The mussurana *Clelia clelia* of tropical America is another snake-eater. One mussurana (as stated, p 748) 6½ ft long that looked unduly swollen was found to have swallowed a 6ft fer-de-lance, the dreaded poisonous snake. The most famous snake-eater is perhaps the king cobra or hamadryad *Naja hannah,* of southeast Asia. It does not constrict its victims and it is not immune to poison, which is why it usually eats non-venomous snakes. It will, however, eat the other kind—including smaller king cobras.

Were it possible to know the truth we should doubtless find that many snake-eating snakes are cannibalistic, if only by accident. A snake is a snake to a snake-eating snake, whatever its species. Even more bizarre things than this have been seen. FW Fitzsimons, the distinguished South African specialist in snakes, tells of a Cape file snake that intervened when two deadly night adders had each seized a leg of a frog. The file snake settled the argument by swallowing all three. Then there was Dudly-Duplex, the two-headed king snake of San Diego Zoo. One night one head tried to swallow the other. This was rescued the following morning. Later, the aggrieved head tried to take revenge—with fatal results for the two heads and the body to which they belonged.

class	**Reptilia**
order	**Squamata**
suborder	**Serpentes**
family	**Colubridae**
genus & species	***Lampropeltis getulus*** *common king snake* ***L. doliata*** *milk snake, others*

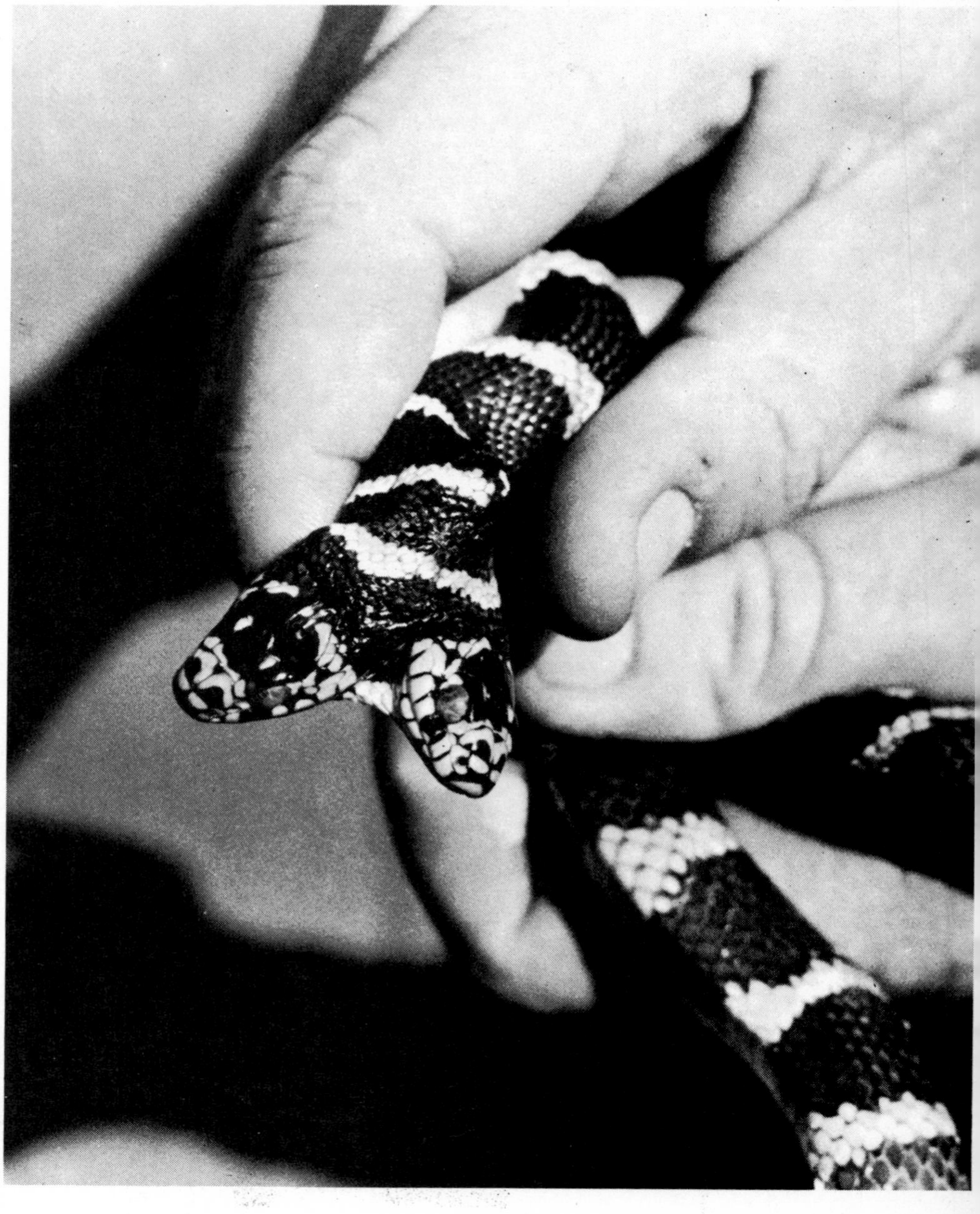

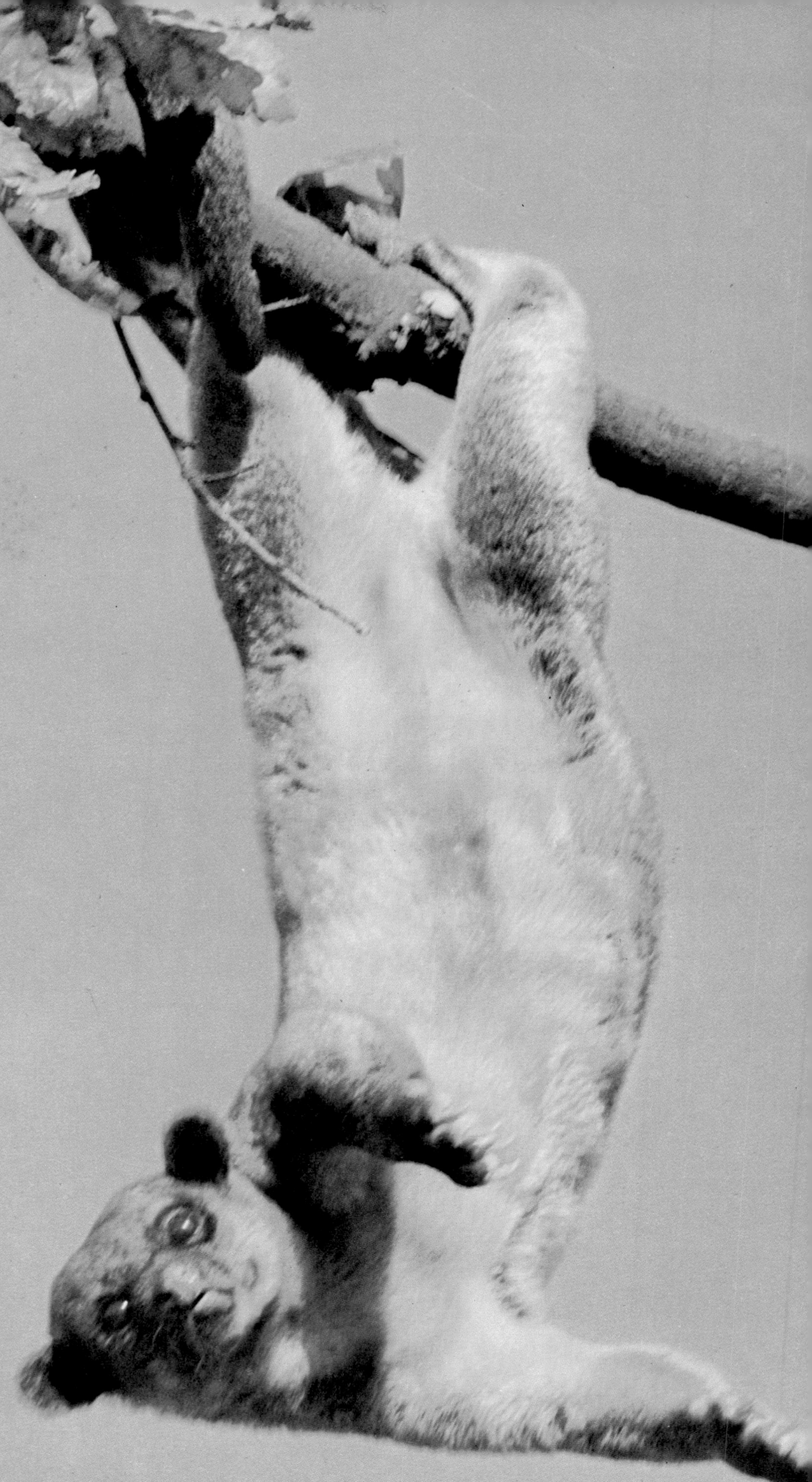

Kinkajou

This is one of many local names for a relative of the pandas living in tropical America, although it is likely to be called a honeybear when sold in pet shops. Another name used by South American Indians is potto, not to be confused with the primate living in Africa.

A kinkajou has a long body and short legs, with the forelegs shorter than the hindlegs. Its coat is of soft woolly fur, dark gold to brown with the underparts lighter. Its eyes are large, its ears small, and its tail is long. Each foot has five toes with short sharp claws. The usual size is 1 ft long in head and body with a $1\frac{1}{2}$ft tail. The height at the shoulder is 10 in. and the weight up to 6 lb. The outstanding feature of this animal is that its tail is prehensile, like the tails of many South American monkeys. The Mexican name for a kinkajou is monkey lion, which aptly describes it.

Kinkajous range from southern Mexico through Central America and into South America at least as far south as the Matto Grosso in Brazil. Within much of this range, from Central America into northern South America lives a closely related and similar animal, the olingo. It is slightly smaller but with a longer, flattened and non-prehensile tail. Its fur is more golden and the tail is marked with dark rings. The fur on its face is paler than that on its body, and the olingo has been called the pale-faced kinkajou. Its habits are much like those of kinkajous and because they are apt to move about with parties of kinkajous they tend to be overlooked, so little is known about them. Indeed, olingos are sometimes sold as kinkajous.

Zool Soc London

The demon drink

One surprising feature about our information on the kinkajou is that although it is called the honeybear very few books say anything about it eating honey. The most complete account of its diet is in Lee S Crandall's *The Management of Wild Mammals in Captivity*. This lists the fruits, vegetables and bread it will eat, adds also raw or cooked meat, dog biscuit, cooked or raw egg, bone meal, cod-liver oil, condensed milk, ice cream—but no honey. In his *Living Mammals of the World*, Ivan T Sanderson says they gorge honey, lapping it up with their narrow 6in. tongues, from wild bees' nests. Most writers say the kinkajou is mild and docile, an affectionate pet, but one that can, if handled roughly, snarl and bite. Sanderson calls it a most dangerous pet because its honey-eating leads to an insatiable appetite for alcoholic liquors. He says that when inebriated a kinkajou goes quite mad, will attack its owner with tooth and claw, holding on with its tail and biting continually as no other animal will. Obviously, a kinkajou is a pet for the teetotal household only!

class	**Mammalia**
order	**Carnivora**
family	**Procyonidae**
genera & species	***Potos flavus*** *kinkajou* ***Bassaricyon gabbii*** *olingo*

◁ *Kinkajou climbing up his own tail while hanging from a keeper's hand. There are only two carnivores, the kinkajou and the unrelated binturong, with prehensile tails, which make a useful fifth limb for when the animal is climbing.*
▽ *Acrobat of the forest treetops.*

Important tailpiece

Kinkajous live in forests and spend all their time in the treetops, sleeping by day in hollows in the trunks, sometimes coming out on hot humid days to lie along a branch or in the tangle of a vine as in a hammock. At night they move about the trees singly, in pairs or in groups as when they converge on a single tree with a ripening crop of fruit. They move quickly and with agility through the trees, wrapping the tail around a branch for added support but they do not leap from branch to branch, as a monkey does. They move cautiously from one tree to another, making sure of the next foothold while anchoring themselves with the tail. Kinkajous are often kept in zoos and there a keeper will sometimes show how the animal will turn and climb up its own tail with the end of the tail wrapped round the keeper's arm. They bark if alarmed but otherwise their call is a shrill quavering scream.

A passion for fruit

Although a member of the Carnivora, or flesh-eaters, kinkajous live mainly on fruit. In captivity they readily eat oranges, apples, bananas and grapes, but will take bread, carrots and peanuts just as eagerly. With the softer fruits they scoop out the pulp with their mobile tongue, holding the fruit to the mouth with the forepaws. They also eat insects, and possibly small mammals and birds at times.

Long-lived in zoos

A number of kinkajou pairs have bred in zoos in Europe and America but nothing is known of their mating behaviour, the time of the breeding season or the gestation period. Usually there is one young at a birth, seldom two, but as many as four have been recorded. If correct, this larger number must be exceptional. The babies are born blind with a soft coat of black fur. They can hang by their tails at 7 weeks and their eyes open at 10 weeks. During the early days, judging from what has been seen in zoos, the mother leaves the baby in a hollow in a tree when she goes foraging, carrying it from one nest to another, if necessary, by holding it in her mouth by the scruff. Kinkajous are fairly long-lived, at least in zoos, the maximum age so far reported being 23 years 7 months.

Leo Rue III: Photo Res

Kissing gourami

This is a popular aquarium fish that has achieved fame for a single trick of behaviour that looks uncommonly like a familiar human action. Other than this the species would have remained in relative obscurity. 'Kissing' is by no means confined to this gourami, which is chosen here to show an interesting facet of animal behaviour.

There are several species of gouramis, all from southeast Asia, where they grow to a foot or more and are used for food. The kissing gourami may grow to a foot long, but when kept in an aquarium it is usually well short of this. Its body is flattened from side to side, oval in outline, with a pointed head ending in a pair of thickened lips. The greenish to grey-yellow dorsal and anal fins are long and prominent and both slope upwards from front to rear. The normal colour of the body is silvery green with dark stripes on the flanks but there is another colour phase, pinkish-white and somewhat iridescent.

Thick lips for breathing and eating

The kissing and other gouramis belong to the labyrinth fishes, which means they have an accessory breathing organ in the gills for taking in air at the surface, as well as breathing by gills. The kissing gourami not only rises to the surface from time to time to gulp air, and therefore can live in water that is slightly fouled, but it also feeds at the surface. The thickened lips probably have an advantage in these two respects. The food consists of both animal and plant matter and in an aquarium kissing gouramis eat dried shrimps and powdered oatmeal, water fleas and dried spinach. To some extent they will feed on the small algae that grow on the sides of the aquarium.

Life history little known

There is still some doubt about their breeding habits. Many labyrinth fishes build bubble nests for their eggs but so far as we know kissing gouramis build no nest but lay 400–2 000 floating eggs. They seem to ignore these as well as the young which hatch in 24 hours. The baby fishes eat ciliated protistans for their first week, taking water fleas after this, graduating to the mixed diet as they grow older. They begin to breed when 3–5 in. long.

Mystery of the kiss

Nobody seems very clear whether this is an aggressive action or part of the courtship. Probably it enters into both. When several kissing gouramis are kept together in one aquarium the larger of them bother the smaller by 'sucking' at their flanks. They will do the same with fishes of other species. This is probably aggressive. When a pair are together, however, they can be seen to face each other, swaying backwards and forwards, as if hung on invisible threads, and then they come together, mouth to mouth, their thick lips firmly placed together in an exaggerated kissing action. Like other labyrinth fishes the male wraps himself around the body of the female when mating. This is preceded by the two swimming round and round each other in a circling movement, after which they again come together, lips to lips, in a seeming kiss.

A touching scene—like mirror images of each other two gouramis 'kiss'. It is not fully understood why this fish, a favourite among tropical fish fanciers, makes this familiar human action. It may be one of aggression or, as we tend to think, a sign of affection.

Paying lip-service

The use of the mouth as a test of strength in fighting is common among the higher animals. It is frequently seen in aquarium fishes, especially among cichlids and labyrinth fishes. One fish butting another with its mouth is often used in courtship, especially by the smaller freshwater fishes, and it seems likely that the mouth-wrestling and the butting lead on to the kissing. At all events, A van der Nieuwenhuizen, in his book *Tropical Aquarium Fish,* takes the view that in the cichlid, known as the blue acara *Aequidens latifrons,* mouth-wrestling is used to defeat a rival as well as court a mate. He maintains that when a pair indulge in a bout of mouth-wrestling which ends in stalemate this means the two are physically and psychologically suited and the chances of their breeding are high. The mouth-tugging, as he calls it, may last for hours and be repeated day after day, to end in a genuine lovers' choice. The chances are that the kissing of the gourami has exactly the same importance, so it is a true lovers' kiss.

class	**Pisces**
order	**Perciformes**
family	**Anabantidae**
genus & species	***Helostoma temmincki***

Kite

The kite is a bird of prey, whose smooth gliding flight has given its name to man-made flying devices. It belongs to a subfamily Milvinae of the falcon family. The subfamily also includes several fish eagles and the Everglade kite (p 727) but attention is given here mainly to the true kites, genus ***Milvus.*** *These have long pointed wings angled at the wrists and a forked tail.*

Both sexes of the kite (sometimes called the red kite) are 2 ft long. Their back and wings are dark brown with lighter borders to the feathers, the underparts are rusty red with dark streaks and the head is greyish, nearly white in old birds, with dark streaks. In flight they show a conspicuous white patch under each wing. Black kites are slightly smaller, darker and their tails are less forked.

The range of the kite includes most of Europe except the extreme north, much of France, the Low Countries and northern Italy. It also includes Asia Minor, the coastal strip of northwest Africa, the Canaries and the Cape Verde Islands. The black kite ranges over Europe and Asia except for the extreme north, Africa except for the Sahara and much of Australia.

A number of other Milvinae have been called kites, the most famous being the Brahminy kite ***Maliastur indus****, ranging from India to the Solomon Islands and Australia. This is the sacred kite of India, 18 in. long, living in the swamps and feeding on frogs and carrion. It is brown with a white head and shoulders.*

There is another subfamily, of black-shouldered kites, sometimes called white-tailed kites, which somewhat resembles the true kites but differs in habits. Species are found in America, Africa, Southern Asia and Australia. Typical of these is ***Elanus caeruleus*** *of Africa. It is grey and white with black markings on the fore edge of the wing. The African black-shouldered kite feeds mainly at dusk and dawn, quartering the ground at low level.*

Masters of soaring flight

The kite lives in wooded river valleys, but it is sometimes seen in broad-leaved forests, most often at their fringes. It may spend long periods perched on a branch, always alert, descending to the ground when it sees food. On the ground it is quite active, hopping rather than walking, and having found food the kite usually returns to a perch to eat it. In the air kites appear more buoyant than buzzards as they drift high over the valleys or soar, glide and occasionally hover on wings more slender than those of the buzzard. When looked at from above, the tail is noticeably red.

No food refused

The kite has a justified reputation for being a scavenger, and will take any dead animal food lying around, including garbage. It

Popperfoto

△ *Black-winged or white-tailed kite* ***Elanus caeruleus*** *can hover like a kestrel.*

▽ *Yellow-billed kite* ***Milvus aegypticus*** *wheels at no great height searching for food.*

will, however, take any small mammals, from rabbits and squirrels to mice, any birds —especially young ones—and older birds that are injured, as well as frogs, lizards, snakes and insects. Grasshoppers especially are picked up on the ground and beetles are taken on the wing. Dead fish and fish offal are eaten and in the Canaries and the Cape Verde Islands kites are familiar in ports and fish markets.

Garbage-filled nests

As with all large birds of prey, courtship is marked by soaring flights and a mewing call. Kites are said to pair for life and about March—earlier in the southerly parts of their range—each pair begins to court in earnest, sailing at great heights, circling around each other or gliding low over the treetops. Sometimes one of them will fly low with a stick or wisp of wool in its talons, the other will follow and the 'plaything' will be passed from one to the other, usually ending up in the nest. The nest is a platform of sticks consolidated with earth, close to the main trunk of a tall slender oak or pine. It is lined with wool, moss and an assortment of rubbish, such as hair, paper, rag, grass, dung, bones and fur. The 2—3 white eggs, lightly marked with brown, are laid in mid-April and incubated by only the female for about a month, the male bringing food to her. He continues to do this for a while after the eggs have hatched and then the female joins him in hunting, both bringing food to the fledglings until they are 2 months old.

Bel Vienne: Jacana

△ *A pair of red kites merge well with the pine tree as they guard their nest.*

▽ *Reputation for scavenging—a black kite stands over the carcase of a red deer.*

Eric Hosking

Black and red compared

The black kite has a similar history except that it tends to live more consistently near rivers and takes a higher proportion of fish carrion. It will also catch large fish swimming at the surface in rivers. In Africa it is noted for preying on swarming locusts or hunting for insects driven out by grass fires. Some red and the black kites migrate, mainly from the northern parts of the range to more southerly latitudes with the approach of winter. The red kite, however, does not move farther south than the Mediterranean region whereas the black kite tends to winter in tropical Africa.

Decline of the kite

In the Middle Ages kites, probably both the red and the black, were numerous in Britain but today only a few pairs of red kites survive, almost confined to Wales, and only five black kites have been seen in the British Isles in the last century. Richard Fitter recalls, in his *London's Natural History,* that the secretary to Baron Leo von Rozmital, visiting London from Bohemia in 1465, noted that nowhere had he seen so many kites as on London Bridge. Charles Clusius, the Flemish botanist, visiting England in 1571, thought there were as many kites in England as in Cairo. They were then protected birds and so tame they would come down for carrion and garbage among crowds of people, or snatch 'bread smeared with butter, in the Flemish fashion, given to them by their mothers from the hands of children'. European soldiers serving in the Middle East have often had similar experiences when eating their rations. By the 18th century kites were rare in Britain, being no longer protected. The last pair nested in Hyde Park in 1777 and the last one seen flying over London was June 24, 1859—over Piccadilly!

Although the list of items of food taken is a long one, kites tend to have different preferences in different districts. Some undoubtedly make a practice of taking chicks and ducklings from farmyards and this almost certainly led to their persecution. People's habits changed, also, and there was less garbage about in London and elsewhere by the 18th century. By 1905 only five red kites were known in Britain, in mid-Wales. By 1910 these had increased to 10 pairs, but by 1938 there were only 15 kites in Britain. Some protective measures were attempted during this period but records were not well kept. In 1949 the West Wales Field Society set up its Kite Field Committee. By persuading farmers on whose land the kites nested to leave them alone and by trying—not always successfully —to keep people away from the nesting areas, the kite has been given protection ever since. The position in 1968 was that there were 24 or 25 pairs, 20 of which nested, and 12 young birds were reared.

class	**Aves**
order	**Falconiformes**
family	**Accipitridae**
genus & species	***Milvus migrans*** *black kite* ***M. milvus*** *red kite*

Kittiwake

The kittiwake is a small gull that differs from other gulls in frequenting open water rather than shores, and in nesting on cliff ledges. It is small, about 16 in. long, and looks like a common gull, but has no white tips to the black edges of its wings. The body is white with grey wings and back, but in winter the grey extends up the neck to the crown. The bill is yellow and the legs black. Young kittiwakes have a black band across the back of the neck and another across the wings.

Kittiwakes live in the North Atlantic Ocean, breeding as far south as Brittany and Newfoundland. To the north, they breed in Spitzbergen, Franz Josef Land and Severnaya Zemlya. A second species, the red-legged kittiwake, breeds in the Bering Sea and North Pacific as far south as the Kurile and Aleutian Islands.

Fritz Siedel

Head for heights

◁◁ *Sheer drop to the sea below—the kittiwake must have a head for heights to lead its precarious life. Kittiwakes nest in large colonies on the narrowest of cliff ledges.*
◁ *Each kittiwake, out of necessity, builds a solid nest of mud, grass or seaweed, so preventing the eggs from toppling over the edge of the cliff. Even when the chicks have hatched they are unable to run about but must stay in the nest for the first few weeks.*
△ *A kittiwake emerges from a plunge dive. It feeds on fish, molluscs and plankton and does not steal eggs and young birds as do other gulls.*

Oceanic seabird

Outside the breeding season kittiwakes spend their time at sea in flocks of 1 000 or more. They can be found on the pack ice of the Arctic Sea, provided there is enough open water for feeding, and have been found within 130 miles of the North Pole. Kittiwakes are rarely seen inland, usually only after a storm. Sometimes a flock is caught by a storm and driven into the shore and inland where many may die. There is a general southward movement in the autumn after the breeding season, returning the following spring. There is also a movement around the oceans; kittiwakes ringed off the British Isles have been recovered in Newfoundland, Labrador and Greenland.

Food is mainly plankton

Kittiwakes are found in the plankton-rich surface waters of the ocean. They usually feed by plunge-diving—diving with wings half-folded but not completely submerging. They do, however, sometimes submerge completely and swim underwater with their wings. They catch a variety of floating animals such as crustaceans, squids, worms and fishes. Occasionally freshwater or shore creatures are taken and there is even one record of a pigmy shrew being taken. Kittiwakes are not usually attracted to carrion and offal like other gulls but will sometimes follow fishing boats and frequent canning factories to feed on the scraps.

Kittiwakes have been reported as attacking grey seals that were carrying fish in their mouths, settling or hovering near their heads and lunging at them.

Nesting on cliffs

Towards the end of May or June, kittiwakes appear around the coasts where they nest in large colonies, sometimes of up to 100 000 pairs. They often nest on the same cliffs as guillemots, fulmars and shags. Occasionally they build on inland cliffs or on window-sills, which are man-made equivalents of rock ledges, and some kittiwake colonies are on rocky islets. There may be competition for nest sites and the kittiwakes nest on the narrowest ledges, to which the pair cling, facing inwards, during courtship. The two kittiwakes bow and rub each other's bills and heads, or face each other and utter their characteristic calls of 'kitt-i-waak', at the same time showing the orange inside of their mouths.

Most gulls build very scanty nests, making little more than a depression in the ground with a lining of grass and other plants. Kittiwakes, on the other hand, build a solid nest of mud, grass or seaweed, forming the cup needed to keep eggs from falling off a narrow, often uneven ledge. The collection of nest material is a community event. Several dozen kittiwakes fly inland and settle on a piece of boggy ground or other suitable place where they can pick up beakfuls of mud and grass and fly 'kitt-i-waaking' back to the cliffs. The nest material is placed on the ledge, trampled down, and finally a lining of dry grass is added. Not all the material is collected on these communal expeditions; kittiwakes regularly steal material from their neighbours' nests.

Both parents incubate the 2 eggs for 3 weeks. Unlike other gulls, the chicks are unable to run about and have to spend their first few weeks in the nest. This means that they cannot practise flying so vigorously as do other young seabirds, or run away if attacked by their nestmates or by adult kittiwakes. If they are attacked they hide their heads in submission, thereby reducing the aggression of their attackers.

Cliff safety first

Gulls that nest on open ground often fall prey to predators such as foxes or stoats, but by nesting on inaccessible cliffs kittiwakes are safe from such attacks. It is thought that this habit has occurred through natural selection and much of their breeding habits have altered to fit the new way of life. In the course of a study on the habits of kittiwakes, Esther Cullen made a list of the changes that distinguish kittiwakes from the gulls that nest on open ground. Because of the safety of the cliffs kittiwakes rarely give alarm calls and stay on their nests until one comes quite close. Unlike the chicks of other gulls, kittiwake chicks are not camouflaged and the parents do not remove eggshells or droppings from the nest to make it less conspicuous. They do, however, swallow or throw away waste food as a sanitary measure. Other gulls do not do this but they can lead their chicks away from the nest before feeding them. At the start of the breeding season most gulls are wary of their nesting ground because of the dangers of predation and pairing takes place away from the nesting ground. Kittiwakes, on the other hand, mate on their nests.

Some changes have been necessary to live on cliff ledges. A solid nest is needed for the safety of eggs and chicks and sharp claws and strong toes for hanging on. The violent, wing-beating battles other gulls indulge in are impossible on a narrow ledge and kittiwakes fight by grabbing and twisting each other's bills. The chicks feed by taking food from the parents' throats. If they were fed by the parent regurgitating food onto the ground for them to peck, the food might be lost over the edge.

class	**Aves**
order	**Charadriiformes**
family	**Laridae**
genus & species	***Rissa tridactyla*** *kittiwake* ***R. brevirostris*** *red-legged kittiwake*

Kittiwakes quarrelling over food in mid-air: a rare photograph of unusual behaviour (by G Rüppell).

Kiwi

The kiwi is the smallest flightless running bird in the southern hemisphere, the other runners being the emu, cassowary, ostrich and rhea. There are three species in New Zealand, each about the size of a domestic fowl, with a rounded body, no tail, stout but short legs, strong claws on their three toes and a long slender bill with slit-like nostrils at its tip. They range in size from a bantam to an Orpington and in weight from 3 – 9 lb, the females being larger than the males. The wings are very small, 2 in. long, and completely hidden by the hair-like body feathers that make up the plumage. The eyes are small but there are many long bristles at the base of the bill which are probably used as organs of touch. The ears are large and are the chief sensory organs used in detecting danger.

Kiwis are so different anatomically from the other running birds that they are probably only distantly related to them. They are more closely related to the extinct moas of New Zealand.

Waddling nightbird

The home of the kiwi is in the kauri pine forests with their tree ferns and swampy ground. Here they spend the day in burrows or under buttress roots of large trees. They are shy, retiring and hard to see in the forest because of the gloom and the birds' dark brown colouring. They come out at night and waddle along, their legs being set well apart. Their run is a long-striding waddle, with the bill held well out in front.

Food for all seasons

When feeding a kiwi moves quietly, probably feeling its way to a large extent with the bill bristles. At the slightest alarm it dashes rapidly to cover. Its main food, when the ground is moist, is earthworms and insects and their larvae. The tip of the long bill overlaps the lower half, so the bill can be thrust deep in the ground, driven by the short, thick neck. The bird tracks its prey mainly by smell. When the ground is dry in summer, the kiwi picks up fallen forest fruits and eats a large number of leaves.

Testing its sense of smell

It has always been assumed that the kiwi finds its food by smell, although most birds have a weak sense of smell. In December 1968, Bernice M Wenzel, of the University of California, published an account in *Nature* (Vol 220, p 1133) of a series of experiments carried out in New Zealand. Sets of tapering aluminium tubes were sunk into the ground in two kiwi aviaries. The tests, repeated over a period of 3 months, consisted of placing food in one tube, earth in another and a strong odorant in a third. By ringing the changes, such as using different odorants and different ways of masking the contents of the various tubes, it was proved beyond doubt that a kiwi can smell food several inches down in a way that no other bird is able to do.

Unusually large eggs

Although kiwis' nests have often been found, not much is known about the breeding or nesting habits. The nest is made in a hollow log or among the roots of a large tree. Sometimes it is in a hole or burrow in a soft bank, enlarged by the bird itself. Kiwis lay 1 or 2 very large chalky-white eggs, each about 5 in. long, weighing about a pound. This is $\frac{1}{8}$ of the hen kiwi's body weight, not $\frac{1}{4}$ as is sometimes stated. The male, as is usual with running birds, does the incubating, which lasts for 75 – 80 days. The chicks are small balls of soft hair-like feathers with a spindly beak. They remain in the nest for 6 days after hatching, receiving no food during this time. Then they follow their parents on their nightly forays, finding their own food, after the male has helped by clearing the ground for them. The normal call of the male is thin and reedy; that of the female is more hoarse. It is a two-note call, made only at night, and sounds like 'k-wee', with the accent on the second part.

At Hawke's Bay a colony of kiwis is kept under protection. Nesting boxes are provided and there it was noticed that during the incubation period the hen tapped at intervals on the box and the male inside tapped back. This may be a means of communication between the two partners.

From pot to popularity

The kiwi population has decreased over the past century. They were prized by the Maoris as a delicacy, and their feathers were woven into cloaks for the chieftains. Then the early settlers hunted them for food. The birds also suffered from dogs, cats, stoats, weasels and other introduced animals. Their habitat has been reduced through the country being opened up for agriculture. In contrast with their falling numbers, their popularity has increased. Their image is seen on postage stamps and coins and on the trademarks of many products from shoe polish to textiles. The name became most familiar to people in Britain and in other parts of the world during the First World War because the New Zealand troops were called Kiwis. The Royal Air Force also perpetuated the name to some extent when its non-flying members were nicknamed Kiwis.

class	**Aves**
order	**Apterygiformes**
family	**Apterygidae**
genus & species	***Apteryx australis*** *common or brown kiwi* ***A. haasti*** *great spotted or large grey kiwi* ***A. oweni*** *little spotted or little grey kiwi*

Earthworm forager afield: the flightless kiwi of New Zealand, with beak outstretched, walks through undergrowth in long-striding waddles.

M F Soper

Klipspringer

The klipspringer is a small antelope related to dik-diks which is adapted, like the chamois in the northern hemisphere, to life on bare and inaccessible rocky places. The klipspringer is 3 ft long in head and body with 2–4 in. of tail and stands up to 22 in. at the shoulder. It weighs up to 40 lb. The thick, wavy coat is yellowish to reddish, with yellowish white or white on the underparts and the insides of the legs. Each hair of the upper parts is minutely banded with yellow and black, giving a pepper-and-salt effect. The hairs are bristle-like, stout and with an inner pith quite unlike those of any other antelope.

The head is broad and triangular with a pointed snout but broad mouth, the muzzle being bare and the nostrils small. The ears are large and rounded, and their inner faces are conspicuously ridged, suggesting efficient hearing because ridges of this kind have been shown to direct sound waves more effectively on to the eardrum. There is a prominent bare opening to the scent glands on the face, in front of each eye, but there are no foot glands. The legs are stout and each ends in a hairy pastern, with black hair, and two cylindrical hoofs, each hoof 1 in. high and the same across, blunted at their tips and with their bases high from the ground when the animal is in motion. The horns are short, straight spikes ringed at the base and usually worn by males only but there is one race in the Tanganyika area ***(schillingi)*** *in which the females often have horns.*

A dozen races have been recognized from Northern Nigeria to the Sudan, Ethiopia and Somalia, south to the Cape.

Splendid jumpers

Klipspringers live in cliff ravines, on high rocky prominences and rocky kopjes, and in the bush surrounding them, where they feed. Traces of them have been found on Mt Elgon in Kenya up to 14 800 ft. They are solitary or form small groups of up to eight. Once disturbed they make off for the rocks or, if already on the rocks, they stand with all four feet together, alert, rigid and hard to see. When not unduly disturbed and if only their curiosity is aroused they give a shrill whistle. On further alarm they retreat, always uphill and on reaching the summit, a klipspringer pauses for a last look backwards before disappearing. The alarm call is a curious discordant squeaking. The name, which is Afrikaans for rock jumper, is from the animal's amazing capacity for jumping from crag to crag. It is a terrific jumper, more surefooted than any goat, bouncing up an almost perpendicular cliff like a rubber ball or dropping down a precipitous face without losing foothold. FW Fitzsimon, the South African naturalist, observed one leap 30 ft from the edge of a rocky precipice to a jutting ledge below, steady itself for a moment, then run at a fast pace obliquely down the precipice.

South African Tourist Corporation

Delicately poised: the klipspringer is renowned for its ability to scale seemingly inaccessible rocky places. It has been claimed that it can land on a point no bigger than a penny!

A bare living

Its food is leaves and grass or, if in a habitat with little or no bush around, rock plants, especially succulents. Astley Maberly maintains that it must get its moisture from dew or small quantities of water caught in holes in the rocks, as it does not visit waterholes.

Statuesque buck

The breeding season is probably extended over a long period, the single young being born between September and the end of January. The gestation period is 214 days. A feature of the rut seems to be for the buck to stand on watch on a pinnacle of rock with the hoofs all close together.

Odds against survival

The probable enemies are leopards, large birds of prey and pythons. The only protection is the almost moss-like coat of brittle hair which comes away in tufts and seems at times to nonplus the enemy. The lost hair is soon replaced by a new growth. At one time when klipspringers were more numerous, they were hunted for this hair which was springy and light enough to be used for stuffing saddles and mattresses. Astley Maberly is of the opinion that the klipspringer's coat serves as a cushion against rocks, or against thorns as the animal scrapes past them. On precipitous slopes it could not afford to have its coat caught even for a moment in a thorn tuft growing among rocks or in a crevice in a rock face. The real long-term danger to the species is that, owing to its special requirements, it is unable to adapt to changes, which often lead to local extinction. At the present time klipspringers still survive in fair numbers in some places but should extinction ever be threatened it is unlikely the species could be preserved in captivity. The animals are not often seen in zoos although one lived for 15 years in the St Louis Zoological Park, in the United States. The experience there, however, where there has been the greatest success in keeping klipspringers, is not very promising. A number of young were reared from a small group of these animals obtained in 1935 and a considerable stock was built up. Then, when success seemed assured, the vitality seemed to wane and the herd 'disintegrated'. A tall kiosk of rough stone was built to resemble their natural habitat but they made less use of this than was hoped and this may have had something to do with their deterioration.

Point of balance

The klipspringer is always figured standing on a pinnacle of rock with all four feet close together, the animal balanced on its 'points'. It has been claimed that it can spring from the ground to land on such a pinnacle no bigger at the top than a penny, which is just over 1 in. diameter. If true it shows remarkable judgement, balance and poise. It may be that the story improves with the telling because the account varies with the writer from a penny to a silver dollar or 'several inches'. Even so, there is an implied skill which compels comparison with a ballet dancer poised on the points of her shoes which are shaped not unlike the hoofs of the klipspringer—and the animal's life depends on their unerring accuracy.

class	**Mammalia**
order	**Artiodactyla**
family	**Bovidae**
genus & species	***Oreotragus oreotragus***

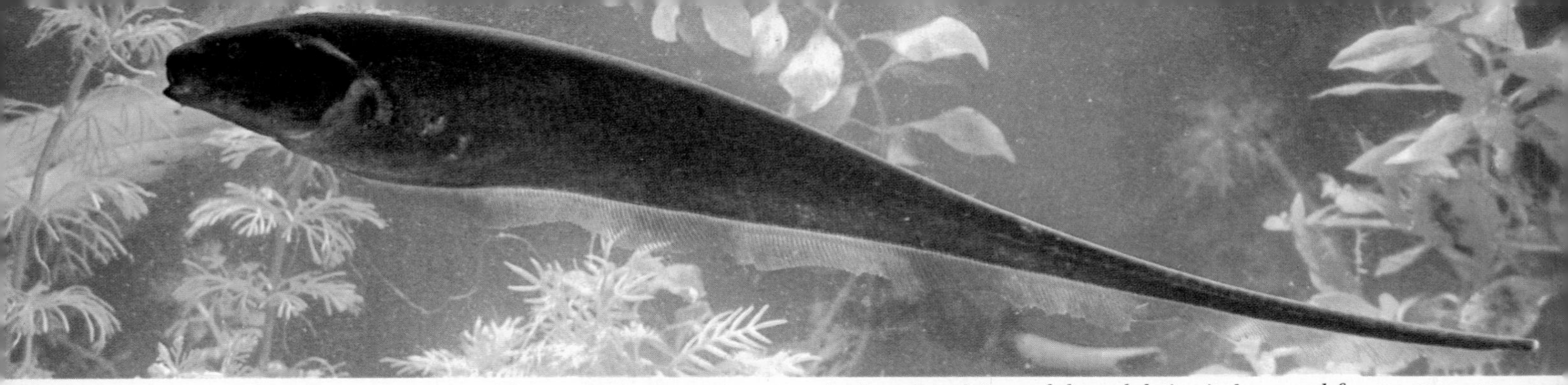

Aptly named: South American apteronotid knife-fish ***Sternopygus macrurus*** *moves backwards and forwards by undulating its long anal fin.* (Jane Burton: Photo Res)

Knife-fish

For a fish to be called a knife-fish its body must be broad and thin. The knife-fish of tropical Africa and southern and southeast Asia, belonging to the family Notopteridae, is very much flattened from side to side and the blade-like body ends in what is almost a point. One member of this family has already been dealt with under featherback (p 741). There are three other families of knife-fishes, living in South America, and they belong to a different order. They are the Gymnotidae, Apteronotidae and Rhamphichthyidae. Together they give us an excellent example of convergent evolution, in which two or more unrelated animals have come to look alike. The last three families are related to carp (order Cypriniformes), the Notopteridae being nearer to the arapaima (order Osteoglossidae).

Knife-fishes are often kept in aquaria and anyone wishing to air his knowledge—or, conversely, not wishing to expose his ignorance—needs to take a second look to know whether the particular fish he is looking at is from South America or from tropical Africa and Asia. Knife-fishes are separated into families on the basis of their anatomy, and one thing that helps us tell straight away whether a knife-fish in the aquarium before us comes from the Old World or the New World is that the South American knife-fishes have a well-marked tentacle lying in front of each nostril.

Forward and backward swimmers

In all knife-fishes, the abdominal cavity and digestive organs occupy a small part of the body behind the head so the vent is well forward, where the pectoral fins would be in an ordinary fish. All the fins are small, even the tail fin, and only one is prominent: the anal fin, which runs from behind the vent along the underside of the body, and is continuous, or nearly so, with the very small tail fin. Knife-fishes, from wherever they come, swim by wave-like movements of the anal fin. When the flow is reversed the fish moves backward with equal ease. This is swimming reduced to a simple formula. With the body held rigid the knife-fish moves forward or backward, using only one fin, the long anal fin.

Two ways of breathing

All knife-fishes live in quiet weedy waters, in the side reaches of large rivers or in stagnant backwaters. In an aquarium they do best when shaded or given dimly lit places into which they can retire. They need to come to the surface to gulp air. In the South American knife-fishes the swimbladder has been transformed into a kind of lung. In the knife-fishes of the Old World, at least in the species studied, air is gulped into the gill cavity and the spent air is later given out through the stomach, intestine and vent. All knife-fishes feed at night or in twilight, on animal and plant food. In aquaria they are fed with chopped meat, worms and rolled oats, as well as small invertebrates such as water fleas, insect larvae and small fishes, although little is known for certain about what they eat in their native habitats. There is no way of telling male from female and little is known about their breeding.

Groping in the dark

The Nile fish, with similar movements and shape to knife-fishes, is a species that has been intensively studied because of the special use it makes of electric organs. It is of interest to note that the South American knife-fishes also generate electricity, from organs derived from outer parts of trunk and tail muscles. These generate impulses at frequencies between 1 and 1 000 per second. Some species produce 1–5 pulses per second while resting, increasing this to 20 per second when excited. Others produce up to 1 000 pulses per second. These electrical pulses set currents flowing in the water around the fish, the pattern of the current being altered by objects in the surrounding water. Animals have a higher conductivity than water, rocks have a lower conductivity. An animal concentrates the current so increasing the current flowing through nearby parts of the knife-fish's body. A rock has the reverse effect. So the fish can tell animal from mineral, food from an obstacle—but the current is not strong enough to kill prey.

class	**Pisces**
order	**Osteoglossiformes**
family	**Notopteridae**
genera	***Notopterus, Xenomystis***
order	**Cypriniformes**
families	**Gymnotidae, Apteronotidae, Rhamphichthyidae**
genera	***Gymnotus, Sternarchus, Hypopomus****, others*

False feather ***Xenomystis nigri.*** *Its sole claim to generic recognition is the fact that it lacks the dorsal fin common to the rest of the family.* Jane Burton: Photo Re

Made-to-measure: with no eucalyptus tree available a koala seems to enjoy a change squatting up a telegraph pole on Phillip Island, off eastern Australia.

Koala

The koala is probably Australia's favourite animal. It is known affectionately as the Australian teddy bear although there are a dozen names to choose from. At various times it has been called bangaroo, koolewong, narnagoon, buidelbeer, native bear, karbor, cullawine, colo, koala wombat and New Holland sloth! The last two have an especial interest. For a long time it was believed the koala was most nearly related to the wombat and was placed in a family on its own, the Phascolarctidae, near that of the wombat. Now it is placed in the Phalangeridae with the opossums. In habits the koala recalls the slow loris and the sloth, two very different animals which also move in a lethargic way.

The koala is like a small bear, 2 ft high, up to 33 lb weight, with tufted ears, small eyes with a vertical slit pupil and a prominent beak-like snout. Tailless except for a very short rounded stump, it has a thick ash-grey fur with a tinge of brown on the upper parts, yellowish white on the hindquarters and white on the under parts. It has cheek pouches for storing food and the brood pouch of the female opens backwards. All four feet are grasping. On the front feet the first two of the five toes are opposed to the rest and the first toe on the hindfoot is opposed. Also on the hindfoot the second and third toes are joined in a common skin.

Ace tree-climbers

The koala is essentially tree-living, only occasionally descending to lick earth—apparently to aid digestion—or to shuffle slowly to another tree. If forced to the ground its main concern is to reach another tree and climb it, scrambling up even smooth trunks to the swaying topmost branches where it clings with the powerful grip of all four feet. Although its legs are short they are strong and there are sharp claws on the toes. When climbing a trunk its forelegs reach out at an angle of 45° while the hindlegs are directly under the body. It climbs in a series of jumps of 4–5 in. at a time. During the day it sleeps curled up in a tree-fork. It never enters hollows in trees. Koalas are inoffensive although they have harsh grating voices, said to be like a hand-saw cutting through a thin board; it has been claimed that they have the loudest Australian voice, other than the flying phalanger.

Fussy feeders

At night the koala climbs to the topmost branches to find its only food: the tender shoots of eucalyptus, 12 species of which are eaten. A koala is said to smell strongly of eucalyptus. Bernhard Grzimek has spoken of koalas as smelling like cough lozenges. Their feeding is, however, more restricted than this. Different races of koala eat only certain species of gum tree. Koalas on the east coast of Australia feed only on the spotted gum and the tallow wood, in Victoria only the red gum. Even then they cannot use all the leaves on a chosen gum. At certain times the older leaves, sometimes the young leaves at the tips of the branches, release prussic acid—a deadly poison—when chewed. So, as more and more gum trees have been felled, koalas have become increasingly hemmed in, prisoners of their specialised diet. One of the difficulties of saving the koala by having special reserves is to supply enough trees for them of the right kind. Koalas are said to eat mistletoe and box leaves as well, and a koala in captivity was persuaded to eat bread and milk, but without gum leaves they cannot survive.

Get off my back!

Another drawback to preserving the koala is that it is a slow breeder. Usually the animal is solitary or lives in small groups. At breeding time a boss male forms a small harem which he guards. The gestation period is 25—35 days and there is normally only one young at a birth, $\frac{3}{4}$ in. long and $\frac{1}{5}$ oz weight. It is fully furred at 6 months but continues to stay with the mother for another 6 months after leaving the pouch, riding pick-a-back on her, which has led to many endearing photographs. On weaning it obtains nourishment by eating partially digested food that has passed through the mother's digestive tract. The young koala is sexually mature at 4 years, and the longest lived koala was 20 years old when it died.

Pitiless persecution

Until less than a century ago there were millions of koalas, especially in eastern Australia. Now they are numbered in thousands. In 1887—89 and again in 1900—1903 epidemics swept through them, killing large numbers. This was at a time when it was a favourite 'sport' to shoot these sitting targets, often taking several shots to finish one animal which meanwhile cried piteously, like a human baby, a fact that caused Australian naturalists to condemn the sport as the most callous. At all times koalas are a prey to forest fires as well as to land clearance for human settlement. Moreover a market was developed for their pelts, their fur being thick and able to withstand hard usage. In 1908 nearly 58 000 koala pelts were marketed in Sydney alone. In 1920—21 a total of 205 679 were marketed and in 1924 over two million were exported. By this time public opinion was being aroused and before long efforts were being made to protect the surviving populations and to establish sanctuaries for them and ensure their future.

Australian News & Information

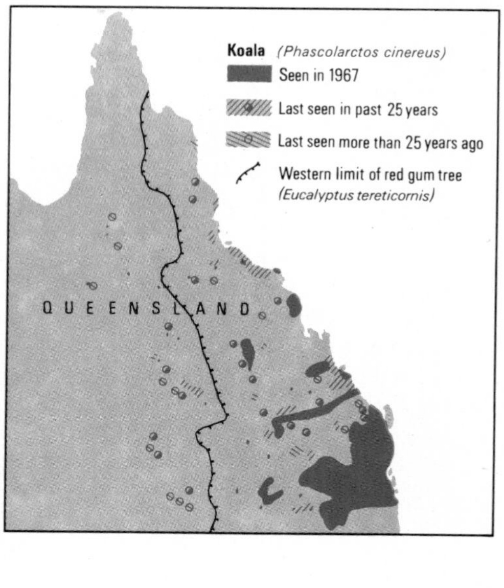

Curious cuddly: favourite of millions, the koala is the Australian teddy bear. It spends most of its time shuffling about its eucalyptus tree-top home. The baby above has climbed onto its mother's back from a downward opening pouch. At a year (right) it is about to leave its mother and find its own gum tree. Numbers have seriously decreased in the last 100 years mainly due to fires destroying their gum trees and from persecution by man. From a 1967 survey in Queensland the present-day distribution was established in that state (left).

class	**Mammalia**
order	**Marsupialia**
family	**Phalangeridae**
genus & species	***Phascolarctos cinereus***

Kob

Kob are antelopes, near relatives of waterbuck from which they differ in their short coat, lack of a mane, short lyre-shaped horns and well-developed face glands, one in front of each eye. They also have scent glands in the groin (inguinal glands). The lechwe, another close relative, has more lyre-shaped horns with a double curve, no face glands and only rudimentary inguinal glands. Only the males, in all three, have horns.

The two species of kob are the true kob and the puku. The first, which includes two subspecies, the Uganda and the white-eared kob, ranges from Guinea to Uganda. The buck stands 3 ft at the shoulder and weighs 200 lb, the doe being smaller and weighing 145 lb. The coat varies across the range from orange or red to blackish-brown with white round the eyes and at the bases of the ears. The fronts of the forelegs are black, often with a white hoof-band, and the muzzle, lips, underparts and insides of the thighs are white. The puku, found in Zambia and part of Malawi, is 2–3 in. shorter at the shoulder, the buck weighing up to 170 lb, the doe up to 140 lb. The coloration of the puku differs only in details: no black on the legs, no white hoof-band, and the white eye-ring is narrower. The coat is longer and rougher.

△ A handy hoof for scratching an ear. ▷ Uganda kob on the alert in Elizabeth National Park. Kob have well-developed face glands, one in front of each eye and a scent gland in the groin.

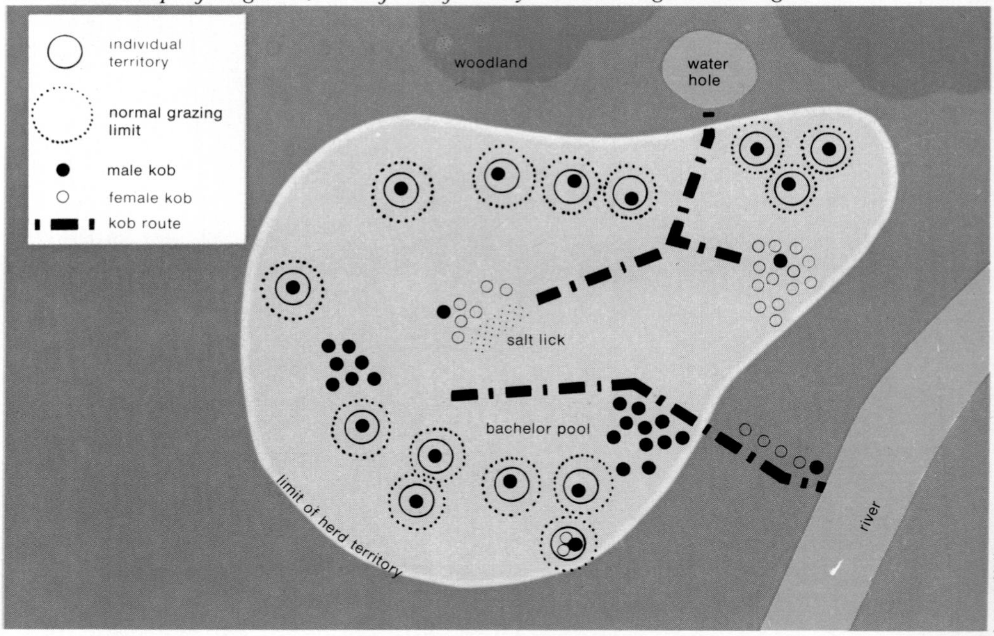

Diagram of typical kob territory occupied by a medium-sized herd. Dr Hal Beuchner from his studies on kob in Toro Game Reserve in the early fifties showed how a large herd of kob scattered unevenly over the plains were actually in orderly territories (see text under Herds within herds) based upon harmless aggressive displays and fights between bucks.

Herds within herds

Kob are animals with a complicated social order. Looking over the African savannah we see a large herd of kob scattered unevenly. In one place we see a few hundred and a few miles away there is another concentration of them. It all seems to be haphazard but when Dr Hal Buechner, of the Smithsonian Institution in Washington, made his now famous studies less than 20 years ago, he found there was order in this apparent confusion.

On closer inspection, a herd of kob is seen to be made up of several groups and some solitary animals, grazing or resting and chewing the cud. A few will be moving about restlessly, but never straying over an invisible boundary line enclosing the territory of the herd. There were 15 000 kob in the Toro Game Reserve when Buechner came to study them. They were spread over 158 square miles and within this area there were 13 breeding grounds. Each ground was on a ridge or a knoll with good grazing, good visibility and fairly near water, and within it, in a central space 200 yd across, were 12–15 roughly circular territories each 20–60 yd across. Some of these were touching, sometimes overlapping, and in each was a single adult buck who spent most of his time at the centre of it where the grass was close-cropped and the ground trampled. Nevertheless, males often displayed at each other across the boundaries of their respective territories by walking towards the boundary with head lowered and feinting with their horns. Usually they had a harem of does within their territories.

Besides these circular territories, within the central space, were groups of bucks—the bachelor groups—and groups of unattached does.

The single individuals weaving restlessly through the herd are likely to be males without territories, quick and eager to get one. They wander around the edges of the central area running quickly to a particular territory and challenging the occupant, or taking possession of one temporarily vacant because its owner has led his harem to water. The males fight with feet wide apart, heads lowered and horns interlocked or beating against each other. Fights are seldom fatal; victory usually goes to the occupant male, the loser being finally chased well away towards the herd's outer boundary. Often he is chased or threatened by all the occupying males as he crosses one territory after another in his retreat.

A buck may occupy a territory for less than a day or up to 2 months.

The love kick

Breeding continues throughout the year although a female is in season for only a day. Then she leaves the unattached groups, which wander around from place to place elsewhere, and enters the territories where she mates with several males. The buck tries to attract a female with a prancing display, which often carries him in his exuberance outside his own territory, perhaps towards another male's territory, where he is chased off. Courtship includes what is known as the *Laufschlag* or mating kick. In this the male touches the female's underside with a stiff

The short lyre-shaped horns are a distinctive feature of the male kob (above left and centre, and previous page), the female being hornless. Kob relish tender, marshy grasses and are usually found near water. They have suffered, like many animals, from man's depletion of their habitat and unrestricted hunting.

foreleg, placing it either under her flank from the side or between her hindlegs from behind. In a great many antelopes—blackbuck, gazelle, dibatag, oryx—this is a preliminary to courtship and is a clear indication of their relationship to each other. The antelopes which do not perform the *Laufschlag* are the hartebeest—gnu—impala group, and the bovine (ox-like) group, including kudu, eland and bushbuck.

New use for old horns

Lions, leopards, hyaenas and wild dogs all prey on kob. A rather surprising predator is the python. Hay and Martin, in the *East African Wildlife Journal* for 1966 record five cases of python swallowing female kob in Uganda. It is probable, however, that even if he managed to overpower a male, a python would not be able to swallow the spreading horns.

Staking the claim

Since Buechner discovered the social behaviour of the Uganda kob, similar modes of life, with territorial and non-territorial males, have been described by Fritz Walther for Grant's and Thomson's gazelles. It was an even chance that similar territorial behaviour would be found in the puku, too. So as soon as opportunity arose, A De Vos went to the Luangwa Game Reserve to see if they, too, had such a remarkable system. He found they had but with certain differences. Puku territories were 8—20 times the size of those of the Uganda kob, and were less rigidly observed. Thus, when a male temporarily left his territory, his neighbour might wander in. The centres of the territories were not close-cropped or trampled like the kob's, perhaps because they were so much larger, with more variety of food in them. The display which the male pukus made at each other, across their boundaries, consisted of a very rapid tail-wagging, without laying back the ears. The displays sometimes ended in a chase, which might even carry the bucks into one of the other territories. Around the territorial breeding grounds of puku are the same 'bachelor bands' as in the kob, and here too non-territorial males wander in and are chased off by the 'owner' of the territory.

class	**Mammalia**
order	**Artiodactyla**
family	**Bovidae**
genus & species	***Kobus kob*** *kob* ***K. vardoni*** *puku*

Van Nostrand: WWF

Lizard giant: a Komodo dragon takes a stroll, forked tongue flicking out to taste its way along.

Sven Gillsater: Photo Res

Gluttons enjoy photographer's bait.

Komodo dragon

Belonging to the monitor lizards—which will be dealt with later—the Komodo dragon deserves special mention. It is not only the largest living lizard—the males grow up to 10 ft long and 300 lb weight—but also the largest lizard of all time, except for the extinct marine mosasaurs which reached 50 ft. The only known rival to the Komodo dragon is an extinct monitor in Australia of about the same size. This lived during the Miocene period, 20—11 million years ago. Although the Komodo dragon is so large, it was unknown outside its native home until 1912. Its native home is a few small Indonesian islands: Komodo, Rintja, Flores and Padar. The first is the largest and this is only 20 by 12 miles, the others being even smaller.

The Komodo dragon has a stout, somewhat flattened body, long thick neck and longish head. Its legs are short and stout and the toes have long claws. Its tail is powerful and about the same length as the head and body combined. The tongue, which is constantly flicked out of the mouth, is long, narrow and deeply cleft. Young ones are dark in colour with red circles all over the body and vertical bands of black and yellowish green on the neck. These neck markings disappear with age but the red circles remain on the grey-brown bodies of adults.

Feats of gluttony

The islands where the Komodo dragon lives are hilly, their river beds filled only in the rainy season. The hills are covered in places with rain forest and the lowlands with tall grasses. The dragons spend the night in holes among rocks, between the buttress roots of trees or in caves. They come out at about 8.30 am to look for food—chiefly carrion, which is located by smell. The tongue seems also to be used as a taste-smell organ as in other lizards and snakes. The larger lizards monopolise any food, keeping the younger ones away by intimidating them, or beating them off with sideways sweeps of the powerful tail. Only when the bigger ones are full are the smaller able to feed. The dragons probably kill deer and pigs as well as monkeys. They eat heavy meals which last for days. An 8 ft dragon was seen to eat most of a deer, after which it rested for a week to complete the digestion. In eating flesh the dragon is helped by its back teeth being finely serrated, like small saws.

Young dragons feed on insects, lizards, rodents and ground-nesting birds and their eggs. Large individuals, feeding on carcases, tear the meat apart with claws and teeth and swallow lumps whole. One was seen to gulp the complete hindquarters of a deer, another to swallow a whole monkey.

Middle-age spread

Mating takes place in July and the female lays her eggs about a month later. The eggs are oval, 4 in. long with a parchment shell, and they hatch the following April. Dragons in zoos have grown at an average of 8 in. a year. They probably reach sexual maturity at 5 years. Up to a length of 7 ft a dragon remains slender in the body. From that size growth in length slows down markedly but there is a fairly rapid increase in girth. Earliest reports told of dragons 23 ft long and although there have been more sober reports since of 12 or 13 ft it seems that even the 10 ft usually quoted may be a few inches longer than the actual maximum measured. Reports differ so much that there can be no certainty in this respect, which is why the figure of 10 ft is to be preferred.

Unique photograph of a Komodo dragon swimming off Lesser Sundra Island, Indonesia.

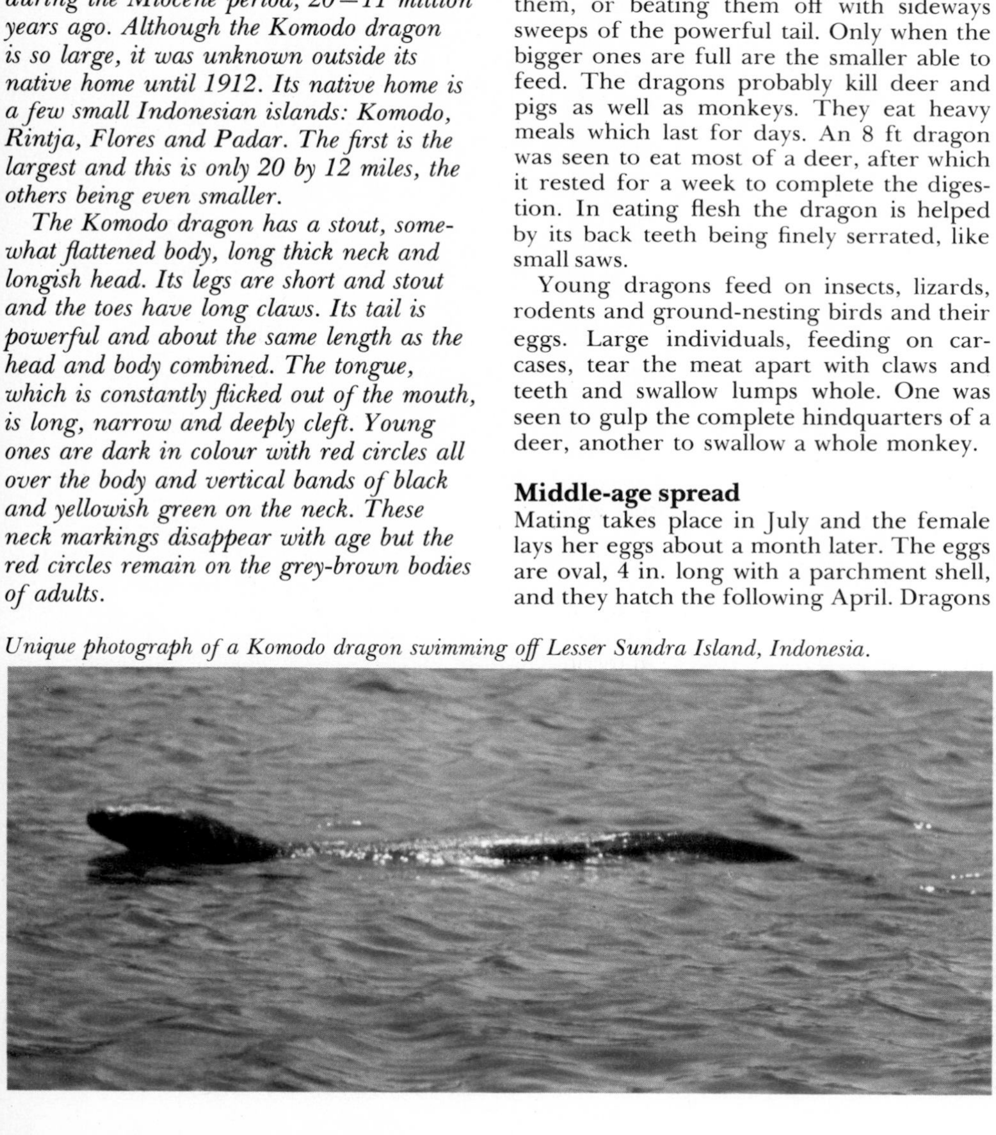

Sven Gillsater: Photo Res

'Land crocodiles'

Komodo was an uninhabited island visited occasionally by pearl fishers and people hunting turtles. Then the sultan of the neighbouring island of Sumbawa used it to deport criminals and other 'undesirables'. Reports began to circulate early in the 19th century of a *boeaya-darat* or land crocodile, 23 ft long and alarmingly ferocious. In 1910 the reports became so insistent that Major PA Ouwens, director of the Botanical Gardens at Buitenzorg in Java, asked the Governor of Flores to look into the reports with the result that in 1912 Ouwens was able to publish a scientific description of this giant lizard. Then the First World War broke out and the giant was forgotten in Europe, but in 1923 Duke Adolf Friedrich von Mecklenburg, a keen explorer, went to the island of Komodo and came back with four skins of this lizard.

There are several reasons why the lizards were ignored for so long. One was that the islands were uninhabited until undesirable or doubtful characters were sent there. The stories they told were coloured by their own fears and superstitions and were so exaggerated that they were disbelieved. The other reason was that it was called a crocodile, and nobody in those days, before the crocodile leather craze, wanted to go all that way to look for crocodiles.

class	**Reptilia**
order	**Squamata**
suborder	**Sauria**
family	**Varanidae**
genus & species	***Varanus komodoensis***

Kookaburra

The kookaburra or laughing jackass, although a member of the kingfisher family, appears very drab when compared with its brilliantly coloured relatives. The famous naturalist, John Gould, writing in 1844, called it the great brown kingfisher. Yet no kingfisher is better known, in its native land or throughout the world, or has been given so many different names. The one by which it is affectionately known to many Australians is 'Jackie'.

The laughing kookaburra, as it tends to be called now in Australian books, is 17 in. long, its plumage a mixture of white, buff, brown and black. It is stockily built with the usual heavy head of its family and the bill is large and heavy. The kingfisher family is divided into two subfamilies, the river kingfishers and the forest kingfishers which usually live far from water; the kookaburra is the largest of the forest kingfishers. Its range is eastern and southern Australia from Cape York in the north to Eyre Peninsula and Kangaroo Island. It was introduced into Western Australia in 1898 and is established in the southwestern corner. It was introduced into Tasmania in 1905 and is firmly settled there.

The blue-winged kookaburra is less well known. Its range is the northern parts of the continent, north of a line from Shark's Bay in Western Australia to southeastern Queensland. It is also found in New Guinea. It is the same size as the laughing kookaburra, and has much the same habits, but it is less vociferous and is mainly distinguished by the blue in its wings.

Popperfo

The bushman's clock

▷ *The laughing jackass or kookaburra is famous for its fiend-like screams and vulgar chuckles.*
◁ *Bills skywards and tails cocked a pair of 'Jackies' salute the day. To the visitor they may be attractive but Australians call them many unprintable names.*
△ *It is also famous as a killer of snakes, the bird above having a vice-like grip on a small but deadly poisonous one.*
▽ *The less well known blue-winged kookaburra. It is also known as the barking jackass as a discordant scream is added to the laughing chorus. This shy bird is usually seen in pairs or small parties and has much the same habits as the laughing jackass.*

C Fr

HJ Pollock: Photo Res

Keystone

Kookaburra emerging from its nesting burrow tunnelled into a termite nest on a tree. After the bird abandons the nest at the end of the breeding season, the active termites patch up the hole.

Good or bad timekeeper?

The original habitat of the laughing kookaburra is open forested country where it can be seen in pairs, singly or in small groups. It has taken readily to parks and gardens, and becomes friendly with people, accepting food from them and tapping on windows to be fed. Because it is a nest robber its relations with small birds are not good. They harass it by flying at it, striking with wings, feet and beak.

Its outstanding feature is the sounds it makes. Gould wrote: 'It rises with the dawn when the woods re-echo with its gurgling laugh; at sunset it is again heard.' Various naturalist authors have since referred to the regularity with which the kookaburra gives out its 'shouting, whooping and laughing chorus'. It has been called the clock bird, bushman's clock and settler's clock but opinions differ on this. Some Australians say the chorus is at dawn and sunset, others that it is at dawn, noon and sunset, and there are yet others that claim the bird's laughing call can be heard at any time of the day. One who had reason to favour the third of these was thrown from his horse and 'a pair of Jackasses in a nearby dead tree burst into a loud chorus, easily understood to be ridicule at my discomfiture'.

Snake-killer

The laughing kookaburra will eat anything animal including large insects, crabs, fish, reptiles and birds. It will not only rob nests of wild birds but has the reputation of taking chicks and ducklings from farms. It is also reputed to be a snake-killer, tackling snakes up to $2\frac{1}{2}$ ft long, seizing them behind the head, battering them senseless or killing them by dropping them from a height. Several kookaburras may combine to kill a large snake.

Calling the watch

The breeding season is September – December. The nest is built in a hollow tree or in a hole in a bank, sometimes in a chamber tunnelled out of a termites' nest. The eggs are white, somewhat rounded, and there are 2 – 4 in a clutch. A detailed account has been given of a nesting pair in a zoo. The nest was in the hollow base of a tree and the birds tunnelled out the earth below so that the nest was finally 3 in. below ground level. One egg was laid then a second the next day and a third 3 days later. Male and female shared the incubating for 25 days. Several times the hen rapped on the tree with her bill. The male responded to this by going in and relieving her at the nest. This should be compared with the kiwi's behaviour. Kookaburras are vigorous in defending their nest and young.

Danger from immigrants

Away from the homesteads and suburbs the kookaburra is threatened by the continued felling of trees and from the advance of human settlement. They are also harassed by introduced starlings taking over the nesting sites in hollow trees. A further menace is that immigrants are apt to shoot the kookaburra for sport.

The vanished nest

A few years ago two men were clearing an area of bush when they noticed two kookaburras returning at intervals to fly to an 'imaginary' spot in the air about 12 ft up, hover there for a few seconds and then fly away. This was at the spot where the men had felled a tree which held a nest. The birds continued this behaviour for days.

We talk with a certain amount of wonder about swallows returning in spring, after an absence of 6 months or more, from South Africa 6 000 miles away, to the same barn or stable to nest on the same rafter. Memory and the use of landmarks are involved and presumably the landmarks are of two kinds: the gross features of the landscape and the smaller details immediately surrounding the barn window, rafters and the rest.

If resident birds such as thrushes are studied from early nesting, the gross landmarks are found to be of the most importance. For example, a thrush may start to build a nest when the trees are leafless and, sometimes within a matter of days if the weather suddenly turns mild, the whole of its surroundings have changed as the buds burst and the leaves unfold. Although the detailed picture of the surroundings is altered, the thrush continues to find its nest, suggesting the bird relies more on the gross features for its bearings.

This seems to be supported and emphasized by the behaviour of the kookaburras. Heavy tree clearance must have entirely altered the detailed picture immediately around the nest, and also the more immediate gross features, as the trees around the nest were being continually grubbed out. For the kookaburras to have been able to fly up into the space, where their nest used to be, they would seem to have been relying on the more distant features of the landscape for their bearings.

class	**Aves**
order	**Coraciiformes**
family	**Alcedinidae**
genus & species	***Dacelo leachi*** *blue-winged kookaburra* ***D. gigas*** *kookaburra*

Psychotherapy Tales

Patients, Doctors, Friends & Many Awakenings

Julia A. Cooper, Psy.D.

Golden Tales Publishing Co.
Greenwich, Connecticut

www.goldentalespublishingco.com

Names, characteristics and other details have been changed.

The diagnoses listed throughout this book provide general, familiar and quick nosological classifications but do not reflect the view of the author or treatment at Creative Therapies. Interpretations herein are based on the author's years of experience, research and study. Nothing in this book is intended to be a substitute for medical evaluation and psychological treatment. The publisher and author are not providing professional recommendations. Nor are the publisher or author liable for any loss or damage allegedly arising from any information herein.

Published by Golden Tales Publishing Co., Greenwich, Connecticut

ISBN-10: 0-9860308-1-3
ISBN-13: 978-0-9860308-1- 9

Devoted to My Mum

A Door

A wise man from another land came to the shores of
America.
Over time, people brought their questions to him.

What is the secret to love?

"A doorrr" said the wise man in broken English.
"Then my door is solid and secure.
Smiled the happy newlywed.
"You mean love is like a door, that opens and closes and
sometimes revolves?"
Laughed the fickle teenager.
"A-doorrr" the wise man repeated, more slowly.
The divorcee exclaimed wearily.
"I have been staring at a closed door so long I see no
windows."
The widow, contemplated,
"My love is beyond the door."
The wise man looked warmly into the eyes of the
innocent child.
"A door," the child giggled.
"Adoor" childhood playfulness connected the words
together.
Adoration the child experienced in the soulful eyes of the
wise man."Ahhhhh!"
The interpreter bowed,
"The secret to love is adore:
May you regard one another with deep respect and great
esteem.

Table of Contents

*Note: When an asterisk precedes a word, that word is further detailed in the 'Glossary and Other Commentary' section. However, to prevent spoiling a developing plot or because it is not yet relevant, some words deliberately do not direct the reader to the end of the book at first use.

Table of Figures

Preface

As a psychotherapist, I enjoyed a fascinating, sometimes challenging, ever intriguing 30-year career. I was brought up in a reserved, quiet English household so I found the expression of feelings thrilling. It was spectacular that patients who knew little about me entrusted me with their innermost private thoughts and feelings that they would not share with another. Furthermore, it was riveting to work with them on their personal growth and witness their triumphs and transformations.

I invite you to join me in this retrospective series through the stages of my career from my young, early experiences of this first volume through to my seasoned years of later volumes. I share a psychotherapy story from every year of my career. Each chapter is a story of a different patient and each story becomes a piece of my journey, which parallels and sometimes intertwines with my colleagues and I.

These stories are based in truth. The hospitals and universities are intentionally not identified. Also, names have been changed, some people are composites, and dates and other details are altered to protect confidentiality.

I wish for this book to open hearts and raise consciousness by: encouraging communication skills; supporting young adults in expressing compassion; appealing to people entering or reconsidering therapy; providing lessons for psychology students and ideas for therapists; heartening more women to write their psychotherapy stories; and educating parents and other caregivers further.

Ultimately, may you be inspired.

Acknowledgments
Thank you God.

Thank you to my patients for entrusting me with their care. I cherish the time we have spent together. And to the families who have allowed me to draw from their files and authorized me to share their stories, pictures and other information to make these volumes possible.

Thank you to my husband, stepson and daughter for gracing my life, and teaching me the depths of love and commitment. For making me laugh every day and for keeping me humble by challenging my theories.

Thank you to Carol, my best friend, editor, sister by request, and godmother to my daughter. For your beautiful love, rare commitment and selfless service.

Thank you to my Mum and Dad for teaching, inspiring, and sacrificing for me. Ask anyone who knows them and they will tell you, my parents are the nicest people you will ever meet.

And, thank you to my friends and colleagues for contributing to the richness and joy of my life. For allowing me to share our stories and, in the process, educate and support others. For encouraging me through the years and times of our lives when I warned, "One day I am going to write about this!" It is a blessing and a privilege to know you and be known by you.

I appreciate you all with all my heart.

To prevent spoilers, some of my thank-yous are given by relationship, not name. You know who your are.

CHAPTER ONE, 30 YEARS AGO, 1987

The Magician Finds Her Magic Words

"Real isn't how you are made," said the Skin Horse. "It's a thing that happens to you. When a child loves you for along, long time, not just to play with, but REALLY loves you, then you become Real."

-Margery Williams
The Velveteen Rabbit

THEIR LOVE GOES WITH ME. I was saying goodbye to the patients at a mental health residential facility. I had volunteered there for years. I began reading self-help books at my neighbor's home when I was ten and started volunteering, helping people, beyond the school ground, at fourteen. Now at twenty-five, college-educated, I was driving off with tears in my eyes, waving goodbye with a small ivy root from the living room plant a patient had excitedly plucked for me. And I was wearing their gift to me, a necklace that dangled a beautiful, gold sun-charm.

They sweetly called out as they chased alongside my car, "Bye, Sunshine." I wondered if anyone would ever call me that again.

The following week I began my counseling job at the top psychiatric hospital in the country, or at least it was back then. After several months I was promoted to the Senior Psychiatric Counselor of their on-site halfway house, providing transitional living for patients discharged from psychiatric hospitals and addiction treatment facilities.

Mary, who had been an obese child, lost so much weight by the time she was eleven that she was diagnosed with Anorexia Nervosa, Early Onset. Now at age 17, and after her sixth hospitalization, she was coming to live with us. We were hoping to prevent the seventh.

We knew that people with Anorexia Nervosa can become desperate when they are required to eat more than their distorted body image, obsessive fear of fat and profoundly wounded heart and soul can tolerate. Often, they engage in compensatory behaviors. For Mary, during this first stay, it was her sleight of hand that was quicker than her chatter. She kept us amused and trusting while unbeknownst to us Mary dropped her thrice-daily snack of graham crackers into her half eaten yogurt container and hid her nightly dinner under her side of lettuce. Then she covered it all with her napkin and threw it out.

Before our very eyes, Mary kept losing weight while we were not gaining any information about how this could possibly be happening. We had lots of time together; we kept her out of the bathroom after meals; we increased her daily caloric intake (see Healthy Lifestyle Plan, Appendix A); and we observed her meals, snacks, medicine and amount of activity. We catered to developing our relationship with her and fed into her charm while she managed to go underfed. She was good at the illusion of compliance while we were the mystified audience unable to see how she had disappeared under 80 pounds. In less than one month, she was readmitted to the hospital.

On my own time, I wanted to visit Mary while we were waiting for her to 're-feed,' to reach her minimum required weight to transfer back to us. I imagined building a strong, genuine bond whereby she would become secure enough to actually want to stay with us rather than repeat her same ol' disconnected trick of disappearing weight and re-hospitalization.

Her doctor authorized my request to visit Mary regularly and asked to meet with me to become further acquainted. When I arrived at this doctor's office, unbeknownst to me, Mary was there. Dear Mary, who worked so hard to hold herself perfectly together, was scantily dressed and stiff in posture while being weighed. As is typical during 're-feeding,' Mary exhibited unusual excess weight in her upper arms and belly. In that moment, I saw a featherless little bird, stripped of all defenses. As she stepped off the scale, understandably self-conscious, the unexpected sound of the weights recalibrating sent her fluttering. I reflexively leaped forward to steady her, and she defensively raised trembling hands to block me.

I assured Mary of her safety and that I respected her privacy by clasping my hands together while looking towards the door. I intonated apologetically, "I…I will just go ahead and meet you out at our table in the common room."

As I walked toward the door, Mary's words invited my eye contact, "Don't tell." She glared at me hard, body rigid yet her words were soft, barely audible.

"I will leave it between you and your doctor," I said and walked out closing the door behind me. I stood there for a moment. I had this nagging feeling that we had inadvertently reenacted a violation. Further, this would imply the hospital's treatment plan, which is promulgated by diagnosis, was incorrect.

It was not the same circumstance, but my mind went to: A male teen, who had been hospitalized and diagnosed with Anorexia Nervosa. He kept removing his feeding tube, so he was tied down and force-fed to save his life. Only after a counselor, he had developed a meaningful relationship with, learned from the teen that he had been restrained and orally raped, was it obvious the treatment was a reenactment of that rape. Then the correct treatment and true healing could begin. Subsequently, the Primary Diagnosis was changed to Post Traumatic Stress Disorder (PTSD) with Anorexia Nervosa as the Condition-Induced Mental Disorder.

My mind came back to Mary, "Why was I permitted to go in there?" I berated myself as I walked into the common room. "I should not have gone in," but then that image of the little bird flew back in. Ah! If I had not been present at that weigh in I would not have seen how tiny or understood how scared Mary was. Magically, that little bird nestled in my awareness, reinforced my understanding of what Mary needed and informed her treatment plan for her growth, healing and eventual flight.

I also took that image of the bird into my daily practice, which included focusing my mind on each patient. This built intuition, *compassion and efficacy in the treatment of my patients. I cannot imagine serving without this routine.

Meditation is my *self-care, and nowadays it is as close to me as my awareness of my present moment breathing: Hamsa. It arises spontaneously from a natural vibration with the sound of 'Ham' upon the air of inhalation and 'sa' with exhalation.

Mary and I reconvened in the hospital common room. She arrived from the weigh-in mishap dressed in her androgynous baggy clothes, with her body hidden and feelings protected. Even her tightly pulled back hair in a perfect, ever present ponytail, revealed her need for control.

When I attempted to talk about what happened in her doctor's office she minimized the interaction. I wondered about this boundary as she returned to her ongoing guessing game of coping through drawing shapes of objects from the halfway house. However, I remained engaged, understanding that this distraction helped her clear her mind and take back the power she needed. As usual, I did not get a single shape correct and I suspect if I had, she would surely have changed what the object was.

That is when it occurred to me; her endless games were similar to my *EBIPS developmental research. I found I was also able to determine what age an adult was traumatized by how her presentation correlated with these child developmental findings. In other words,

Fixation in adulthood reveals the age of trauma in childhood.

Specifically, Mary was behaving like an eight-year-old with a constant desire to play games, make up rules and if losing, cheat to win.

I could see clearly now, Mary was stuck at age eight and, of course, this included her physical size. Now the task was for her to locate this trauma from that age. This was essential to her healing. However, this journey would have to be in her time, on her terms, to allow her full expression of feeling and for the hidden *True Self to be found.

Unfortunately, our time was up for the day. This is a moment where sometimes patients reveal a serious issue from which they can then 'escape' or receive 'special,' extra time. Mary persisted urgently with her game and the next shape she drew was an oval, followed shortly by a confession:

"The mirror in the foyer?" I guessed, while I continued to search for clues to other questions in my head.

"Nope" she smiled, and then slowly and precisely drew a line across the center of the oval.

"The divided tray at our din...?"

"...Nope..." she eagerly interrupted before my usual three failed guesses and revealed, "It's a Xaaaanax pill." I was struck again by her childlike appearance as she expressed with satisfaction and a smirk, "I got you again." Then she confided that every night when we had observed her taking this tablet, she did not swallow it, "I *cheeked it!"

She briefly gave me the details. I thanked her for telling me. I credited her with progress in lifting the veil between us. I reminded her that this was the type of information I must pass along to our medical director and her hospital doctor. Again, there it was, now that I was familiar what it looked like. I saw in the rigidity of her body the "Don't tell" cry, as if she expected me to collude with her.

I reassured her again before I said goodbye. Then I turned my attention to the concern that the sobriety of residents in recovery could have been jeopardized. My mind raced, *Wait, not just the residents in recovery, but all of them were vulnerable. What if one of them had found and taken or sold or, or was planning an overdose on the pills? Oh my God, I have got to find those pills.*

I casually walked out the common room door, closed it quietly and...bolted down the stairs. I ran down the bumpy lawn, past the tennis court, through the mud parking lot, across the grass and over the road. All the while, the uneven terrain made my speedy run awkward and connected my brain to the running skit I saw on television weekly during my childhood in England; The theme music to the Benny Hill Show. It was playing in my head and continued as I leaped onto the patient path, my body-sidestepped right "Pardon me," sidestepped left, "Sorry." I arrived at the halfway house, tripped up the stairs, ran directly to that office chair, huffing and puffing. And there just as Mary had described, tucked in the crevices of the therapy chair – barely hidden I might add – was the equivalent of her twenty-three nights with us, of schedule IV, controlled substance, Xanax.

Thankfully, every tablet was accounted for and I was relieved to know none of our residents had been compromised, but now Mary's return to us had been. I sat in with Mary's hospital doctor, while the Medical Director negotiated terms for her readmittance to our halfway house. The agreement had to assure Mary's safety and everyone else's as well. This serious matter took less than a minute to resolve. Their prescribed plan was to stop prescribing a prescription she did not comply with. They shook hands agreeing, "Problem solved."

Of course, Mary's transfer would happen only once she had reached the required minimum weight.

When I met back up with Mary in the hospital common room she was aflutter. She said, "You're in big trouble, you shouldn't have told our secret. You are hurting others and untrustworthy."

I found her perceived consequences to be revealing – though of what, I did not know. But what I did know is, Mary had a secret and to tell would distress the people she was keeping it from, expose the person she was keeping it with and sadly, she would see it as a betrayal of herself. We were close.

I explained the information was helpful to her treatment, I did not get in trouble and this her honesty would make us closer. I did not want to defend myself; rather I wanted to encourage her to remain genuine while at the same time experiencing she was accepted. I reassured her of my long-term commitment to her, her safety and her health. It took until our next visit for her to settle back into the trust and sweetness of our relationship.

As her weight continued to increase on the hospital regime and our bond strengthened with my regular visits, we discovered the crux of why she was truly afraid of gaining weight. It happened when we were the only two visiting in the hospital common room. We found it as a missing memory when we unlocked the magician's code of symbols.

Mary volunteered, "I have this recurring dream." She said as if I had earned a gift, "Do you want to hear it?"

I was thinking,

Yes, yes, of course yes!

But, my therapeutic task was to allow her to "tell" on her own terms and not because she was given permission. So I put it back upon her casually. "If you would like to," I responded.

She stalled, "Well, it's not like any of the usual

recurring dreams that tell me about my emotions like the naked in public one when I'm feeling vulnerable, the missed my course but have to take the exam when I'm unprepared for life or the being chased when I'm anxious."

She had clearly been reading up on the meaning of dreams.

"It's more like a memory is awakening. I am walking to the house we lived in when I was a kid. When I wake up that is all I can remember."

It was time. "Sit back, close your eyes and inhale deeply, making the sound Hammmm." After she did that I instructed, "exhale long to the sound of Sssaaa… Continue, Ham…sa." I spoke knowing that as her visitor I should not have been pursing a treatment.

Her eyelids flickered just like in REM sleep when the eyes are rolled upward. She seemed settled in and far away. On her next outbreath, instead of "sa" she said, "Sssooo. I am walking to my old house…" she repeated. Then her lips kept moving, no sound came out.

I whispered, "Take another deep breath" to encourage her stifled words on the next exhale. My laconic encouragement and her feelings of safety with me, kept her in a relaxed, cooperative, available state.

Her story changed significantly with the addition of just one more word, inhale "Haaam" exhale, "Ssaa, I'm walking to my old house with…with…"

I observed the same behavior as she attempted to continue and no sound came out.

"Again," I encouraged.

Inhale, exhale, "I'm walking to my old house with Mr. Jim…I can't…I can't…"

This was followed by a long silence, other than the sound of her Hamsa breathing. I intentionally did not interrupt.

"I can't…" her eyes were flickering underneath her closed lids accessing a memory.

"I-I can't…" Then with a burst of energy, she exclaimed, "I can't tell my dad."

"You can now," I spoke authoritatively, overriding the "don't tell" voice of her past.

"Mr. Jim squeezed my boobies," she revealed with the immature language and upset facial expression of a younger self. This denunciation escaped faster than her hands could cover her mouth and swallow the words.

She moved her hands down exposing her tightly closed lips. She felt her chest of skin and bones. She remained frozen in this position.

"Use your words and tell him, 'No!' " I said strongly.

She yelled, "No!"

I waved to the RJ the security to communicate, "All is well."

"Push Mr. Jim away," I said to Mary, encouraging movement and a sense of power.

Eyes still closed, she thrust her arms forward.

I proceeded, "Tell your dad."

She opened her eyes and jumped up.

"Wait," I said, "what, what is happening?"

"I'm gonna tell my dad," she said pointing at the pay phone, assuming I had meant literally. "Mr. Jim said, he trusted me to keep our secret and don't tell or it would hurt my dad and we'd be in big trouble. That's ridiculous."

I can still see the way she said, "ridiculous" today. Before my eyes, she matured her body softened and her words flowed strong. Her adult self understood how preposterous the threat was.

"Oh, okay. I, I will wait here" I said excited about the suddèn potential of this recollection to support her true healing. "Then Mary, we will go back in and tell your doctor," I said reinforcing the tell while ironically uncertain of the big trouble I was in for pursuing this, in the hospital common room, no less.

I could hear Mary talking to her father on the nearby pay phone. From what I could tell, he was endorsing the legitimacy of his daughter's recollection. A parent's belief is an essential quality, critical to the healing process. Through tears she asked her father if he still loved her and from her relaxed body language I could tell he had reassured her. The two of them progressed to a loud, relationship-transforming discussion, bonding on how angry they both were and how disgraceful Mr. Jim was.

After the call we went to tell Mary's doctor. We came to understand that after the sexual assault, this 'don't tell' threat resulted in an unconscious, self-protection whereby she closed her mouth and was no longer able to tell or to eat. Over time she lost her obese, budding third-grade body and the traumatic memory. In other words, Mary had without awareness she emaciated her full figure so that she would never be desired, never be touched and never be violated again and did not remember why.

The repressed memory had been decoded. Only with this recollection did Mary's presentation make sense. Now Mary's not eating, not maintaining weight and not maturing were able be treated from the root cause. This provided her with the most accurate and effective treatment plan for her true healing journey. The strengthening of her ego was underlined and a new treatment plan outlined.

Unhealthy behaviors were now disappearing. I knew the eating-disordered thinking was healing when Mary's 'tell' of continually burning extra calories disappeared: Mary stopped chewing gum. While this might not sound like much, at approximately ten calories per hour and 5 hours a day of chewing, she could burn an additional 1500 calories a month, for the loss of another two-thirds of a pound minus half an hour, daily, for the five calories in the sugar-free gum. I share that, recognizing just as patients take on our positive qualities as well as our idiosyncrasies, we take on theirs. I told Mary, for example, through our time together, I had at times admired, been challenged by or had absorbed her 'attention to detail' skills.

As we laughed and because she had trained me well, I suddenly wondered, *"Hey, how many calories does laughter burn?"*

At this point in her care, delighted by my disclosure, ready to heal and encouraged by our bond she told me more of her food tricks. She said she used to cut English muffins in horizontal thirds and throw out the middle part, spend most of dinnertime moving the food around her plate rather than eating it and replaced our house cheese with a low calorie imitation cheese that she had purchased on a walk to the local country store.

Next, I was excited for her to transfer this energy and intelligence into her new interest to attend a local university. We were now counting up pounds and down days until she could be discharged from the hospital and back to our halfway house for her yearlong stay.

It was a gorgeous, early summer day, as Wordsworth famously wrote, "of splendour in the grass, of glory in the flower." During my break, I took my final walk over to see Mary. However, I didn't go inside the hospital because an excited Mary and her eager father had already packed up his sports car, with the exception of the gift he gave her when she was readmitted to the hospital this past time.

I greeted them with, "Am I too late to help?"

"Hi" Mary beamed, "would it be okay if you carried this across campus for me?" she pointed. Mary's endless games were maturing into a relaxed playfulness. She was secure, letting down her defenses, and allowing herself to be seen as less than perfect. As she was willing to be vulnerable she became more authentic, real.

"You want it at our halfway house?" I clarified, as if surely, there was a different plan happening.

"There's no room in the car, would you?" she pressed on, surrounded by her childish possessions while addressing me with her maturing assertiveness skills.

"Sure" was all I uttered. But I wondered, *am I the only one who saw the paradox of this gift?*

As they drove off, Mary looked back and called out with a huge smile, "See you at home."

And then I picked it up: the huge, honey-colored, stuffed toy animal with the big, red, silk bow. I kept thinking, "Surely, this big-bellied bear was metaphorically the wrong gift for someone hospitalized with a fear of fat and the diagnosis of Anorexia Nervosa. "Well," I grinned and galumphed, "we've got a year of work ahead of us."

This was the beginning of my relationship with Graham, named after Mary's crackers. Graham and I began our journey with the warm sun high in the sky and the short shadow of the afternoon visible. Graham's giant body obstructed my view and his smiling face, like Mary's, looked back on where he had been. I wanted to be at the halfway house to welcome them. I waddled and he wobbled as we made our way as fast as I could manage, down the lawn, past the tennis court… And as a result of how memories connect in related sensations, emotions, thoughts and images, the same Benny Hill theme song, began anew…

PART TWO, Ten Months Later
"Will You Still Love Me If…?"

MARY CAME HOME WITH A GREAT DANE. According to her countdown, it was 40 days before her discharge from our halfway house that had been her home for the past year. This several weeks prior to discharge was a vulnerable, testing time seen in many graduating residents. So, we discussed this in anticipation, and guessed her test would be around the theme, "Will you still love me if…?"

Sure enough, my following shift, she returned from the Humane Society with an underfed Great Dane named Scooby.

Typically, we recommend to our graduating patients, start with a plant.

I appreciated that Mary was establishing a new bond in preparation for a secure transition to her next home. Graham had been Mary's transitional object into the hospital. I was her transitional object out of the hospital. And now Scooby was taking over. Scooby was my warm, fuzzy, flea infested, replacement! Interestingly,

The roles reversed

as Mary was now the caregiver refeeding her patient, Scooby.

But had she compromised her stay? We discussed therapeutically, how she had tested our relationship, boundaries, conditions and then… Well, we had never had an animal at our halfway house. It was so far-fetched we didn't even have a policy about it, so without skipping another heartbeat, not to mention without getting permission, we welcomed Scooby. We embraced him with our open arms and tasty kitchen delectables including real cheese. We loved this rescued dog and he loved and rescued us right back. And now indubitably, it was doubly hard to say goodbye to Mary.

On Mary's last day with us, she wanted to play one more memory game with me. Now that her memory was free from the 'Don't tell' message, she was able to recall a beautiful memory from each year of her life, from standing in her crib to standing before me, present day, in a time before cell phones held our memories. It was remarkable how her mind had opened and her intellect had expanded since she was no longer spending energy blocking out the recollection of a violation.

With her *graduation letter, I gave her the book, *The Velveteen Rabbit*, a story about a bunny that was loved so much she became real.

Mary then offered me Graham, her giant, overstuffed bear, who as a sign of her maturation had moved Graham from her bedroom to our living room many months ago. "I've outgrown him," she said proudly.

"Thank you, Mary, Graham will be loved so much."

Funny, as much as I had not wanted Graham to come along a year ago, he would now be with me for many years. I took him to my play therapy rooms, where we had an eventful and most wonderful long-term relationship….

And then, Mary and I began her 'Days of Health' count up.

Nowadays Addendum - 2018

Mary moved into a nearby apartment with another graduate from the halfway house. She came to visit less and less over time. She went on to complete her under graduated degree locally then moved back, near her hometown, to pursue her doctorate.

Mary is now a middle-aged psychologist. She still sends an annual family holiday card, a request I have of all my graduates. Her photos and notes are evidence of a healthy, happy woman with an affectionate husband, two large healthy dogs and three snuggly sons. She is soon to have her own empty nest. Sometimes just for fun, she continues the 'count up,' – today is 11,222. In homage to Mary, I wrote this book, one story from every year of my career, 'counting up.'

CHAPTER TWO, 29 YEARS AGO, 1988

A Call for Compassionate Inclusion: On-the-Spectrum-of-Perception

We can't help everyone, but everyone can help someone.
-Ronald Reagan

W*HAT DID I LEARN FROM A PATIENT IN A YEAR?"*

I would explore this question in my journaling, before the end of each graduating patient's one-year stay at our halfway house. I loved this inquiry and how it inspired my writing of their graduation letters. This letter would include their ups and downs, inspired moments, healing lessons, and more from their brave and adventurous journey that I felt blessed to be a part of.

"What did I learn in the first session?"
I learned to

Be still
to awaken a deeper awareness.

I learned to mostly listen, and to observe casually yet closely our incoming patients. I was discovering a fascinating non-verbal world. I saw that:

When people described a traumatic event, their eyes flickered at the detail that overwhelmed them most.

I called this, "*point of trauma." This showed me just where to go in the treatment.

I noticed excess salivation in eating disordered patients expressing an urge to binge. This taught me to talk further with residents in recovery who displayed this while requesting to leave the premises, for example to, "Oh, just go for a drive."

Which brings up what I found most intriguing; observations of patients as they lie. The task was to see the duplicity of the protective *False Self and use this knowledge to help guide patients back to their True Self. The right-hand dominant person entering treatment for alcoholism looked up and to his creative right brain to devise a lie about his drinking. Those who were not telling the truth experienced itchy sensations on their face then their fingers scratched at their suddenly itchy Pinocchio noses or men rubbed their eyes vigorously, women more gently as if to block out the brain's truth telling view. The constantly moving patients went still when lying while the still patients moved. Some stared beyond what would be considered a normal length of time, others fake coughed as if to clear their lying words and/or cover their mouth to not let the deceptive words escape. Of course, reflexes like sudden sweat and heavy breathing are noted. The feet would start moving as if to communicate, "Let's get out of here."

The body tells the truth.

The observations were riveting and I used these body confessions as 'tells' to help patients get healthy, but not by revealing how I knew. If I told them how I knew that would actually train them to become better liars and next time they would deliberately control that impulse.

I challenged myself by completing first visits with incoming patients before reading their hospital file so I could meet them with fresh eyes. Sometimes, I would make observations and possible interpretations not in their file: a scar on the middle finger knuckle from teeth (self-induced vomiting) with the top of that same finger being wrinkled or discolored from the acid; fast movements towards oneself (self harm); or movement, touching, or tapping rituals (in response to obsessions and compulsions).

It was all there and I was interested in it all. How they acted, what they thought, how they walked, looked, talked, what they said and did not say, it went on. I had found my life's calling. Of course, this passion was complicated on another level, yet relevant to their best care, as it was also easy to see the patient's starry-eyed crushes from confiding their private world and receiving care from a genuinely interested counselor who was around their age.

"What did I learn in the first few seconds of meeting a patient?"

Now this was fun, wonderfully inspiring and fine-tuned my senses. I learned in that very first moment when I initially meet a patient, I see with greater accuracy. For example: at first glance, we can catch the slightly off body dimensions of the undernourished teen compromised by long-term starving herself; the asymmetrical facial features such as the hidden in plain sight sad side of the face, a startled eye or a raised eyebrow of doubt. Then we blink and these imbalances self-correct. After a while, I learned to spend the first few seconds systematically scanning a patient from what I called, 'toe to head.' I did not use 'head to toe' because scanning the body after eye contact makes a person feel judged. So, I proceeded with 'toe to head,' wide-eyed, to delay my blinking and enhance my scanning time while hopefully not seeming too wild or giving away too much off my own *slate.

From there, I furthered my exploration by going over to the hospital to introduce myself to new patients, see their rooms and welcome them before their transfer to our halfway house. My observations included these possible interpretations: undeveloped hands (developmental delays); dry, cracked hands (repetitive hand washing/fear of germs); acne (rage); slumped posture (poor self-esteem); cartoon posters on walls (formal education too young/anxiety); methodically arranged room (obsessive-compulsive), drawn on eyebrows (hair pulling) and the list went on. The more I worked on these skills and discovered what to pay attention to, the better my accuracy and the greater my intuition developed. This was reinforced by the good fortune of receiving confirmation from the patients, doctors and, of course, the records.

The other half of my week, when I was not working at the halfway house, I attended a nearby university for my master's degree in Clinical Psychology. It was concerning, and not unusual at the hospital and at the university, to hear of a wide range of mental health concerns amongst the staff and at the expense of patients and students, respectively. This included the misuse of power, a lack of responsibility, hiding behind antiquated mores, insensitive dark humor, and narcissism that ran far and wide.

My classmates and I had a particularly difficult time with one of the thesis board professors, Dr. Karp. Though we appreciated his expertise overseeing the analysis of our data, we dreaded asking for his signature of approval for room assignments, changes in the number of participants, extended due dates and such. The rumor was this tenured professor's social awkwardness was diagnosable as what is now called, *Autism Spectrum Disorder.

We noted Dr. Karp's 'Yes' or 'No' responses correlated with the kind of day he was having. His decline

ed triggered more by an excess of
stimulation than by how reasonable

d a plan to gauge his agreeability by
iate to assess him. We used my, *"What did you ...* *e first few seconds?"* and the *SOAP standardized method (Subjective, Objective, Assessment and Plan) of note taking, which includes thoughts, observations, concerns, steps of treatment and a plan. This style of clinical note taking also includes patient quotes.

This time we were sending in my dear friend, Davisman. When he returned to the hallway from the task of assessing Dr. Karp's amenability to authorize those quick approvals, we gathered around him. "Okay, SOAP us," we asked with bated breath.

Davisman proceeded, "He's laughing loudly, amusing himself with those word plays and he's 'Running-the-Spectrum-and-on-it too.'"

"That's a 'play on words' yourself there Davisman." I lightheartedly called him out.

He smiled at me sarcastically and continued to the group, " 'Annnnnyyywaaaay,' he's unpredictable today. You know he actually said to me, 'Boy-you-annoy.'"

"Jesus, Davisman, what you do?" said our Spanish classmate we fondly called, 'The Boy Named Sue.' "You no touch him? He hate that."

"Of course I didn't touch him. Okay shit, I might have. Well, no problem that just reinforced the Plan: Do not go in there; do not make any requests" and for effect he added, "and no sudden moves. The Plan is: Shhh! Walk away slowly."

So we all turned, screamed and ran.

Occasionally though, Dr. Karp's mood went in our favor. For example, one time when I was the 'designated examiner,' I came out of his office and informed my classmates: "He turned towards me, made eye contact, seemed agreeable enough, and greeted me by name. Your wish is as good as granted. The Plan is go in, speak softly, ask a 'yes' question, get his signature and get out."

The line formed outside his door.

Another day when I required a signature, and just Davisman and I were around, he offered to evaluate Dr. Karp for me. Davisman returned from Dr. Karp's office a little too quickly and gave me the thumbs up with a nod. He bowed and with an arm-welcoming gesture inviting me through Dr. Karp's threshold.

Now Davisman was a wonderful man, older than us, divorced with an 8-year old daughter, and would go on to become a brilliant medical doctor but he never got over the fact that I was awarded top diagnostician in our class. So, consequently, he competed, challenged and bickered with me. (I read this to him in the present day and he interjected right here, "No, I don't!").

I knocked on Dr. Karp's open door and walked in, strategically leaving it open for a possible quick escape. "Excuse me, Dr. Karp, may I have…"

"…Jellybeans?" He said loudly, bursting forth from the corner of the room. He held out a small round glass bowl, bumped into his desk and kept coming. All I could see were the predominantly black licorice jellybeans moving rapidly towards me.

"Oh? Oh, yes, please" I replied, wanting to be gracious. They were those nasty tasting, vintage (well, nowadays considered vintage), big jellybeans, which came in just a few colors. I dove my hand in, fished for a white jellybean, hoping it would be the most plain on my picky palette, netted it in my mouth and garbled, "Mm, thank you." I nodded. Then, because engaging Dr. Karp in conversation was not only difficult but also risky, I said, "So, about my thesis…"

"You just took one-plain-one, one-plain-one. You don't like all the colors-Cooper?" He stated loudly, "You're-disfavoring-flavoring!" Jellybean spit was accumulating at the corners of his mouth as he soothed himself, repeating "Disfavoring-flavoring, disfavoring-flavoring."

Oh Boy, I thought to myself, *wait till I get my sticky hands on you Davisman.*

"Actually, Thir," I lisp trying not to chew the offensive jellybean while planning its exit and mine, "I-I just took one to be polite, but I-I need water. I will Thop back later." I exited his office fast, closed the door between us slowly, and just as I turned to run off, there was Davisman. He had been eavesdropping and was laughing to himself. I playfully stuck my white colored tongue out at him revealing the disgusting jellybean laying on it. It began to fall out and I panicked, sucked it back in and to my dismay, I swallowed it whole. As I ran off Davisman laughed progressively louder.

While washing my tongue in the hallway water fountain Ronnie, one of the other students in our class, who told everybody everything, walked by. She looked at me with judgment, specifically, intolerance. It was just for a second, but I felt it and it did not feel good. There, as I rinsed my tongue again, I concluded that we students, all of us going into caregiving professions, must develop '*Compassionate Strategies of Inclusion,' beginning with Dr. Karp.

After classes, my unlikely comrades and I went to our usual late 'Thursday Night - Thesis Group Meeting' dinner. We were working on various graduate degrees with some overlapping classes and all required to write a thesis. Though we have often told stories of how we would have found one another anyway, we are forever grateful to Dr. Karp for matching us up. He had organized our class alphabetically and in tables of three, Hulk, Davisman and I. He had one student left over, an intimidating looking male with a female name. To this day the story is told that it was because everyone else was looking down that Dr. Karp circled back to me.

"You!" Dr. Karp pointed. "You-take-the-boy-named-Sue–sue-me."

Davisman made a face at me, as if to say, *this is your fault.*

The Boy Named Sue is a song written by the poet Shel Silverstein. This instantly became his official nickname, as rumor had it; his own history was similar to that song's story. The Boy Named Sue silently walked over to our table and dropped his belongings down. They spilled around him.

"What's with all the envelopes?" Davisman asked him, trying to make small talk but coming across judgmental.

"None your business," grumbled the 'Boy Named Sue' tightening his long, curly ponytail.

Hulk and I eyed one another and then turned towards 'The Boy Named-Sue.' We tried to smile and he attempted to smile back. Good enough.

Soon Davisman, Hulk, 'The Boy Named Sue' and I, became known as the "Four Musketeers," perhaps nicknamed because we were inseparable…but there could be other explanations.

Now, the four of us were sitting at our weekly dinner. While I picked at my dressing-less salad, I told them, "Dr. Karp was right, I do 'disfavor-flavor.' I have been brought up on bland cooking and, as a matter of fact, yes; I am 'disfavoring-flavoring.' Pass me the dressing!"

Davisman slid over the whole daunting tray of condiments, "Hey Jules," he laughed, *"Do you need wah-ta?"* This relentless joke, combining my barely audible British accent with what he called the 'Jules Jellybean Incident' did not get a laugh from me. Not then or for the next 29 years.

I interrupted, "I've got an idea, an Inclusion Plan…"

Davisman looked at me. I could not read him the way I read others. This appealed to me. His sparkling, penetrating, green eyes, like his behavior, gave off the conflicting impression of boyish insouciance and deep intensity. Then, in a cross between a disagreeable rebuttal and an agreeable advocate, he said, "Well, bland Cooper, tell us your wild plan."

"I think we'd be more successful, lest I mention" I leaned in "respectful," if we change our perception of Dr. Karp from this limited, inconsistent professor that the students have diagnosed 'On-the-Spectrum,' to meeting him where he is…"

I was met with a chorus initiated by Davisman. "How?" he sang.

"How?" Hulk chimed in laughing.

And "How," The Boy Named Sue sang gruffly as if obligated. He looked a little nervous.

As if the fourth member of a quartet, I harmonized, "In our hearts where compassion embraces judgment and encourages understanding to seep in.

"Tell us Coopermeister," Hulk encouraged, exposing a mouth full of greens. Hulk was adorable, dressed well and worked out every free moment. He was easy to talk to and had lots of girlfriends, but I just couldn't get over the way he chewed his food…. I noted this while ironically vouching for his and their non-judgment.

"Dr. Karp's just trying to connect with us with his wordplays and, ok, little truths." I gave Davisman an exaggerated wink and continued, "I think an *entry point into his world is though particular interest in jellybeans…I…am…going…in."

"I think you might be sugar coating this a bit, Jules."

"I hear you, so you Musketeers can be on hallway back up. If it goes sour, by all means, come on in. One for all and all four for one." I raised my glass.

'The Boy Named Sue,' who had told us he did not drink alcohol anymore, took off his spectacles and clinked my glass. Then we all clunked glasses together and shouted, "One for all and all four for one."

They were in.

Davisman threw back another shot of his homeland Irish whiskey and chased it with another beer and no further words.

The following week I returned to Dr. Karp's office and ignored the telltale warning sign, 'no line outside his door.' I noticed I was a little sweaty. I knocked and stepped in, "Dr. Karp?" He jumped. I jumped.

"In the interest of developing my 'favoring-for-flavoring,' I brought us lunch," I said, having rehearsed it many times.

I tilted the brown bag and his head tilted in imitation, and then out slid the box.

He clapped his hands and burst out laughing. It was an unnatural sounding roar that ordinarily cast us away. Now that I was listening to him without a clinical *label I could hear the sound of sluggish karmic forces blocking his potential.

What I had brought was a gift box filled with trays organizing 40 different flavors and colors of Jelly Beans.

He was smiling from ear to ear, "You know what Ronnie said?"

"No Sir. I am thinking, *God knows what Ronnie had said now and what she would say to everyone later.*

Dr. Karp continued, "He said.

"He, Sir?" I gently, though now that I think about it, boldly, interrupted.

"The President of the United States…" he said maniacally.

I was beginning to think, *this was a bad idea.*

I shrunk away from his intensity. He ignored this non-verbal communication. *Oh! Of course,* I soothed myself; *he does not connect my body language to my emotion.*

Dr. Karp went on to tell how Ronnie Reagan loved jellybeans. He quoted President Reagan,

> "You could tell a lot about a fella's character by whether he picked out all of one color or just grabbed a handful."

"Brilliant!" I exclaimed. "Let us make our own 'Jelly Bean Personality Test' for your visitors."

He snorted.

I proceeded, feeling a connection had been made and together we developed our own 'P for Plan.'

Shortly thereafter, when I walked out of Dr. Karp's office, there they all were, the Musketeers ready to come to my rescue, if needed. This memory of them standing there, loyal and protective is one of my favorite images of them together.

As we walked across the quad, Hulk right behind

doing 'walking lunges,' I filled them in. They were mystified, shocked and maybe a little impressed, though Davisman would never admit any of that.

Over the remainder of the term I joined Dr. Karp during his Thursday office hours for 'Jelly Bean Late Lunches.' I developed my taste buds for a variety of flavors. Dr. Karp noticed I had a growing "expansivity of creativity" based on my advancement to gourmet blending of two jellybeans at a time. I created flavors such as piña-colada, chocolate-banana pie, and apple-cinnamon tea. He also found my rescuing of jellybeans that were stuck together or in some other way not like the others, "a good ration of compassion."

We invited each visitor coming in for a 'signature of approval' to also make a jellybean selection and if they wanted to ask Dr. Karp what it meant about his or her personality. It was a hit! Whereas previously, students had been intimidated to come into his office, now students and even faculty were enjoying receiving Dr. Karp's sweet, quirky, and remarkably accurate observations.

Well, except for Davisman, who from the spectrum of jellybeans, selected every time the same treat that was both a candy and a drink: the gold jellybean that was named, Irish Crème. Dr. Karp's assessments of Davisman's selection were tuned in, penetrating, but atypically not sweet. He told Davisman:

"Two treats in one, a too-conflicted one," and the second time "Drinking sours, sweet thinking."

Davisman shot Dr. Karp a defiant look, took a handful of Irish Crème jellybeans, leaned in a little too close, popped them in his mouth and left with the signature he had come for.

And then there was Davisman's famous third and final 'Jellybean Test' when Dr. Karp recited,

"It's hard to be the favored one, your parents' praised 'Golden Child.' You lack insight, esteem, have jealousy and get feasibly, easily riled."

Wow I thought. *Did he just make that up on the spot?*

It was impressive and accurate about the challenges of a 'favored child,' and of course, of Davisman. Dr. Karp even had the color of the jellybean represented.

But that was it! The be-all and end-all. We didn't know what the issue between them was, but 'The Dr. Karp and Davisman Game' was over. This moment went down in our shared university history as "Bad Boyo's Limit."

I remember this was also the turning point in my development of more understanding for Ronnie. It began with Dr. Karp's response to her selection of the Sour Cherry jellybean.

"When you plant judgment, you feel safe, but it's your own cherry tree flower that will sour."

Over time Ronnie systematically took one of every jellybean and each time Dr. Karp's responses was specific and poignant to her. Through the process, the essence of her "Karpisms" conveyed that really underneath all her gossiping, she was hurting and just wanted to be included and liked by each one of us.

Students now lined up outside his office more often with less fear while Dr. Karp became interested, involved and extremely helpful in our research with few refusals of our requests. As people became more accepting and even enjoying what they used to call 'his peculiarities,' Dr. Karp became less insecure, though never quite relaxed.

Along our way, I apologized to Dr. Karp for how I perceived him through a label before I knew him.

He smiled his very large smile, "It's okay Brave Heart, we all rolled according to our roles."

He added, he knew he was a "ball of odd, oddball."

"And a genius mathematician" I added, which was also absolutely true.

He snorted this force of breath, which I had come to adore. I understood now, he only made this sound when he was very happy.

I elaborated on how helpful he was in scrutinizing our data samples. I appreciated his great interest in numbers and his intense focus on accuracy. I wondered out loud if I in return could help him relax more with us. From the discussion that ensued I made him a sign that we posted only during his office hours,

Voices: Low

Movements: Slow.

After he viewed the sign, Dr. Karp had an epiphany: his own behavior was opposite from these needs. This sudden realization created no evident anxiety, guilt or shame, and seemingly no inner transformation either. However, this solution allowed groups of two or three students to come into his office, provided they honored the sign.

The inclusion of all had grown into a graduate thesis student family, except Dr. Karp was no longer the *identified patient.

We advanced our 'personality test': visitors were to assess their own jellybean selection. This activity in the group environment encouraged students to open up to one another, which stimulated our natural caregiving inclination to be supportive, and we grew close as a class. We're still in contact to this day.

Then Dr. Karp began reflecting our inclusion strategy back. He invited a student to join us who, who like he used to be, was eating alone. The following day, I atypically arranged to see Dr. Karp. While I was eagerly awaiting his arrival outside his office door, I overheard (admittedly I did not stop myself) his answering machine pick up. It was the mother of that student yesterday expressing her gratitude for Dr. Karp.

> "If each of us did just one compassionate act a day, our society, as a whole, would be happier and healthier."

And underlying her beautiful message was another truth: Compassion aids the wellbeing of the receiver as well as the giver.

When Dr. Karp arrived outside his door he was not wearing his usual blue polyester, 70's leisure suit. Dr. Karp you're wearing a different suit."

"Green suit Friday."

"Dr. Karp, you have more than one suit?"

"Gray suit Monday, black suit Tuesday, maroon suit Wednesday, blue suit Thursday, green suit Friday," he recited.

"Well you look very smart in green as well. Would you consider mixing it up so our class could see you in another color other than blue on Thursdays?"

He stared into the distance, tilted his head and matter-of-factly said, "No." He unlocked his office door and walked in.

Over time, Dr. Karp's had authorized my thesis, *Childhood Sexual Abuse Antecedent to Eating Disorders*, to become a large project, expanding to 100 female participants. I would have included men, but there were so few who came forward at that time in history. Dr. Karp was remarkably supportive with this project, thoughtful in his recommendations and wonderfully generous with his time. I went on to dedicate my thesis, to him acknowledging that it would not have reached nationwide acclaim without his contributions.

And over that school year, we came to genuinely met Dr. Karp where he was, managed feelings, solved problems, and improved behavior patterns. Through our approach, we all changed for the better, just as what happens in any good doctor/patient psychotherapy experience.

Meanwhile, "Ronnie" Reagan, after 7 years of complimentary Jelly Bean deliveries to the White House, in this, his final year of office, decided he preferred M&M's.

When I graduated, I went to Dr. Karp's office for a final goodbye. I read him the note of appreciation I wrote him and gave him a sign I had painted of "Ronnie" Reagan's jellybean quote.

He glanced around his cluttered office. "Here." He grabbed the fish bowl glass with its sugar-encrusted remnants from the old, big jellybeans it once contained. He turned it upside down on my head.

"Thanks," I laughed. He snorted. "I crown you most likely to help most."

And that one time ever, he hugged me.

Over the years, Dr. Karp went on to realize his own dreams by publishing his work with the assistance of his graduate students. Then, in the year 2000, Dr. Karp retired. Thankfully, he would not have to experience the Harry Potter/Bertie Bott's Every Flavor Beans that arrived that year on the Jelly Bean market. The flavors included soap, dirt, earwax, booger, rotten egg, skunk spray, and vomit.

Addendum - The Power of Perception and Forgiveness

It is not what you eat,
it is what is eating you.

"And *what did I learn from my thesis?"*
In my study, *Childhood Sexual Abuse Antecedent to Eating Disorders*, I learned from the participants who shared deeply personal experiences, that their childhood sexual traumas were followed by significant eating issues. These issues extended beyond their relationship with diet, weight, and body image.

There were many variables that contributed to the degree of the trauma in childhood sexual abuse, such as the familiarity of the perpetrator; single or multiple incidents; whether the child was believed; if the parent(s) were supportive; if the care was immediate; and, of course, if the diagnosis was correct and the treatment effective. The hypothesis was that the degree of sexual abuse would correlate with the severity of the eating disorder. In actuality, my research found that

The severity of a woman's perception of the sexual abuse is determined how acute the subsequent eating disorder was.

This faculty of perception, which creates our reality, is developed through many of life's influences, such as genetics, interpretation from culture and appraisal based on early conditioning and life experiences. However, this faculty is open to change, growth and healing with good psychotherapy treatment.

Another interesting discovery, though beyond the scope of my study, was the controversial question of forgiving the abuser. This was a greatly misunderstood, highly volatile topic amongst the participants. To be clear, this difficult, often confusing work of forgiveness was not, in any way, for the sake of the abuser.

The process of forgiveness does not mean to betray oneself. It does not mean to forget, pretend, or accept but rather to free oneself from bitterness, rage, and revenge. Rather, to explore the painful experiences, seek soulful transformations and stop ingesting the toxic hatred that poisons insight and harms compassion. After all, the outrage from the past, while directed at the abuser, has no effect on that person, while the outrage, hatred and suppressed anger, internally, continues to hurt the abused. The goal of forgiveness is to release the weight of resentment, cry about the pain, and let go to advance to a freedom where self-acceptance, peace, happiness and gratitude for life exists, and a brightest, best life is possible.

However, only a few participants in my study had accomplished this delicate therapeutic goal. Those who did succeed had undergone over two years of this work with psychotherapists they described as feeling very connected to. Furthermore, and importantly, these same women reported a greater sense of general health, stronger immune systems, less stress, decreased depression, reduced hostility, better self-esteem, healthier relationships, a deeper capacity to love, and a stronger connection to spirit.

When you cannot forgive - pray.
Pray for yourself and
pray for the other.

-Suelita

My research was only the tip of the iceberg. Vincent Felitti, MD et al. (1998), released a study entitled, *Relationship of Childhood Abuse and Household Dysfunction to Many of the Leading Causes of Death in Adults.* Their conclusion was "a strong graded relationship between the breadth of exposure to abuse or household dysfunction during childhood and multiple risk factors for several of the leading causes of death in adults." The *Adverse Childhood Experiences (ACE) test is available online.

Also poignant was Shonkoff, J. et al (2012), *The lifelong effects of early childhood adversity and toxic stress.* This research demonstrated a lasting signature affecting brain architecture and predisposing one to chronic health problems and early death. This understanding explains why many diseases should be viewed through a developmental lens.

Of course, good psychotherapeutic treatment decreases the vulnerability to these reported outcomes.

CHAPTER THREE, 28 YEARS AGO, 1989

Who Put the Cover on the "No Trifle Matter"?

Never, never, never give up.

-Winston Churchill

3 AM: KNOCK...KNOCK, KNOCK, KNOCK. I awoke to this rare occurrence. I was in the counselor's overnight room, during my Sunday to Wednesday shift at the psychiatric halfway house. I jumped up, leaped to the door, and as I was opening it heard… "I can't stop thinking about killing myself," 19-year-old Sue greeted me. We talked for a few minutes, and according to protocol, I phoned her medical doctor, Kolten. I requested Sue's re-hospitalization, anticipating Kolten's intolerance for this mandated call.

With his tragic dismissal of his own patient's needs, Kolten responded with his usual sarcasm and lack of compassion. He snapped, "Congratulations, you've just been Borderlined."

First of all, "Borderlined" no such word. Borderline

Personality Disorder (BPD) is a disorder with such a bad reputation that it will have to be renamed. BPD is an ongoing instability in mood, behavior, self-image and functioning: A diagnosis that Kolten never gave her and Sue never had.

His dismissive, irresponsible words reverberated, "Congratulations, you've just been Borderlined."

And no pat on the back for you Kolten for being a narcissist, I did not say, but in my mind where his words repeated many times I tried out an equal number of retorts.

After this phone call to Kolten, I SOAPed my brief exchange with him and imagined he had easily fallen back to sleep. My comfort level, however, was different; I would remain with Sue until she went to the hospital's Day Program. Then I would meet with the Halfway House director – who would surely authorize her rehospitalization. Sue and I stayed up, talking, and eventually we enjoyed the beauty of a new day rising.

At this point, we were laughing as we recalled the evening when she was assigned the rotating position of the house chef, and she proudly cooked us a dinner from her Southern heritage, which included an okra side dish. She loved my confession of how slimy and unappetizing the okra looked to me, and she appreciated how I wanted to protect her feelings so I hid it under my lettuce.

She then declared she didn't like okra either. We laughed with comfort and ease in that sunrise moment where everything glowed and all seemed well.

Having recently taken to flavors and cooking myself, our 'okra confessions' gave me a therapeutic idea. I told her I would return for my next shift having made her a traditional British dish. I imagined I would be bringing this to her during visiting hours as she would be readmitted to inpatient facility. "What are you going to make me?" she smiled.

I playfully suggested, "I might prepare toad in the hole, spotted dick or jellied eels." Secretly, I was delighted to prepare a trifle for her the most luscious, quintessential English pudding made of alternating layers of sponge, custard and berries and topped with whipped cream.

"Oh, but you are just going to have to wait," I said, making plans for her to look forward to.

Hold on, I prayed, *hold on.*

Four days later I returned for my next shift. I began each shift a little early so I could catch up on the residents, before they returned from their weekends away. I could not find any communication on Sue from my last shift: missing was Sue's entire Resident Log where I had 'SOAPed' details about the early morning time I spent with her; gone were the notes from our staff communication log with the medical doctors, where I had written about my exchange with Kolten; and torn out - was a single page from the House Log which described my meeting with our Medical Director, Simon, and contained my second request for Sue's rehospitalization.

Simon, who was never there on a Sunday evening, walked in my office carrying a briefcase. We were surprised to see one another, "Simon what's going on?"

He responded stoically, "Sue killed herself."

I was shocked.

His callous briefing made him seem cold-hearted. The residents called him "Simon smug." But in the vulnerability of this moment, he spoke with uncertainty and insecurity exposing his compensation for his actual inferiority complex. I wondered if he was emotionally numb from years of exposure to trauma without treatment. *Perhaps,* I wondered, *has he been suffering from*secondary trauma?*

He left unceremoniously and I sat there for a long while. I could not grasp: how Sue was denied the help she asked for, that she would never be with us again, and that she had left no goodbye note. I could not comprehend that Sue was gone…

I returned to the refrigerator, opened the door and peered in at the pudding I had made Sue. It was a *trifle, garnished with a single slice of okra, and in that instant my overwhelming sadness and the trifle blended in traumatic association. I had to close the door, get ready, and support the residents who would be returning momentarily.

While Simon had been devoid of emotion I knew the residential patients would be overflowing with it. The sharing of the news had to be handled delicately as the *Werther Effect of emulating suicide is an even greater risk amongst the more vulnerable psychiatric patients. For this endeavor I received no supervision and no additional staffing.

The next day, I was called with Kolten, Simon and

other staff to a mandatory hospital in-service, more accurately, a 'control their own damage' meeting. I was also informed I was not to talk about the case and to leave it to the lawyers. What was going on?

Prior to that notification I had already discussed the missing records with one of the day program counselors, who I phoned, to discuss how each of my residents in their attendance was managing the news. So through a grapevine that traveled faster than my solitary walk to the meeting, everyone knew my notes had been plucked from my office.

Regardless, the next hour was spent sitting through a disingenuous, basic lesson to make sure we document and how to document the correct SOAP way. Were they going to claim that I had not documented my time with Sue? Had someone read my SOAP notes and saw I included Kolten's 3AM, reprehensible, congratulatory statement? Because this training seemed directed at me, protected Kolten, and spared the hospital any responsibility.

"What are we doing?" I spoke up. Simon startled. Kolten glared. "Why are we not taking responsibility?" I asked, unaware how common this was in the profession. "Without responsibility, how can we truly speak from our hearts, and most effectively care for our patients, one another, and even ourselves?"

Kolten took a controlled sip from his cup of water.

Above and beyond all else, the room was blanketed in a *fog of fear: A palpable, disharmonious breath that obscured clarity, confused loyalties, and threatened that any utterance of agreement with what I just said, could throw any one of them, out and under, as well.

"It is like there are sides," I continued, "Am I the only one on Sue's side?"

"Sue-i-cide" a psychiatrist mocked.

The staff glanced around, ignored my question, and connected with a forced, low laughter.

I burst into tears…and not one caregiver dared comfort me.

Since no one spoke, I took a breath of courage and pronounced, "God bless Sue." I looked at Kolten and added, "God bless all of you." They followed my gaze to where Kolten sat *atop it all. He flushed and they all saw this telltale truth, but it would change nothing.

I turned on my heels and walked toward the exit. But then, who should saunter in, catching me off guard, but my own coping strategy when dealing with this depth of pain: Diversion.

"Is that Sue's trifle?" Diversion asked.

Someone had covered up Sue's trifle and placed it on the snack table. In this distraction from my upset, I thought, "That is not right."

I wished we could have sat around and processed the loss of Sue together. We would share tenderhearted stories: "Hey," I would say, "let me tell you about one of my meaningful walks through the garden with Sue… or about the time she generously offered to make me a *gift of one of her beautiful rings…or just how funny she was."

It was insult to injury to think they were going to

enjoy the delicious trifle I made for Sue after their distasteful meeting. I took the cover off. The okra was buried now. Then I grabbed the bowl and took the trifle. Yes, I took the trifle and left! I know, I know. It was technically mine anyway, but because this was multi-layered, I spent quite some time talking about it with the psychotherapist…I now needed to find.

Simon admitted he had covered the trifle and brought it up to the meeting. Initially he expressed disappointment that I had taken it, then annoyance to outright anger. Then it occurred to me Simon was *projecting. The next and final time he addressed me on his supposed loss of enjoying the trifle I told him, "The way you feel right now is the way I feel about the loss of Sue…and I think your relentless upset with me is a cover up for your own sadness about how we lost Sue." He smirked, which is really as close as he ever got to a smile. Thereafter, he treated me like I was his therapist.

When people die by suicide, loved ones deal with not only the fact that they died but also how they died. I would lay in my bed at night haunted by the details of how Sue shot herself. I had learned she purchased a rifle because, other than getting a gun illegally, this was the quickest permit to receive. After the three-day *waiting period she left our residential halfway house, telling a counselor she was going to her volunteer job, but instead, she drove back to the gun shop to take possession of the rifle. Next, she drove one block further to a parking lot behind a vacant store. She leaned back on her car windshield, positioned the rifle so as to use her big toe on the trigger and shot herself through the heart.

The sound of the rifle shot reverberated, waking me from my disturbed sleep.

By morning light, I would wake asking myself: "Did it really happen?" "What if I had…?" and "If only…"

I phoned Davisman for our daily 'elevenses.' It is our British habit of taking a late morning pause for a cup of tea, biscuit, and telephone chat.

"Jules, we can talk about this as much as you want for as long as you want, but also you need your own therapist."

Davisman knew this was not about me taking medicine to blunt my emotions and prevent my grief process but rather about allowing for the time to experience the stages of grief. He recommended three psychotherapists for me to interview on the phone. I selected a Russian psychologist, Igor. I chose him not because of anything particularly profound that he said, rather it was how he said it. He was warm and genuine and reminded me of my own dear Grandad, who had died too young and completely unexpected.

In therapy with Igor, we traveled through Elizabeth Kubler-Ross' heuristic Five Stages of Grief: denial, bargaining, depression, anger, and acceptance. It was a long therapeutic journey with a supportive elderly psychotherapist who expertly navigated the map and, at 85 years old, sometimes, took a nap. He worked through these five stages, often revisiting those I thought were resolved with wonderful new insights.

Even while I write this, all these years later a new

'What if…?' beckons me. What if the reason Sue's parents did not pursue a negligence case against the hospital was because a part of them was relieved? No, that could not be it, maybe they simply needed to let go and move on with dignity for Sue and grace for themselves. I remember from the day Sue was admitted, how warm, concerned, and loving her parents were. If only love was enough.

During treatment with Igor I shared an entry from my journal at that time. I have loved journaling through the years, expressing myself through various formats, art supplies and techniques. I encourage my own patients to do this as well. Journaling decreases stress, improves mood, and supports health. (I rarely get sick.) As an added bonus, my journals have built my skills of observation and insight through time and are useful references as I write now.

I wrote: "It is dawn and I have a dream so real it was as if Sue was actually here. She was standing at the foot of my bed holding a glass bowl in front of her heart. It was a trifle layered with the same ingredients as the one I made for her, though her trifle was much, much larger. I was aware that with an *empathy that both helped and hurt me, I wanted to assist her, but she gestured for me to 'let go.' As each teardrop of her sorrow fell, another spirit was summoned, perhaps for her support, but because she had suicided, more likely she had to answer to them."

The dream analysis of the 'people, places, and things' began… Igor said,

"How do you feel about…? "

And then he would fill in the blank with various symbols from my dream.

"How do you feel about trifles?" Igor asked as if he did not already know how I had unconsciously displaced my heartache into this trifle, but it had to come from me.

Of all the theories on the interpretations of dreams that I have studied, this is my favorite. The interpretation is in my decoding of my unconscious rather than determined by another source. Alphabetized listings might report that pudding symbolizes that: I am lethargic; I should not believe it 'til I see it; or that I am going to have a baby. I did not relate to any of that. For me, trifles had come to represent layers of suffering, mine as well as Sue's.

We discovered that the size of Sue's trifle and her crying suggested that since her *death by suicide, her suffering had not ended, but worsened. We knew from patients who reported near-death experiences that there is a life review and we are accountable in death for our lives. With this understanding that suicide carried a heavy weight beyond this life, Igor and I could cast a scythe of doubt in patient's wishes, fantasies or plans to end suffering if they were willing to consider the peaceful ending pursued could not come from a violent death.

The executioner of suicidal ideation lives in the realization that by ending one's own life,

suffering does not stop, in fact it may well intensify.

People with suicidal ideation must attend counseling. The basic *suicide prevention safety plan includes: awareness of warning signs (behavior, environment, images, mood, and thoughts); coping strategies (distraction, exercise, and relaxation); the names and for phone numbers of safe people, professionals and agencies to contact for help; and a 'worth living for' list.

Each individualized treatment plan is expanded upon from there and includes goals such as improving emotional intelligence (through self-awareness, self-management strategies, and an anger management program); building a reverence for life (by spending time with elders); and developing love and value for self and others (by examining and eliminating negative conditions; showing up for others which also allows own despair to go on pause and exploring the powers of attitude, positivity, and kindness).

Our analysis of my dream gave me a permission that I did not know I needed: to

Let go

Soon thereafter, I planned with Igor to prepare for our next session a smaller replica of that trifle. Often it is creative moments like this, outside the typical boundaries of traditional care, where progress happens.

As I proudly set my trifle down before Igor, he closed his eyes and breathed in the smell of the pudding, "Mmmmm." He said a prayer, then looked at me and added, "God Bless You." We sat in silence and ate. I saw another side of Igor as I watched him enjoying this trifle. Maybe I was simply noticing how we are different when we are not in our therapist-patient mode. I cherished our therapist-patient relationship and would honor it always.

This is when I realized, over a second serving of trifle and small talk that while I had initiated psychotherapy with Igor to help me cope with the loss of Sue, the benefits, of course, had extended beyond such. By spending time with a wise and wonderful elder I had improved my service to my own patients, and discovered unprocessed sadness in my heart, from the loss of my own Grandad. Due to the gift of time with Igor and his excellent treatment of me, this loss softened as well.

When Igor finished eating, he took a napkin and slowly wiped a spot of custard from his beard. He was tranquil, not at all self-conscious, and there was something more vulnerable about him than I had detected before.

Not long after my discharge, Igor died peacefully of old age. He was sitting in what his wife, Noona, called, his "reading chair" and his body naturally shut down. Igor had taught me about loss and death and now in this, his final lesson to me, I was emotionally equipped to grieve his death. Though certainly, Igor's death of natural causes made a huge difference in my process. I was sad that Igor had died, that Noona, like my Gran, was alone, though surrounded by visiting family, and that I would not see Igor again. But I was okay.

After Igor's funeral, I gave Noona a poem I wrote about him. Unexpectedly, right there, she held my hand while she silently read it. She did not comment on what I wrote, she squeezed my hand and invited me to come back to their home. She said she had something for me from Igor. Of course, I had been in Igor's home office but never in their private home upstairs. So while I accepted, I also felt uncomfortable at the invitation because I would be privy to a part of Igor I never would have known as his patient. I planned to stay only a moment.

Igor's pregnant great-granddaughter, whom I met at the funeral, answered his front door with a welcoming smile, just like Igor's. I followed her through the entrance hall to where I requested to wait as she went back through the house to get her Great Babushka. There I stood, suddenly realizing, I was in Igor's library. The sun shined through and spotlighted his vast shelves filled with books from a variety of literary genres. These books were organized behind family photos and delightful tchotchkes.

I was drawn to a black and white photo capturing a young Igor in Communist Soviet Union. I reflected on Igor's defection, his influential life's work, his radiant great-granddaughter and then I noticed the seven-piece set of Matryoshka nesting dolls in a line of descent. They spoke of the success of Igor's life. I could see who he was and how he chose to live his life had graced and benefitted the quality of his family for the next *seven generations.

I basked in the love present in his home and right there in his library. I saw his comfy reading chair, his thick lens eyeglasses, and in the space between my stillness and my thoughts, a warm sensation of peace came over me. I could only describe it as Igor arriving to remind me "All that is between us is a door."

Noona entered and must have sensed something also because she tiptoed across the room. She carried, in her tiny arms, a mammoth bowl. She leaned in and whispered warmly, "He love you too, Solnechnysvet."

Then with great pleasure she presented me with a magnificent crystal bowl, "Igor say this is gift for you."

I lifted it out of her arms and ran two fingers around the words etched into the thick lip of the bowl,

"Love is the only ingredient that matters."

I hugged it, "Thank you Noona, I love it." And figuring she knew what I was talking about, I said, "I'm going home right now to make a trifle."

Because through my time with Igor I had come to embrace my own suffering and could now make a trifle based on its new representation – Love. Love for Sue, love for Igor and a newfound, gentler self-love.

The Davisman Addendum - 2018

Every Wednesday afternoon, my favorite time of the week, I read Davisman the next chapter of this volume. "Therapists don't express love," he asserted.

"It is all about love, love is the point." I dangled it out there.

We were staring at each other, silent.

He broke the silence with a change of topic, "What does that Russian word even mean?"

"Oh. I did not know either; I wanted to convey the beauty of the moment, regardless because Noona had said it with such love."

"Do – you – know – now?" he said slowly, enunciating every word.

I nodded. "Recently, I contacted Igor's daughter who still lives in town for permission to include her father in this chapter. When I sounded out Solnechnysvet phonetically as I had written it in an old journal, she gave me the actual spelling and told me what it meant."

Davisman and I compromised that I would put *Solnechnysvet in the glossary.

And then, from a person who had not believed in life after death, Davisman slowly offered up a profound idea, "Don't you think Igor, on the other side, is helping Sue and others?"

"Yes," and I cried, "That is so beautiful." And I cried for so many reasons.

CHAPTER FOUR, 27 YEARS AGO,

The Many Seasons of Sabine

"I am struck by the fact that the more slowly trees grow at first, the sounder they are at the core, and I think that the same is true of human beings. We do not wish to see children precocious, making great strides in their early years like sprouts, producing a soft and perishable timber, but better if they expand slowly at first, as if contending with difficulties, and so are solidified and perfected."

-Henry David Thoreau

I HAD REACHED MY LIMIT. I was going to quit my job. I was invigorated as I drove with the convertible top down through the bucolic backcountry, breathing in the fresh spring air.

My plan was to quit my job at the hospital and create and implement home treatment programs, beginning with a 17-year-old, named Sabine. She was in recovery for drug abuse and was recently discharged from her third inpatient stint in four years. 'The Boy Named Sue' referred this family to me. He had a curious, unspoken

the hospital. I did not ot ask, though in the

terview with the mom and then was driving to their impressive home thiest communities in America. my car at the entrance gates, awaiting auth on, I thought, *who or what are you trying to keep out* and because I was a psychotherapist I also wondered, *who or what are you trying to keep in?* The massive, ornate metal gates opened, I drove through and as they closed behind me I saw a lengthy, tree-lined driveway span ahead of me. The cherry trees were in full bloom with gorgeous, pink double blossoms that filled the air with the lure of their fragrance. Paradoxically, their perfume was a bittersweet invitation. I continued down to their home, noting the sun and the shadows flickering through the trees, creating a temporary, mesmerizing effect.

The mother greeted me at the giant double doors, the side staff entrance to her extraordinary home. As we walked through a series of rooms, to her office for our interview, the rooms were brimming with inconsistent design and substance. It was as if she was seeking who she was on the inside from her outside surroundings.

After the success of our meeting she introduced me to her daughter. Sabine had returned from rehab to live with her mom and stepfather, in their extravagant home with a chef, housekeeper, gofer and essentially whatever she wanted… provided she "behaved."

Journal (J): *The First Few Seconds*, Overall, with Sabine:

She was pretty; 5'4; 25 pounds overweight; hunched posture (insecure, low-self-esteem); tired; looked harder and older than her years; immature syntax; uncertain which hand to shake with; and left-hand dominant (learning disabilities?)

J: *The First Minutes*

Sabine spoke in short, simple, and halting sentences (learning/emotional issues); her Mother finished her sentences (overbearingly at times); low mood; no interests, unfulfilled, street smart, not book smart; sensitive to changes in tones and expressions; the manners of an adult, and the laughter of a child.

She called her mom, "Mother," with an uppity tone heard amongst the privileged, and otherwise unlike Sabine. This gave me the impression that the survival of her youth depended upon the creation of a False Self to reinforce for "Mother" that she was revered. Sabine was too busy holding back her emotions and meeting her mother's needs to develop awareness of her own.

J: *From Toe to Head:*

Expensive shoes; fashionable, ripped, pale denim jeans; quality grey short-sleeved shirt exposing heroin track scars; excess of glamorous, expensive jewelry; bitten fingernails (parent conflict); "LOVE" tattoo on her inner right wrist (ouch!); a smile that didn't reach her eyes; dark circles under her eyes (allergies or laxative abuse?); eyes that dart with hyper-vigilance; excess saliva (binge eating? but no gland swelling, colloquially known as "chipmunk cheeks," indicative of vomiting); grey skin tone with short, brittle hair (from substance abuse). Note: I requested full physical.

At the end of this meeting, I was offered and accepted the position to create and implement a treatment for Sabine and her family in their home. They officially became the first clients of my new business. As I waved 'Goodbye' and drove off, that day, an excited Sabine waved freely with one hand while her 'Mother' tightly held down the other one. 'Mother,' waved like the Queen.

I gave my two-week notice at the hospital. After warm goodbyes with the patients, visits from former residents and weekend parties with the Musketeers. It was my last day of work at the hospital. Simon surprised me with an extravagant, unexpected gift of an exquisite fountain pen, "for your journaling" he insisted.

I thanked him, though could not help thinking, *How perfect, since all he really wanted was my silence.* I put the pen on my desk then away in a drawer, and while I kept it, I've never used it.

I thought about 'Mother' and Sabine. 'Mother,' had a beautifully made-up face, with blonde hair coiffed to one side. She was 5'10 and about 175 pounds. Although she professed herself a homemaker, I would come to find her rarely in town.

That first morning she had worn a business suit adorned ostentatiously with diamonds and other jewels. It was evident she wanted to stand out, be admired above all, but her rigidity and need for control revealed her hidden feelings of inadequacy.

I reflected on that initial conversation with 'Mother.'

She had boasted about how Sabine was a precocious child, able to anticipate her mother's needs but now, as she neared adulthood. 'Mother' described Sabine as a troubled, needy child who 'held her back' and 'let her down.'

I planned to explore with 'Mother' her deeper feelings and most likely reveal a multi-generational pattern of, in actuality, it being the parent that held back and let down the child. Although this would be a difficult journey for 'Mother,' only through this process would she have the insights and compassion to break patterns, see how she had abandoned her child and genuinely find Sabine in the empty, lonely place of pain, anger and numbness where Sabine lived and her 'Mother' pretended not to.

Sabine lived in stark contrast to her environment and especially to her mother. Sabine had a grey, thick body, and unruly short hair. If 'Mother' was the canopy layer of the rainforest that both overpowered and overshadowed, her daughter Sabine was the stunted tree below. This diminutive tree was just like the one she would draw at our next visit, as part of the initial assessment.

The drawing of a tree is considered a basic self-portrait. A few interpretations of her drawing (Figure 1) are: clipped branches—cut off socially; small crown density—mental productivity issues; and an overall presentation of looking stunted—trauma. Yet in speaking with Sabine, her medical doctor and family, along with reading Sabine's file, which included her evaluation, history, and full clinical background, no trauma had been reported.

I named my new business, the 'Three-Quarter-Way Service.' The name ideally explained, in a fraction that it was a program to support patient's transition and progression from little independence at the hospital to 'Halfway' independent at the Halfway House and then on to the 'Three-Quarter-Way' independence in their own homes. The goal was for patients to progress towards 100% independence.

Research suggested that nationwide relapse statistics were as high as 75%, but this new service soon improved upon that locally by extending patient programming forward to the home. Prior to this additional support, some patients, upon discharge, would stop on their way home at the liquor store or grocery store and binge in their car. Alternatively, their relapse was triggered when they returned home to their unresolved issues with "people, places and things." This Alcoholics Anonymous/Narcotics Anonymous (AA/NA) slogan is cited in the patients initial assignments to identify, manage and avoid negative influences that tempt, trigger and increase risk for relapse. Furthermore, a growing list of positive "people, places and things" is developed as patients journey from abstinence to sobriety.

Each individual treatment plan included multi-dimensional goals and objectives overseen in four areas: Daily Living Skills such as the maintenance and accurate self- administration of their medication from an observed weekly Mediset; Social-Emotional Skills, such as by the daily attendance at AA or NA (proven to be the most

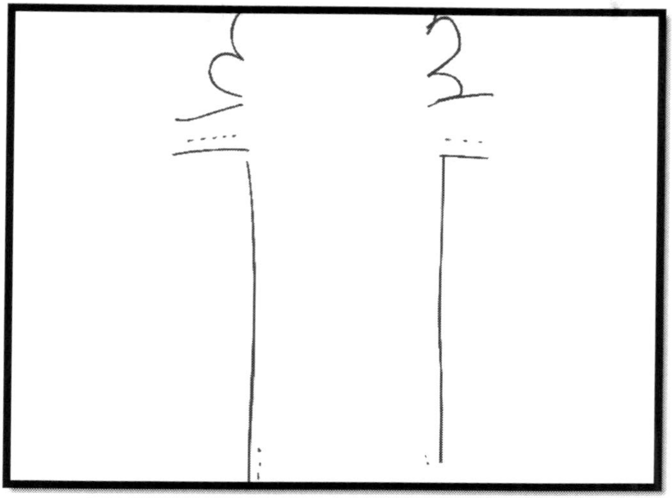

Figure 1: "Draw a Picture of a Tree"
Pencil, First Day of Care, Sabine

effective way to remain sober); Structured Activity including a minimum of 20 hours a week of which could include school attendance, volunteer work, or job participation; and a Leisure Activity, such as participation in a meaningful sport, hobby or other interest.

In support of Sabine attending and building a positive new social life I attended 'an open to the public,' NA meeting with her as an observer. The security guard RJ from the hospital saw me there during, asked me out after and spread the word that I was in recovery thereafter. He did this despite the AA/NA program's promise of personal anonymity and of course, the fact, I was not even in the program. I was concerned how this rumor could negatively impact my career, yet unexpectedly, I was revered. It boosted patients desire to bond and work with me.

Davisman and I went out for a drink.

"Don't worry about it," he said while I sipped ginger ale and he had what he always had. However, after attending that open meeting I was now counting; he was having too many whiskey shot and beer chasers. He continued, "What are you going to do make an announcement, 'sorry everybody I am not in recovery'? Then what? The rumor changes to 'she has fallen off the wagon?' "

"But this is disingenuous, to accept new patients under this guise."

"Therapists can't talk about themselves. Boundaries. All you can do is address it if they bring it to you."

"There is something about being sober, out with someone who is not, to talk about how they think I am in recovery and not informing them that I am not. Did that even make sense?"

Davisman laughed his glorious laugh and reminded me to lighten up.

One informative, challenging aspect of this program was the family involvement. At Sabine's home, my conversations with 'Mother' were providing her with accountability. She was accessing some authenticity behind her own self-alienation as she loosened the grips of control on her soon to be 18-year-old adult daughter. For example, we had agreed on the catchword, "merry-go-round" to increase her integrity through awareness of her cyclical behavior of manipulation and rage. She was willingly working to stop controlling her daughter with lavish, empty approval, overbearing attention, and extravagant gifts she gave with prices, expectations, and soon devolved into "Mother's" disappointments, intense anger, swearing, name-calling, and withholding her love.

Sometimes the 'Three-Quarter-Way Service' accommodated extenuating circumstances. Since Sabine's stepfather, a Trader by occupation, was typically unavailable, the stepbrother, (age 21 and home from college for the summer) along with Sabine and I, met with him, on what he called, "my turf," the World Trade Center, North Tower. I remembered which tower but I did not make a note of the floor number, not knowing that would become a typical modern-day question.

What I do remember is his stark, cold, dimly lit office. It still makes me shiver. It was accented prominently by a black steel-frame containing the symbol of a large dollar sign crafted from one hundred dollar bills. This was hung on the wall behind his desk and looked as if it was growing out of his head. I found this sight incredibly distracting along with the sounds of loneliness and the odor of superiority.

As we began our session the stepbrother, who clearly idealized his father was sought his approval by picking on Sabine. He called her "annoying" and bragged that when he was drunk he had pushed her down the stairs.

Despite the pall that came over the room, I addressed the brother's aggression.

Sabine's stepfather began nervously brushing at his

jacket. His fingers swatted the cuffs of both sleeves, as if to dismiss previously hidden dirt. This was followed by a two-handed, harsh, 'stop,' hand gesture to his son. It was a loud and clear communication, "Shut-up, I got this."

The stepfather exploded, "She provoked him." He pronounced this so loud the room echoed in agreement.

I said his volume was intimidating, to which he silently continued to speak through gestures. He smoothed down his lapels and then tightened his necktie as if to regain control by separating the thoughts in his head from the emotions in his heart. No wonder Sabine was so adept at hearing tones and reading body language—it was a matter of self-protection. Then I felt the command of the look he shot Sabine. The fear I saw in her eyes has surely limited access to her emotions through time and consequently limited her behavioral, intellectual and social responses. Sabine anxiously submitted, "It was my fault."

Despite my attempts to educate them all, that the stepbrother was solely responsible for his own aggression, each of them, for their own reasons, strongly opposed me. I looked around, we were in cell walls, strengthened by the collusion of denial with the language of minimization, we're not mistreating or mistreated. With that, the stepfather abruptly ended our meeting, refused further involvement, and I never saw him again.

I *reported the stepbrother's physical abuse to the Department of Children and Families. Usually this results in an angry parent dismissing the therapist. When "Mother" did not fire me for this required duty, I assumed we would now talk freely about the abuse and treat the family trauma.

The stepbrother was hardened with a protective shield of contempt and a suit of full armor that protected his own emotions from how he too had experienced an upbringing of abandonment, betrayal and exploitation. Unfortunately, he followed his father's suit and was the next to refuse to speak with me.

I figured at least the mandated anger management course would soften him and hopefully guide him into psychotherapy, perhaps with a kind, insightful male therapist. Then he could gain access to his repressed intense feelings rather than retrieving them through alcohol. However, the stepfather, in a misuse of money and influence received approval for an alternative plan. He gave a private doctor a lump sum of money for a supposed series of individual sessions with his son in lieu of attending the group program. His son attended neither.

Despite the father and son's refusal to participate Sabine's progress continued. By autumn, there was improvement in her mood, stress management, identification and expression of feelings and establishment of stronger boundaries with family members. She was becoming less reactive, sleeping better and had increased energy.

However, 'Mother' continued to collude with them, unwilling to consider an alternative to "It was Sabine's fault." She refused to discuss it further. I was appalled that she would sell out her daughter. This is when I realized "Mother' was experiencing financial abuse, whereby the stepfather used the household finances as leverage over her and her behavior. Until then I had not understood it was a form of abuse.

In our supervision Davisman assured me, "Therapists cannot force patient admissions. You must guide her or you will lose her and worse she will re-lose herself. We must honor her process in her time frame. You cannot effectively pull her along."

This was seen in the family system as they one-by-one pushed back by extricating themselves from the program. Next 'Mother,' decided to get her own therapist and she would no longer meet with me. I was hopeful that her new therapist would confer with me on the abuse issues. Further, I wanted her to help 'Mother' address her fear of standing up to her husband, her expectations of her daughter, and her increasing jealousy and competiveness with each of her daughter's accomplishments, especially Sabine's successful weight loss and healthy eating.

Additionally, I wanted to discuss how 'Mother' was *acting out in shocking ways towards me, perhaps confused by the softer boundaries of me working out of her home. She made outrageous, dare I say, evocative comments, such as "I want to strip you naked of your outfit" and "I would stay with my husband if he fucked you."

From the shock alone, of that last comment, I can vividly recall the details of that moment. I was just a kid in my twenties, getting my feet wet in the field. I was disturbed by her language and frankly, 'grossed out' by her suspicion of me having any interest in a 58-year-old man. I could digress, but for now, that's in the "*Four Walls."

Unfortunately, 'Mother' slowed down our work with the purchase of her "yes mam" therapist that she saw an excessive three times a week and used as a sounding board for validation and enabling. Davisman and I call this an "expensive friend." This therapist provided little help and at a great cost. It was clear this was as far as each of Sabine's family members would go.

I continued to address abuse concerns, by building her skills of protection and healthy wellbeing while Sabine insisted, like the rest of her family had taught her, there was no abuse it was "all a big misunderstanding." I struggled with this block to her treatment. It was incomprehensible to me. While therapy offered her orientation I was becoming disoriented. My confidence was undermined and I began to endure some of Sabine's challenges of confusion and self-doubt. I managed this in supervision. Davisman validated me time and again,

"I believe you."

These powerful words from his heart, held me together when I was coming unglued.

By winter, Sabine's mood had stabilized and as would be expected, her anxiety spiked. She became more agitated, questioned her care and often confronted me in unconscious attempt to turn me into her disapproving mother. Also notable during this time in her healing was that she was having dark and vivid nightmares. Sometimes during her biofeedback sessions her finger temperature was low by ten degrees or more. Women tend to store trauma, in their extremities, complaining of cold hands and feet, as if to freeze out or harden to their traumatic history.

We explored various leisure activities in search of what would nourish her soul. I was also interested in movement that would engage and warm her cool hands. After ruling out baking and pottery, she discovered it! Action painting. And soon we were creating an art studio where she splashed, dripped, and threw paint on canvas and flicked her cigarette ash as inspired by the artist, Jackson Pollock.

Her artistic endeavors created in the family basement expressed the unspoken underground network of family emotions. Initially it began when after each piece was completed she gave the artwork a title. Every title related to a current emotion or challenge. Soon thereafter, she advanced to selecting her title first then expressing it through her movement, color choice and other aspects of her creative process. This process was her outlet with which she finally felt safe to identify and express herself. As an example, her painting, "Just Balance Envy" was created predominantly with green paint. She confided her process: "Just BE is a piece that communicates how my mother's aguish makes me flick, flick, flicker – I think her anguish is aggravated by my progress, flick, no her own fears, flick, my progress, flicker no, her own fears. I wish she could just be." This was a profound insight that also demonstrates her remarkable improvement in vocabulary, grammar and overall expression.

A canvas she threw tiny droplets of red paint upon was titled, "Addiction" she confided her "secret subtitle: throwing at 'Mother' what I could not tell her."

Another was titled, "The Guilt of Disappointing." She explained, "I was too young to understand manipulation, and now too old for people to believe I just don't see through it." Her suppression of her Mother's exploitation of her from Sabine's preverbal childhood experiences were coming out through her body. This was happening through the action painting, and regardless of her intellect's attempts to silence or understand the forbidden messages.

I comforted her, the way Davisman profoundly did for me. "I believe you," I would say and she would cry. Her True Self was peeking out through her art, a modality allowing to safely explore her emotions.

Sabine's passion for action painting inspired her to complete her GED and continue on to an Associate's Program in the arts. Her choice of college included a program with services for her learning disabilities that would provide her with the support she would require to successfully complete a two-year degree.

The 'Three-Quarter-Way Service' had grown quickly. Additionally, the doctors I had previously worked with at the hospital were referring their patients, so much so, that I had to hire my own staff.

As the 'good word' of the success of this service

spread, parents began requesting home care for their younger children who needed more than weekly psychotherapy but not hospitalization. This resulted in the creation of a sister program called, '*In-Home Care,' whereby I would create individualized programming and my staff would implement the in-home treatment for the children and family, including parenting skills for the adults.

As with all patients, upon closure of their year of programing, they continue on, as was required throughout, to see their doctor for therapy sessions. After a year of travelling to patient's homes I wanted to shift gears to be the one they came to see. So as I wound down the year of my personal involvement with Sabine and the other initial families, I continued on as the director of the 'Three-Quarter-Way Service' and 'In-Home Care,' but collected them under the auspices my new business, '*Creative Therapies.'

Sabine had blossomed beautifully during this year and no longer required this level of care. She was fortified with education on physical, psychological/mental and emotional/verbal abuse, what to do when she or someone in her family was upset, including signs of when to walk away.

She was attending a twelve-step group daily and had a sponsor and sober friends. She was involved in services for her learning challenges (which helped her overcome her weaknesses and importantly, developed techniques to support her strengths as a visual learner). She received treatment for binge eating and laxative abuse and was eating a balanced diet, which included getting the right nutrients to allow her to reduce and naturally maintain a healthy weight. She was exercising daily to stimulate the healthy hormones that nurtured her body and mind. Even her hair had become strong and lustrous.

While we will never know what specifically made the difference for a patient, I do know they benefit from the vital

Basic abc's: acceptance, belief, and compassion.

During my final visit, "Mother" was away in Europe and unfortunately, never made time to say goodbye to me. Meanwhile, Sabine excitedly said, "I have an angel present for you," and then she handed me a white, cobbler apron that she had splattered and swished with white, iridescent paint. On the back, she had etched wings into thick paint. "When you wear it everyone will remember there's an 'Angel present.'"

On this last day of care, Sabine's drawings demonstrated her significant improvements. Of course, Sabine's final "Draw a Picture of a Tree" (Figure 2) would express her ongoing exacting nature seen as perfectionism. Also, the branches looked like a hand, which suggested though no surprise continued control issues. Next, there was an observable bump noted that could be a pregnancy. We never talked about and I never

Figure 2: Comparative "Draw a Picture of a Tree"
Colored Pencils, Final Day from Care, Sabine

read or inquired about if she had ever been pregnant. I followed up on that with the doctor she would continue to see for treatment.

As the layers of the onion are peeled back in care, new emotional topics are released that make us cry and lead us further within, to our sweet center.

Overall, Sabine demonstrated tremendous progress compared to the quality of her initial tree. This time she drew with confidence. The 8 ½ x 11-inch paper was no longer spontaneously turned sideways, which had resulted in the creation of a smaller tree suggestive of low self-esteem. Now the tall tree grew to the full size of the page with a healthy trunk-to-crown ratio, which expressed greater and more full potential. This tree compared to Sabine's initial drawing, reached for the sky with thirteen (the age she began using drugs) flowers replacing the dots on the branches and roots (that represented the heroin scars on her skin - arms and feet on figure 1). While there was a knothole suggestive of trauma, attention was not drawn there as it with the concern when heavily shaded. I questioned her one falling flower and she believed it was a sign of no longer hiding her thoughts and feelings.

Four seasons had passed since our first meeting. It was another sunny, spring day as I said "Goodbye" to Sabine. She stood tall, independent, wearing a soft, pink cotton dress and a warm, healthy glow. There was a blanket of cherry blossom petals beneath her bare feet and several of the flowers in her hands.

"Never forget me," she said offering me the pink flowers.

I placed them in the passenger seat of my convertible, already abloom with fallen cherry blossoms. Then I came back around the car and we hugged long.

"I will always remember you." I whispered.

As I drove off, she waved freely; both arms swaying overhead.

Then for the very last time I watched the massive gates silently close and lock behind me. *"Oh!* The realization startled me*, she is locked in there… she is not free… not yet.*

It is common that after a season with younger children and usually no more than a year with teens and families, the work is done. However, during another stage of the patient's development a new challenge can arise, perhaps an unaddressed issue in the body was triggered, a remnant or deeper level surfaced, or a compulsion to repeat an unresolved wound cries louder. When this happens even years later, and the individual is under stress, the person repeats coping behaviors related to that emotional state, eventually reaching out to the therapist who successfully helped before.

Sabine was 22. She phoned me.

PART TWO, Four Years Later, 1994
The Reverberation of the Unresolved Past

"Anybody can become angry – that is easy, but to be angry with the right person and to the right degree and at the right time and for the right purpose, and in the right way – that is not easy."
-Aristotle

"DON'T CALL THE COPS," SABINE GASPED. Her voice was sober, tone stressed, and breathing labored. I remained silent. I don't make deals. With no formalities, Sabine's words quickened: "It doesn't happen that much…I feel bad, it's not usually this bad...I can usually read him, fix him, but it was a really bad day and besides *he has gone back to drinking and…" She atypically rambled, "…I should have known better. He is just trying to teach me how to be a better girlfriend…"

"Where is he right now?" I was assessing her safety.

"Maine," she said sadly.

She was physically hurt and speaking like an abused woman. She was not telling me about her and what he had done to her. She was focused on protecting him. *Oh,* I cried to myself, *this was just how she had been conditioned in her family.* She was distorted in her thinking, excusing his behavior, and blaming herself.

I am listening, wanting to interrupt for her phone number and location, but knowing her well enough to know that if I upset her, she might hang up (this was before I had Caller ID). So, I waited for the opportunity, a pause, to quickly, calmly interject. "Sabine, I am glad you called me, what number are you calling from?"

I was surprised she willingly provided her number. I continued, "And your address there?" Again she did not refuse to answer, which further evidenced her need for help.

"Stay on the line, I am calling you an ambulance." I said, not waiting for her reaction.

From my FAX line, I dialed 911, and the dispatcher asked me questions and determined that because she was having difficulty breathing, Sabine required emergent assistance. I returned to the phone with Sabine and I told her an ambulance was on its way. She was fading. I kept her talking and told her I would meet her at the hospital and that I would make arrangements for a counselor from the *Domestic Abuse Council's 24-hour Hotline to join us.

After what seemed like a long time, though to be fair only three minutes had passed, I heard sirens. Apparently, five fire trucks, three police cars, some volunteer trucks and one ambulance had arrived. Soon I heard voices, the door being forcibly opened and the sound of the EMT's in the room. It was noisy and chaotic and I could no longer hear Sabine. A first responder came on the phone, identified himself and said, "We've got her."

For now she was in safe hands.

"Thank you," I wanted to say along with a dozen other comments and questions but the line went dead…

I drove to the hospital. I was informed they planned to keep her for two nights, until Friday morning. So that was the timeframe, unobstructed by him, for her to heal physically and us to reach her emotionally. If we did not succeed, she would return to this abusive relationship.

It was the first day of winter, the longest night of the year. After receiving care Sabine, was laying in the hospital bed continuing her storyline, using language riddled with an abused woman's thinking, illustrating his manipulation and control, and her damaged self-worth: "He is willing to risk his own trouble with the law to teach me…Please tell them not to arrest him…He trusts in our love that I won't tell…It was my fault, I triggered him...I deserved this."

It is common that people who have experienced trauma in their childhood are revictimized due to familiar patterns, ego deficits, poor coping skills, emotional dysregulation, and inadequate cognitive functioning. So while my primary goal was to be there for her, as a healthy comfort and safety, I also wanted to confirm for future treatment that there was more abuse in her history. From this place of honesty we could shine light on the similarities between her past and her present abuse, and then we could build relevant treatment strategies to freedom. She may be older, but I now had four more years psychotherapeutic experience and many more ideas on filling in the gaps since her previous treatment was compromised by her denial.

If she admitted a history of abuse, it would explain how she sought refuge in abuse. It was a familiarity that bred a comfort, despite that it was not safe. Her past abuse was creating a pleasure where there should be pain, a running toward rather than away, and a denial where there should be a scream. It was time for her to learn that her upbringing did not have to be her future.

Her family denial had resulted in untreated abuse issues, which 'provoked' a vulnerability that a present-day abuser would prey upon to soothe his own hidden shadows from his childhood wounds that compel him also to repeat his trauma.

I began, "Sabine, could you control your stepbrother' attacks?"

"Sometimes," she responded succinctly. She wittingly or unwittingly confirmed there was more violence in her past than she or her family had previously admitted.

I stay with the plural, "Did his attacks get progressively worse."

"Yes."

I continued, "Did he promise he would not hurt you again?"

"Yes," she cried softly without detailing. She had reverted to her monosyllabic communication style of the old days, early treatment when her fear limited her access to her emotions and generated poor social and behavioral responses.

"Did he stop?" I gently pressed on.

"Never," she sobbed.

"Sabine, do you still see him?"

"I can't" she gulped.

"I know you want to trust him, it must be very

difficult for you to come to terms with the fact that he is not worthy of your trust and the violence will continue. You cannot fix him no matter how…"

"I have to," she interjected, "I'll do better." She followed my lead and we were now speaking about her present relationship.

"What makes you stay?" I inquired. This important question is about the underlying 'benefits' as to why a woman is stuck, which will then help us address solutions and alternatives together.

She bit her lip, "Nobody else would want me." He had convinced her that he loved the unlovable. This shadow instilled in her childhood would benefit from working with a psychotherapist that could provide her with genuine love and acceptance. This would allow her to safely identify and discuss all the darkness and details behind her belief that she was unlovable; to then release to the light the idea that this made her unworthy and punishable. But this was not a task for this weekend.

She slowly turned her eyes towards me, sensed my concern, and burst into tears.

I wiped her tears with a Kleenex from the packet I would carry for my own tears on my drives to and fro these visits. We were both silent during this tender moment.

I asked softly, "Where are your sober friends?"

"Julia, you know I am still clean and sober. He just made me drop them when he started drinking again." This is another typical form of control used to further isolation, deepen reliance, and allow abuse to escalate.

"Sabine, he cannot make you."

"Well I go along to get along." She is describing the codependence of annihilated boundaries and the social withdrawal and retreat that happens to victims of ongoing abuse in their home. Typically, passivity and perfectionism are also prevalent in attempts to control the environment and keep her safe.

"And 'Mother?'"

"She moved to Long Island after my stepfather traded her for someone half his age." She laughed her pretend laugh.

I cleared my throat of all the words that wanted to speak on that and said, "Let us call your sponsor." I assumed she had not been in touch with her either. Then just like I taught her years ago, to compensate for her weaknesses with a strength she used her strong ability for tone discrimination to sing from memory her old sponsor's phone number. I saw a glimmer of light in her eye.

Understandably, these few days in the hospital would be physically and emotionally difficult for Sabine. We created a supportive team made up of her sponsor, the new counselor from the domestic abuse center, and me. The three of us agreed upon a rotating schedule of who would visit her when and what treatment we would provide throughout her Sabine's stay.

On the morning of day two, I arrived several minutes late for the beginning of visiting hours. As I walked out of the elevator a nurse grabbed me, "Julia," she said with urgency, "Sabine has a male visitor."

I took off walking fast towards Sabine's hospital room. I thought, *there's an APB out for his arrest and we all know what he looks like…would he be so bold, so righteous to dare to show up here?* I broke into a run; *surely someone on the hospital staff has called the police by now.*

I stopped short, in the hallway by her door. Others had gathered and were listening to a melodious male voice singing. It was my all time favorite song. At the end of the song Sabine clapped and called out, "encore."

I took a breath and barged in.

I gasped but did not say, *what are you doing here?* And, *You know how to sing?* And more than that, *You were just acapell-uh-ing 'Amazing Grace!'*

It was 'The Boy Named Sue!'

Goosebumps ran up my arms. I was stunned by this magnificent musical side of him that I had never been privy to in all our years of friendship.

"Hey," I whispered keeping the shock out of my voice.

"Hey," he said looking incredibly embarrassed.

"I-I will just put these flowers here for you Sabine, and let you two visit. I will come back in an hour."

"Pink! You remembered. Thank-you Julia. See you soon," she said. As I turned to leave 'The Boy Named Sue' attempted to smile and tightened his ponytail.

I went to the hospital's medical library to study, as I did every free second I had, for my psychology doctoral program. After only a few minutes, knowing exactly where to find me, 'The Boy Named Sue' came running my way, unable to wait until he arrived he called out,

"Cooper! Four Walls!?""

Someone stood up and shouted, "Library voice!"

When he actually stood in front of me, huffing and puffing, I said quietly, "'Four walls' what? What is it you do not want discussed beyond our walls?" It came out with a sting. "Look, I have respectfully not asked how you know Sabine. But 'Four Walls' what?" The tears were welling up in my eyes. "That you were here? That you knew her from the hospital? That you know her at all? What? I do not even know what you are asking of me. Why are you so secretive with me? Why won't you let me know you? I want us to be closer."

Again, he did his nervous tell and tightened his ever-present ponytail. He divides the pony in half and pulls the two sections away from one another. He reached out, hesitated, then cradled my face with his big hands and tenderly wiped my tears with his thumbs.

"Why you not just ask?" He responded softly.

"Oh." I said, as years of what I thought were secrets from me corrected to my polite English manners preventing greater intimacy between us. *Why was I direct with my patients and not my friends? Why do I not ask my friends meaningful questions and express my deeper feelings with them? I will have to journal about that. No, no, I will have to use this awareness and just do it.*

"Cooper. Cooper," he repeated, seeing I had turned in. "I here because Sabine invite me. I know Sabine from time I was hospitalized for drinking and she was there, but please, I do not wish others to know I sing."

"You don't want others to know you sing? I repeated

what he said to be sure I understood. Your issue is about keeping your…your beautiful voice a secret?" I tried not to smile.

"Cooper, please, I am not ready."

"Ready for what?" I asked quietly, his body close and his hands still on my face.

Quietly, he explained.

"Oh?" I wondered out loud.

He continued.

"Oh." I nodded.

He expanded…

"Oh!" I smiled broadly. "Of course, 'Four Walls.' Thank you for telling me." I excitedly threw my arms around him while he awkwardly relocated his by floating them in the air above me.

I could feel him hesitating. I waited. Then something new happened, slowly, he lowered his hands and put his arms around me. He actually hugged me back. My ear was squished to his heart and my smile to my ears.

"Thank you, Cooper," he whispered, then stepped back. "IOU" then he turned and walked away.

"Alright then." I said looking for a less abrupt closure than that, while talking to his back. "I'm on the schedule for two visits with Sabine today." "I'll call you in between."

He waved in acknowledgment.

On my walk back to Sabine I thought, *One day in the future when everyone knows about his incredible voice, we'll have an Opera party…Oh, we could have a Phantom of the Opera party, one day…*

3 hours later, in between my visits with Sabine, I phoned him and collected on that IOU.

Admittedly, it was a very different plan. 'The Boy Named Sue' agreed to record a children's song in Spanish for one of my young patients.

When I returned again to see Sabine, this time in the early evening, she was elated, anticipating her discharge. I was surprised, though I should not have been, because her response was textbook. She was smiling in a way evident that feel good endorphins were surging through her body as she fantasized about him bearing gifts and a bouquet of flowers and going on and on with apologies and doting on her with promises of undying love.

During my visit earlier that day, I had taught her about the patterns of behavior in 'The Abuse Cycle,' thinking this awareness would prevent this exact scenario. Now here she was after an abusive "incident" in her hospital bed, her shadow prowling outside the light of consciousness, prepared to dual.

She was high on thoughts of a passionate "Reconciliation/Honeymoon Phase." This was despite my teaching her about the pattern and how this would be followed by a "Calm" before the "Tensions Rebuild," and then another abusive "Incident" would occur. And yes, then "Reconciliation" recycles.

I used to understand the Abuse Cycle as a circle that goes round and round, but I drew it as a graph, illustrating how it goes up and up because abuse progresses in frequency and severity.

While I was certain he had his own history of abuse,

which taught him to psychologically, verbally, and physically assault under stress, I was clear I would not compromise her care by discussing, let alone trying to understand him.

"Sabine," I interrupted, closing the curtain on the lurking evening shadow and turning on the light, illuminating the room. I continued by offering a gesture of taking responsibility, "I am sorry I did not have the information to teach you…"

"You're sorry?" she snapped. "You're sorry you did not teach me!" she accused. She was angry and confused by her learning challenges that blocked her understanding of what I was saying or more so, what I was going to say.

She continued, "So, you're responsible for not teaching me, but when I don't teach him, he is responsible?" Her abuse mentality inflamed with such intensity that her body flailed, aggravating her injuries, increasing her physical pain.

Sabine was hurting herself. There it was and it still makes me cry. I attempted to gently calm and reassure her. I wanted to be the soft, warm pillow to her harsh, rough self. "Sabine, I am not going to argue with you. I am not going to hurt you and you may not hurt yourself. Let's work together."

She stilled. We were both quiet.

I broke the silence, "Remember our old agreement when one or both of us was upset? One of us would call a 'Pause' and both of us would respect it." During the pause Sabine and I would do a relaxation technique to support us in peacefully returning to our conversation.

"He will not 'Pause' or take a 'Time-Out' or any other 'Stop this and do that' supportive plan. When there is an emotional upset between you and him it leads to your physical pain. The *process you have described is five pronged:"

"1-He will go on. He will not calm down. He will blame, insult you and intimidate you."

"2-You, then try to smooth things over."

"3-He will swear, threaten and become physically violent toward you."

"4-You then agree with him. You have turned against yourself. You bully and blame yourself convinced you did something wrong and deserve this."

5-"He will finally storm out. You lay there in physical pain but your emotional pain is greater, so great that all you want is for him to come back.

"Sabine, unless you ask me to leave, I would like us to call a 'Pause' here and work on a calming skill. We could both do the silent guided imagery technique, like we used to. Then when we are calm and ready, we could resume our talk."

She agreed. I sat still in her hospital room visitor chair with my eyes closed, modeling relaxation breathing, and waiting. I could feel her emitting intense anger my way so I imagined myself as a ball filled with light, no negative energy could penetrate.

After several very long minutes, she uttered on a calmer breath, "Okay."

I opened my eyes slowly, looked at her warmly and asked softly, "Would you like to go first?"

"You."

"Sabine, since every person is responsible for his or herself, I find it helpful to ask myself:

What is on my plate?"

To provide a visual cue to support her comprehension, I took two of the extra paper plates from underneath the plate of cookies I had brought.

"Juliiiaaahhh," she digressed, "you baked Jackson Pollock cookies?"

"Stay with me."

She nodded.

I put a paper plate in each hand and took out my pretty case of watercolor pencils. I wrote "His" on one plate and "My" on the other. I held one in each hand and lifted the "His" plate higher. "His aggression, his violence – his plate." I switched the positions and now holding the "My" plate higher said, "Staying away from him, keeping yourself safe – that is on…"

"My plate" she said.

I asked her questions about responsibility and she motioned in the direction of whose plate it was on, soon becoming conversational.

When I said, "Now it is your turn."

Rather than proceed with discussion about her upset she asked me to write some of her realizations about responsibility down. What we had was the two paper plates so that is what I wrote on. She listed words for her plate, "My hurt, behaviors, thoughts and words are on my plate and his are on his plate. I get it."

She asked me to put the plates on the table in front of her so she could review them later.

"Is there anything else you'd like to talk about?" I asked.

"Yes" she replied, "thanks for caring about me…and thanks for not yelling or leaving, you know, when I got angry."

"Sabine, you're safe with me. Actually, also notice how safe you are here."

"Hey, yeah," she marveled, "I'm actually safe to sleep."

We both sat quietly for a moment before I stood up to go. I said, "I'll see you in the morning before you are discharged. Sweet dreams."

"I get it, it's not like sleep tight it's like sweet dreams. I am going to paint that."

That return to her passion was a good sign. The following morning was her discharge. And as I turned the corner towards Sabine's room, there she was wide-awake, out of bed and standing tall. The curtains were open and the shadow had surrendered to the light.

"I just had the best night of sleep in a long time. I am taking back my life, my self-esteem...everything is going to change." She detailed her plans to stay away from him, move into a sober house for women that her sponsor was coordinating right now, and return to her 12-step program with its supportive social system.

"I'm remembering who I am before I believed who

he said I was.

With a smile that reached her eyes she continued, "I'm returning to my action painting, too. I can't wait." She showed me the plate and read to me what she had added: "I go to bed and sleep safe every night, all night. His violence is not my fault, that's on his plate. The only cause of his abuse is him. No matter what, I never deserve to be touched roughly or beaten. I have a right to a peaceful life."

She had colored "His" plate in with my black and blue watercolor pencils then using her fingers and water she blended the colors into what looked like a bruise.

And there, peeking through, in the light of this new day, was her True Self, demarcating a new juncture of facing her own shadows, so the outside world wouldn't reflect them back (See Appendix B). Her sponsor arrived and the three of us walked out of the hospital together.

The sun was directly overhead, shadow underfoot. This was the third of the three days of the winter solstice. It is the process whereby the sun reaches its most northerly point, it has given the impression that it was standing still when in actuality it had been reversing.

Sabine gave me a tender, one-armed hug goodbye.

As I watched her and her sponsor drive off, she was laughing, light and free. I exhaled a breath of cold winter air. I was suddenly able to relax enough to feel my exhaustion for the first time since Sabine phoned me. This is a common occurrence in caregivers working with people in crisis.

I stretched towards the sun.

Sabine was scheduled to meet with her Domestic Abuse counselor the following day and from there they would have a set weekly appointment. The seasons passed. Her person to call was appropriately, yet sadly, no longer me.

An Autobiography in Five Short Chapters

Chapter 1

I walk down the street.
There is a deep hole in the sidewalk.
I fall in.
I am lost…I am helpless.
It isn't my fault.
It takes forever to find a way out.

Chapter 2

I walk down the street.
There is a deep hole in the sidewalk.
I pretend that I don't see it.
I fall in again.
I can't believe I am in this same place.
But, it isn't my fault.
It still takes a long time to get out.

Chapter 3

I walk down the same street.
There is a deep hole in the sidewalk.

I see it is there.
I still fall in…it's a habit…but, my eyes are open.
I know where I am.
It is my fault.
I get out immediately.

<u>Chapter 4</u>

I walk down the same street.
There is a deep hole in the sidewalk.
I walk around it.

<u>Chapter 5</u>

I walk down another street.

-Portia Nelson

On the Wall in the Domestic Abuse Council

Addendum - Celebrating with Davisman - 1994

The next day was Christmas Eve. Davisman's "Ma," had asked everyone to arrive earlier than usual for her annual feast due to the approaching Nor'easter that threatened to send everyone home early.

I was late. They were already out caroling. I let myself into the grand and gorgeous Edwardian home. I placed a pie and flowers on the table and plunked myself down amongst the blankets on my favorite cushy couch. This house was over 100 years old, uninsulated and yet the big, bright, airy rooms were filled with warmth. I stared out the casement windows at the dance of the snow flurries in the soft wind gently preluding the approaching severe storm.

Davisman entered from the kitchen, "Hey Jules."

I just knew he would be there waiting for me. "Hey, sorry you missed the caroling because of me." I stood up and passed him the pie.

As the good friends we were, he responded with genuine understanding not reprimand. "I'm so glad you're here," he said blowing the apology off and breathing in the pie. "Is this what I think it is?"

"Your favorite," I smiled.

He laughed in delight, put his fingers in the pie and said, "Let's eat it right now to celebrate."

"You got it?" I said. He was nodding and I was jumping. "You got it! Oh, my God, of course you did!" He was pursuing his mid-life dream, a degree in psychiatry, at one of America's finest universities, thanks to the trust fund his father recently left him. He got the residency he wanted. I was so happy for him, and yet tears were streaming down my face at the thought of him moving into the city to manage his 80-hour workweek.

"I'll be home a lot" he assured. "After all, you and Maolisa are here. Nothing is going to change. Now come on, let's eat pie."

Shortly thereafter his huge Irish family trickled in from the Boot Room, caroling, 'Joy to the World' and the house was aglow with happy faces, holiday lights and warm fireplaces.

"There's me dearest lad," Ma said with her loud, Irish brogue. She grabbed and held Davisman tight. I always bring Ma flowers, this time a holiday bouquet, because she loved decorating inside and out with flowers. She thanked me and then my favorite part she hugged me. Ma was the epitome of her home; big, strong and nothing was more comforting than being in her embrace. However, this glorious moment was interrupted when she noticed over my shoulder, "Is that a hof eten pie befur dinnr?"

Davisman grinned that appealing grin that warmed the entire house. He grabbed my hand, pulled me away and we ran off down the wide corridor, up the narrow stairs and into his childhood bedroom. We talked and talked over a game of Scrabble with wooden tiles that were older than me.

Davisman picked up my hand and twirled my bracelet, "Jules, I love your voice."

"Really?" I deflected the compliment. "It's the

English accent, isn't it? It reminds you of your heritage." I said in a heavy English accent though in reality, after all these years in America, I thought it was barely audible.

"No" he shook his head with a smile, and with that Maolisa, his fourteen-year-old daughter, bounded into the room. I jumped up. Davisman said, "Jules we should finish."

I was not sure if he meant our conversation or the game. I went with the competitive side of him and teased him still using my heavy accent. "Sorry you're not winning mate but Maolisa and I are off to have some girl time."

I turned towards her, she was now at my height, "Let's get the rest of the pies and the English pudding from my car, while you tell me the latest on 'you know who,' and your Da here cleans up."

As Maolisa and I focused on walking down the steep servant stairs to go out the back parking area, he called after us, "Um, I - I'm going to leave the board just like this. We can pick up where we left off later."

"I'd love to," I affirmed and the bare ceiling and walls bounced back in confirmation, "love tu, love u."

Maolisa jumped down the last several steps asking one word per stair, "Are – you – in – to – my – Da?"

I imitated her jumping and responded, "I – am – going – to – catch – you." Then she squealed as I chased her through the vestibule and giggled when I caught her in the Boot Room. "Now, tell me more about that boy you like" and we were off…

That night the worsening snowstorm sent me home

soon after the feast. So, that partially played Scrabble game became the first of our saved and returned to boards over the years. We called it 'Perpetual Scrabble' and left our unfinished business at various homes, offices, hospitals, in the future one church and soon – at Davisman's fabulous new city apartment and then… everything was going to change.

CHAPTER FIVE, 26 YEARS AGO, 1991

Holy Haunted House and Two-House Therapy

Your willingness to wrestle with your demons

will cause your angels to sing.

-August Wilson

PEOPLE MAY NEVER TELL YOU, BUT HAVE THEM DRAW A PICTURE AND THERE IT IS. The three drawings, House-Tree-Person (HTP), a projective technique created by John Buck, yield rich clinical insights into the inner sanctum of personality. These drawings, followed by an interview, elicit further fascinating clinical clues, such as strengths, weaknesses, and abilities to manage psychodynamic conflict. I revised this technique by replacing the request for the drawing of a Person (P) with a Kinetic Family Drawing (KFD) and began administering this combined series, H-T-KFD to every new patient. This addition enhanced treatment plans by bringing to life invaluable information on the patient's perspective toward their family. For example in KFD's I observed: heavy scribbles of anxiety at the location of the mother's former breast cancer; drawing only the tops of family member's heads at a dissociative distance; and a detailed phallic tree branch next to a family with no mouths to speak about it.

I hold the faith from the beginning of care, when parents are often afraid, sad and struggling. I know healing will come. These drawings along with follow-up questions on their first day will be readministered on the day of graduation from therapy, and at that time will validate the transformation and healing.

The heavy scribbles described above are replaced with lines of standard pressure that denote the release of the daughter's anxiety about her mother's health; the tops of the family's heads are replaced with full body drawings now that the boy is safe and can be present; and the family that had secrets now all have mouths because they have told what happened and received treatment.

Bart, almost ten was brought in for treatment by his single mom. Dad lived in another state and was rarely involved. Bart's mom expressed concern about her son's anger issues, including biting and his difficulty falling and remaining asleep. No childhood trauma was reported.

As with many of my approaches, I have exceptions that are guided by following the child's energy. This was the first of many extenuating circumstances or special exceptions that I would be making for Bart. The request was for him to "Draw a picture of a house." This usually begets an illustration of the exterior of the home lived in. However, due to the alarming nature of his drawing, I did not proceed with the other two drawings that visit. Rather, I began immediate inquiry.

"Tell me about this picture."

"One now" he demanded.

I was so focused that for a moment I did not know what he was talking about. "Oh," I realized, I had agreed he could have another treat after he finished the drawing. I had offered this to balance establishing rapport with building cooperation, earning trust, setting boundaries, and developing respect. I passed him my glass fishbowl of peanut butter cups. He took two.

"One," I reiterated firmly, and then without tantruming, he put one back.

I do not typically provide sweets, but they were Halloween leftovers and the healthiest of the market choices.

Bart took a bite, he closed his eyes, the treat seemed to soothe him, and then he continued where we left off. "This is me when I was four."

"And this?" I asked, casually tapping on it.

"That's the demon that waked me every night." He spoke matter-of-factly, "We lived in a haunted house" (Figure 3).

In the treatment of non-directive play therapy the therapist follows the child's expressions and communications with non-judgment. Therefore,

Figure 3: "Draw a Picture of a House"
Colored Markers, Bart

whether we believe him or not is irrelevant to his care the child simply goes where he needs to go.

In the beginning children come for care typically because of their parent's wishes, so at the end of the first session, I make a point of asking the child if he would like to come back.

"Yes," Bart confirmed, as they all do. Then as he was walking out, he turned back and asserted, "Have more of those peanut butter cups every time."

And I did.

Before proceeding further with Bart, I scheduled interviews to meet with his older sister then his mother. Both confirmed stories of a demon in the "haunted house" they lived in, five years ago.

"How did this not come up at school or elsewhere?" I asked them individually.

Their responses were similar variations of learning to

be silent and isolated. They realized: "We couldn't talk about it…nobody believed us and nobody helped us. They just judged, labeled, and alienated us."

I referred both of them out for treatment. Both returned to me fór care.

The older sister's horror lived in her body as physical symptoms, school absences, and mood issues. As she found her words, processed and assimilated what happened new behaviors took hold and her physiology began to heal. This was not a quick fix, it had taken time for her to become this symptomatic and it took time for her to heal. She would go on to enjoy a healthy, full, and fun life.

The mom, who was overwhelmed and in a constant state of shock, would also begin to heal as she processed her trauma with words in a safe non-judgmental environment. However, psychotherapeutic healing in adults is a longer journey towards health, complicated by years of multi-faceted layers, maladaptive beliefs and behavior patterns.

During my next visit with Bart, while still in the formal assessment phase of his care, he spontaneously continued talking about the demon. Unlike the judgmental messages that had previously silenced his family, he felt safe and open to talk spontaneously with me. This was a sign of our developing rapport. He even requested to draw the demon again, this time life-size.

I agreed, provided he left it and all the thoughts about it here with me. (Bart never gave the demon a gender, so neither did I. He called it an 'it,' so, so did I.)

He agreed that if he thought about it outside of the playroom, he was to say, "Not now, tell Julia," clap his hands together and then rap, something he loved to do, to distract himself away from the thought.

He selected the 4-foot wide, blank newspaper for his 'actual size' drawing. I began rolling the paper out slowly. "Was the demon this big?" I unrolled more. "Was it this big?" I kept going until Bart confirmed its size at over 8 feet tall. I was overwhelmed with emotion for him, he was so small comparatively, let alone how tiny he was at age four. He proceeded to tell of many encounters, while he colored with Sharpies, an eerie black creature with red slits for eyes, sharp teeth, and claws.

That evening before he left, for closure to this topic, we rolled the drawing up tight, and took it into my office. Bart clapped his hands together and transitioned back to his mom rapping.

It is true that children show the psychotherapist what it is like to be them by making them feel as they do. After he left, I rolled it back out and took the photo (Figure 4) on the following page. (Note: Preferring authenticity, to retouching, the quality of this image is shown in its compromised state due to the brightness of the flash.)

We planned to use it as a prop, so we agreed that before his next session I would glue the demon onto thick cardboard and cut it out so it could stand up. After I did this, I stood it up. It looked ominous at almost the height of my ceiling. I went out to my kitchen, returned back to my office, flicked the light on and yelped!

As I finished my paperwork, I felt like I was being

watched. And of course, I could not let any of the other children in my practice see or feel this monstrous demon, so I laid it sideways, resting against the far office wall behind my desk, only bringing it out when Bart was there.

For Bart's treatment, safety was the priority, self-regulation the task with reconstruction and restoration of his memories the plan. We worked on skills such as developing his ability to identify, speak, and process his emotions rather than freeze, rage and/or bite. Our connection as is true with all patients was paramount.

Furthermore, I worked with his mom on be consistent, implementing routines, and establishing clear limits with psycho-education that considered additional skill-set relevant to Bart's unique needs. We would use the very first edition of '*PATH,' my home program for parenting children who are quick to lose their temper.

After I finished the initial assessment, playing detective was over and Bart's treatment began. My therapeutic task was to provide him with a safe place with the space, materials, and permission to go where he needed to go to pick up the 'pieces of himself,' to rework and master his trauma. My therapeutic role included trusting, following, and supporting this process while he re-enacted, reconnected, and retrained memories of traumas one would only want to forget.

At Bart's next visit, he ran straight to my office where I had prepared for his visit by deliberately diminishing the presence of the demon. It was placed 'cardboard side up' on the art room floor. He smiled young boy smile, "It's Batman!"

He requested the newspaper roll again, this time to place under the cardboard of the demon as a giant stencil to outline. This time he drew Batman (Figure 5). Upon finishing he requested my help in cutting and gluing it on the cardboard side. Terrifying memories were up for

reexamination with a playfulness & creative thinking that supported liberation.

As he had colored in Batman, he talked non-stop about how this superhero could rescue the terrified 'little boy.' He told adventures of encountering the demon with Batman, and together we resolved them with returns to safety, security, and comfort. He laughed and laughed. In therapy, laughter is suggestive of healing when new understandings soften old fears. Suddenly he enthused, "Call me Bartman!"

There were times when I thought Bart was old for play therapy, as many boys are ready to sit and have a 'talk therapy' session by this age. However, without fail, when he arrived weekly, "same Bat time," he would eat a peanut butter cup and then off he would go, leading us back to his traumatic past. In the beginning, we would role-play his imagery driven scripts. This allowed him to rework his stories, *abreact, put together pieces with

Figure 4: Spontaneous "Demon"
Black and Red Permanent Markers, Bart

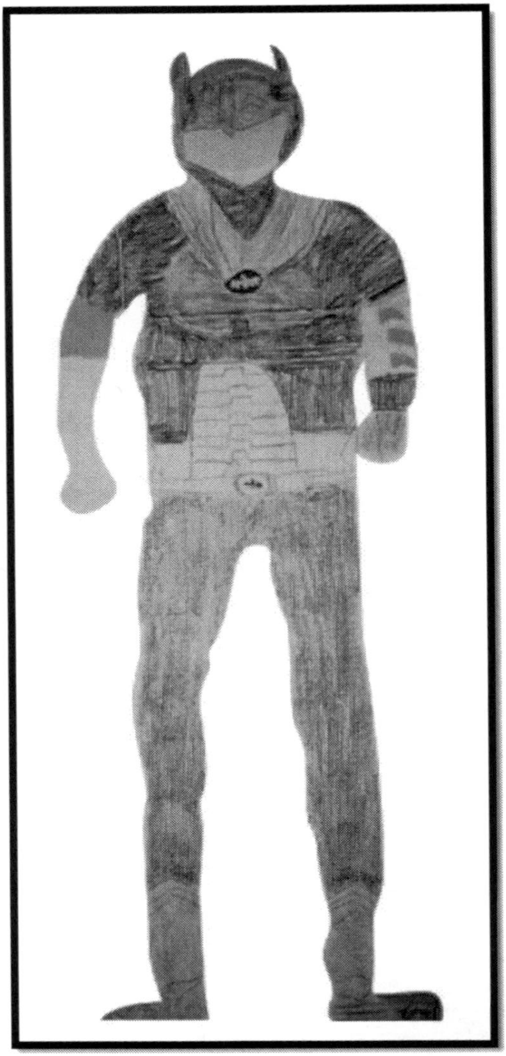

Figure 5: Spontaneous "Batman"
Permanent Markers and Pastels, Bart

understanding, and gain control and mastery over his trauma.

He assigned me the character of Robin, Bartman's trusted ally, and together we would encounter the (cardboard) demon. We would use loud interjections and onomatopoeia, such as WHAM and POW! We also used exclamations "Holy" this and "Holy" that.

He led and Robin, his sidekick, followed.

He instructed, "Say, BAM!"

I responded, "How loud?"

I set limits only where necessary.

He directed, "Close your eyes."

I informed,

"I will close one eye."

Sometimes he would repeat the same painful element of a memory. It would be a grave misunderstanding of treatment to allow the re-enactment to keep rehashing. This would exacerbate the trauma and its associated symptoms, such as rage, terror, and sleep deprivation. At these moments when a specific piece of trauma repeated three times, I would aid him through this terror with general questions: "What else could we do?" or "Is there another way to do that?" And if that was not effective, I would become more specific: "Do you want me to go first?" "Shall we have an angel join us?" This placing of the decisions on him is to empower him to find his own inner resources from which courage, self-esteem, and self-control developed.

If he did not respond, I trusted that I was still sparking his flexibility in thinking and supporting the development of his decision making process to interrupt scary patterns and build his ability to find his own solutions. Near the end of the session, still wearing our silk capes we would drive off in our Bartmobile of attached chairs with wheels and return to safety, to the present. From there we would wind down, talk and have what Bart called our "POW-WOW." While his "play," which Einstein called, "the highest form of research," was strengthening his memory and confidence, and reducing his outbursts at home, the "POW-WOW" was initially devoted to putting words to the details, feelings, and effects of his haunted house terrors.

With time our POW-WOW expanded to build skills, reduce his responses to stress, remain present, and be socially connected. He participated in numerous interventions including psycho-education, mindfulness meditation, interoceptive (bodily sensation) exposure, cognitive restructuring, and relaxation training, (especially breathing exercises to calm and ground him in the 'here and now.') We also used his interest and pleasure in scrubbing (moving vinyl records back and forth on a turntable) to copy one another's vocal rhythmic patterns to build social connection. This also improved his positive skills of imitation, eye contact, taking turns and, of course, there was fun and laughter.

Trauma and its memories were imprisoned in his mind and trapped in his body. Due to how the brain's wiring is altered in trauma, fragments of memories, scary images, and instantaneous reactions could be triggered at any time by thoughts, emotions, or sensations, such as images, smells, or sounds.

One day, when Bart and I were in play, he leaned towards me and I naturally responded by extending a protective arm towards him. This movement triggered a horrifying flashback that Bart later described as the demon's arm reaching through the wall at him. He stood frozen, helpless, reliving the past as if it was happening in the present.

"Do you want to go our Bartmobile?" I suggested not realizing I was triggering him with my arm motion as I moved again to encourage his movement. He grabbed my arm and bit me!

I had deliberately made Bart my last appointment of the day, often having him stay later than scheduled to address powerful feelings and to ensure an adequate "wind down" and closure to his session. He came to trust this process, experiencing the depths and complexity of his emotions, yet by the end of the session, capable of moving through to safety, security, and comfort.

After these sessions he would run up and down the hill in my backyard, with my neighbor's lonely dog on the other side of the picket fence. Grover, like so many dogs, freely offered love, connection, and even eye contact. Their running together helped Bart release additional energy after his session as well as smooth out the transition back to his mom.

One evening after his session, I gave Bart the box of dog biscuits I had for Grover. When I peeked out my kitchen window, I saw Bart and Grover munching away on them. Rather than make one more parenting challenge for his dear mom, I emptied out the remainder of the dog biscuits in the box. I replaced them with home-baked oatmeal biscuits shaped into dog-bones, healthy for dogs and dog people.

Around this time, Bart, his mom, and sister adopted a rescue dog named Lucky. They began benefitting from his unconditional love, connection, and joy.

I was learning and expanding Creative Therapies to become a unique, play therapy center. I read every play, art and sand tray therapy book I could find. I continued attending workshops and conferences and giving presentations. I invested in additional therapeutic games, toys, puppets, art supplies, and children's books I deemed therapeutic for my growing *bibliotherapy lending library. Beyond that, I trusted that if a particular object for a child's play was not available, they would make it from art supplies, use an alternative object or simply produce it from their imagination.

I also was thrilled to participate in a 'Think Tank' with Davisman at his university where clinicians actually brought patients to consult with our group.

Then Davisman's Pa died suddenly. He was grief struck and overwhelmed with the responsibility of his father's very large estate and his family so I stepped in to help him with juggling the demands of his doctoral program and his scheduled time with his eleven year-old daughter.

When Maolisa and I were out shopping, I found a

dollhouse that I thought could represent the haunted house. I will refer to dollhouses going forward as "houses" primarily to avoid gender role stereotyping. (As some parents and clinicians label dollhouses "toys for girls" and restrict boys from playing with them. They say this without realizing the therapeutic and developmental EBIPS benefits of playing with the houses for all children.) Ultimately, I found two gender neutral, wooden houses. I liked each for different details, so I purchased both.

I placed the two houses on a long, low table next to my sand, water and sensory trays. This location invited the use of the drawers filled with *miniatures also. Regardless of what children played with they created a microcosm of their own world.

I waited. I assumed Bart would gravitate to one of the houses. He did not.

However, other children did. This was the era when many children came in for treatment due to their parents' separation or divorce. (See Appendix C titled, *Divorce: Some Basic Considerations on Behalf of Your Children.)* These children gravitated to the houses and suddenly I had a new therapeutic modality. I called the technique, "*Two-House Therapy or 2-HT," created a manual, slideshow and trained clinicians across the country. It was fascinating that children, with or without words turned one house into Mom's and the other into Dad's. Therapeutic play quickly showed where these children's issues and concerns were. For example, the play therapy showed where the warmth and comfort was, who was bulimic, who took prescription drugs, which parent was in another relationship and so much more.

In one *initial phone inquiry and intake, the parents reported it was their divorce that had so traumatized their son that he refused to speak. However, his 'Two-House Therapy' revealed it was physical abuse that had caused his silent rage. The answer to the question arose from his silent play, "Who was the caregiver in both homes?" The boy's new nanny.

Back to Bart, while he did not gravitate to either wooden house, he did find the four-inch black demon with red eyes and claws, like his drawings, that I made out of polymer clay. It was deliberately tucked in one of the drawers of miniatures. Over the next few sessions, he went from checking on it, to poking at it, to biting and eventually burying it in the soil of my large, ivy plant. Play themes of hiding or burying suggest there was more to be found.

The following session he dug the demon up and walked over to the sink. I assumed he was going to wash it off. However, he filled a four-inch bottle with water, spoke 'positive words' into the bottle, and flicked what Bart announced was "holy water" onto the demon.

"KAPOW!" He said and broke the demon in half.

He immediately looked at me, searching my eyes to see if he was in trouble. He saw I was with him, without judgment. This was all the permission he needed to proceed, he banged, he hammered and he smashed the demon to smithereens. When he seemed satisfied with its destruction, he blew the dust away and triumphantly declared, "POOF! Gone!"

Bart had shown us the way to exorcize the demon from his nightly fears. I scheduled the next session at his home. When I arrived at his home, Bart and Lucky were waiting in the front door to greet me. They were standing in an arched tunnel constructed from thousands of mini marshmallows held together with toothpicks. On closer examination, I could see this was a mathematical structure tediously built from hundreds of connected small tetrahedrons; triangular pyramids individually assembled from four mini-marshmallows and six toothpicks. I ducked and followed them through the sticky path to the den.

As I looked back and stared in awe, I searched around my bag and pulled out his "holy water." He smiled, grabbed it and ran off down the hallway sprinkling the "holy water" as he went. Again, I followed him, to find him in his bedroom blessing the walls, curtains, furniture, and even his posters with the "holy water."

Although this home was not the haunted house where he had seen the demon, through this action he resolved his fear and he now believed he was safe. At ten years old, that very night, he remained in his own bed, going to sleep and sleeping uninterrupted for the first time in over six years.

The first stage of play therapy is testing for safety, boundaries, and protection. The second stage is entering into play/work where Bart had picked up the pieces of his trauma and processed the traumatic events. He was no longer terrorized by the flashbacks and, subsequently, he began getting sufficient sleep, self-regulating, and socializing. Thereafter, he soon announced he was done with therapy and with that, we entered the third stage, discharge planning and termination.

At Bart's graduation, he drew his final H-T-KFD, validating his incredible resilience and healing. His house drawing was the more typical portrayal, the outside of the home he lived in, and his family drawing included his smiling mom, healing sister, Lucky their dog, and himself with no signs of the demon lurking (Figure 6).

His mom and sister still look heavily defended in the shoulders as if continuing to guard against attack.

Figure 6: "Draw a Picture of Your Family Doing Something Together"
Graduation Day from Therapy, Colored Markers, Bart

Comparatively, this was considered a testament to the therapy he had done and the therapy they had not yet completed.

As remarkable and profound as his healing, and as improved as his mental health and home life appeared, I was haunted by a lingering feeling. It did not come out until another year…

The Davisman Addendum – 2018

Davisman had supervised me on this case, all those years ago.

"Do you have that unbelievable little terror's drawing?" He asked.

"Of course." and even though he knew what was coming, I said, "You are just going to have to wait."

Doggy - People Homemade Healthy Biscuits - 2018

Preheat oven to 375 degrees Goldie woofs these

Whisk Together

-½ cup Justin's peanut butter
-2 eggs
-¼ cup vegetable oil (substituted because dogs should not eat butter)
-1 cup canned or cooked sweet potato or pumpkin or spinach, or carrot or applesauce. (Harmful to dogs: sugar, honey, milk, raisins, nuts and even bacon.)

Add to the above, mix with hands until incorporated:
-2 ½ cups flour
-½ cup oat flakes
-1 tsp. baking soda
-up to 1/3 cup warm water (added if the dough is crumbling)

Then shape into a ball, cover and place in refrigerator for 20 minutes.

Next, working on a surface sprinkled with oats, roll out dough to a half-inch thickness, (approximately 8x8)

Cut into the shape of dog bones, hearts, stars or however the dough takes shape. You can make a paper stencil to cut around or, nowadays, you can find dog bone cookie cutters and silicone baking trays available at retail stores.

The biscuits do not spread when baked, so they can

be placed close together.

Bake at 375 degrees for 15-18 minutes. Shortly after the edges are golden and you can smell them, turn off the oven and let them dry out in there, ideally overnight.

Thoroughly cool!

Drizzle topping

-¼ cup of Justin's Peanut Butter and enough warm water – enough to drizzle off a fork on to each dog treat.

In 2018 I switched the water in the drizzle topping out for castor oil to dissolve a fatty deposit 11-year-old Goldie had. I gave her three-a-day, and even though, at first, she sniffed out a difference, she still gobbled them up. Goldie's fur softened, lightened, and a bald patch regrew hair.

One of the Four Musketeers who is still somewhat health-oriented, helped himself. I do not know how many biscuits he ate before I stopped him. Be sure to limit intake if using castor oil: it has a laxative effect!

CHAPTER SIX, 25 YEARS AGO, 1992

Truth Will Out

"All in, all the time."

-The United States Navy's
Sea, Air & Land's Motto

"TAKE A DEEP BREATH IN THROUGH YOUR NOSE AND OUT, LONG FROM YOUR *NOSE." That is how I begin the hypnotic induction of my patients. I discovered that trauma was underlying many mental health issues. So I decided to further my skills with this powerful tool, hypnosis, by taking an advanced course with weekend internship hours. My goal was to help patients, who were naturally dissociating anyway, to structure and organize their experience.

I found one of the course instructors, Dr. Thomas, particularly exceptional. His presentations were riveting and he was especially insightful and, well, handsome. I looked forward to seeing him and after a while, it became evident there was a special bond developing between us. In this powerful draw to one another, we ignored our time in history where there still remained a stigma towards interracial couples.

After the course, this bond led to a dynamic personal relationship, including lecturing around the country together. Post-Traumatic Stress Disorder (PTSD) was finally receiving wider acceptance and research funding and new treatment options were being discovered. The demand from clinicians for PTSD training was high. Thomas' background as a Navy Seal Captain during the Vietnam War inspired his work and impassioned his training of clinicians and the treatment of others with PTSD. We combined his experience and work with my own PTSD research, treatment, and history of presenting to create 18-hour weekend workshops for clinicians around the country.

At these workshops, Thomas and I discussed the assessment, treatment, and healing of PTSD in adults and children. Additionally, on our breaks, clinicians could schedule to meet with us for private consultations on their individual cases. Sometimes, when the location of the workshop was in a psychiatric facility, we were asked to evaluate a patient and provide recommendations. We were delighted, honored, and volunteered our time for these extremely interesting extra hours.

At one of these psychiatric facilities, a location that specialized in long-term substance abuse treatment, we were asked to meet with a 32-year old resident, named Darcy. We were told that Darcy had transferred to them one month ago. She had been in the mental health care system for seven years and had moved through many different hospital programs. She received numerous misdiagnoses, improper treatments, and unfortunately, wrong medications. And after all this time and treatment, she reported to the staff, "Nothing's helping me." In short, two weeks prior to our visit, Darcy went Code Green ('Eloped,' a fancy hospital word for ran away). This generally quiet, discreet woman was documented by the overnight staff to have returned the following morning, talking a mile a minute and apparently bragging about "a wild night of sex with different partners for drugs."

Three hours later at the group breakfast, Darcy showed, remarkably, no signs of a crash, hangover, or even fatigue from this proclaimed escapade, and then… no knowledge of her reported event. She participated in the 'Inpatient Day Program' where the staff continued to inquire about the details of her elopement and she repeatedly denied it all. Her frustrated doctor ordered blood and urine tests. To the night staffs' astonishment, the results all came back "negative" for alcohol and drug use.

After we were provided with this information and reviewed her file, we met Darcy. We bonded quickly and easily and she agreed to be hypnotized. During the hypnotic induction another identity named Nancy emerged. Nancy admitted she was the one who eloped and returned to the facility boasting the following morning, That was why when Darcy later returned to consciousness she had no recollection of that night.

Furthermore, this meant that as her psychology

shifted, so had her biology. It was reportedly an identity named Sara, a young girl, who took the blood and urine tests. Though surely impossible, Sara produced negative results for alcohol and drugs despite she was the same body.

Thomas and I recommended Darcy's transfer to a psychiatric hospital where a Dissociative Disorder Unit had recently opened. It was directed by Dr. Mark, a psychiatrist I greatly respected, and knew would take excellent care of her. Mark confirmed our findings and provided Darcy with the proper treatment for her diagnosis of Multiple Personality Disorder.

It was a privilege to meet Darcy and learn about such a rare and controversial disorder. We would visit one university that would confirm this disorder existed, and then we would drive a hundred miles to another university and its existence would be denied. Even the professionals were split.

A few weeks later, Mark and I discussed Darcy and her progress and the fascinating alterations in her affect, behavior, memory, perception, cognition and sensory-motor function *(Dissociative Identity Disorder, Diagnostic and Statistical Manual of Mental Disorders, 2013, DSM-5)*. Also to our astonishment he had found when she "switched personalities" (dissociative states of consciousness), there were changes in her physiology such as heart rate and breathing patterns, her conditions such as food tolerances and allergies and her senses whereby the vision of one identity required corrective lenses. Another intriguing fact was that during a three-week period of time she had taken a number of pregnancy tests with inconsistent results.

Was she pregnant, or was she not?

It depended upon which identity took the urine test.

A few months later, although I never found out how she got my phone number, Darcy left a grateful, loving message on my answering machine with a request that I return her call. After consulting with her doctor, Mark, I phoned Darcy back. She said, she did not remember calling me and asked me the details of the message. I told her, and because she now had appropriate care including psycho-education, she was able to understand and explain that another identity must have phoned me. Then she said, "I know it was me that said that because I know what is true for me."

I still think about Darcy's response, and whenever there's chaos, doubt, or confusion I encourage patients to:

"Inhale and follow your breath into your heart and there you will know what is true for you.

The next time I was asked to assist after one of our workshops, it was to conduct an assessment of a seven-year-old girl named Melissa. We had given a workshop at a clinic located just outside a navy base. Their head supervisor of the clinic was in attendance, and during a break, he privately requested we consult on a high profile, alleged sexual abuse case. A naval officer, up for a prestigious promotion, had been accused, by his soon-to-be ex-wife of orally raping their daughter. Apparently, the girl, named Melissa had explicitly reenacted the molestation.

The girl's therapist reluctantly allowed me to review his file, clearly offended a second opinion had been ordered. The file included the initial intake form completed by Melissa's mother. There were no reported medical issues, hospital visits, or other notes of a remarkable history. The family's last name had been blackened out throughout the documents.

Melissa did not have difficulty separating from her mother though she seemed nervous to meet with me. I took my time to establish rapport before beginning the evaluation. This is Melissa's KFD of her family doing something together (Figure 7). She was provided with eight colored markers. She selected only the black marker.

The most prominent feature in her drawing was the colored in heavily shaded necks of each family member. I wanted to see how she would draw other people. I gave her another piece of paper and requested, "Draw a picture of your grandparents doing something together" (Figure 8).

The result demonstrated the same fixation with the neck.

"Do you have any animals?" I asked.

Figure 7: "Draw a Picture of Your Family Doing Something Together" Black Marker, Melissa

Figure 8: "Draw a Picture of Your Grandparents Doing Something Together" Black Marker, Melissa

"Yes" she said and drew her cat, also with a heavily shaded neck (Figure 9).

Figure 9: Drawing of Her Cat
Black Marker, Before Treatment, Melissa

I returned to the drawing where her neck was colored in and tapped on it lightly, "What is happening here?" I asked quietly.

She extemporaneously leaned back in the chair, closed her eyes, tilted her head back and opened her mouth. She was silent and still.

She appeared to be in a trance, reliving a memory.

"What is happening?" I started with a general

question.

She did not speak.

"What do you hear?" I asked to engage her senses and continue efforts to encourage her to talk.

"Quiet" she commanded, though not of me. "Stay still," Melissa imitated with an aggressive deep voice.

"Open your mouth. Stay like that."

She reopened her mouth and became still again. I waited, observing, then asked, "What are you feeling?"

She wiped the right side of her neck, "Sticky."

"What is sticky?"

"The stuff squirted on my neck." She said, continuing to wipe at it.

I paused here, to choose my words carefully as it was imperative not to lead her by putting any ideas in her head or words in her mouth. And before I spoke, she loudly exclaimed, "The globbery!"

She opened her eyes alarmed, sat forward and looked around. If we had stopped here, we could see how the adults had assumed this reenactment was an oral rape with semen discharge on her neck.

I encouraged Melissa to create her own beautiful "Safe Place" in her "mind's eye" which is also known as the imagination. This is ordinarily created before induction but given her spontaneous reenactment I did it here. I encouraged her to visualize by giving examples using different senses: "You could think of walking in a colorful meadow of flowers, imagine sitting in grandma's kitchen breathing in the smell of fresh baked cookies or feel yourself floating peacefully along in a soft, cottony cloud. You decide." Given her reenactment, none of the imagery included that she lay down.

She nodded.

"This is your special, 'Safe Place,' just for you." This creation, kept to herself, would allow me to take her back through the traumatic memory, returning her to her "Safe Place" for support when necessary. Also, this would teach her a lifetime coping skill for learning to self-sooth.

I circled back, "Melissa, tell me about your neck?"

She pulled down the collar of her roll neck sweater and revealed a fine lined, two-inch scar on the right, anterior side of her neck.

"What happened?"

This reactivated her. She leaned back in the chair, closed her eyes, tilted her head back and opened her mouth.

"Quiet" she began again, same deep tone, same severe demand.

"Who tells you to be quiet?" I interjected.

M: "The lady."

I was surprised to hear this voice was female. "What is *she* doing?" I could now ask using the gender that she had indicated.

M: "Squirting the sticky stuff."

"What happens next?"

M: "She's rubbing a thing on the stuff.

"And…"

M: "I can see it on the TV." Melissa began to cry.

"Put your hands over your eyes if you do not want to see it," I suggested, encouraging movement and control over her experience. She immediately covered her eyes. "You can peek or move your hands away from your eyes whenever you want, if you want," I added, further allowing her to modulate the intrusion with her own power.

Shortly thereafter, to develop her sense of control over the memory, I said, including simple hypnotic power words, "*Remember* your 'Safe Place,' *imagine* you are there *now, because* it calms *you.*"

She relaxed and then after a minute she reopened her mouth wide again as if it was happening in the 'here and now.'

"What's in your mouth?

"Nothing" she answered shaking her head. She reopened her mouth.

I playfully peeked in, while seriously ruling out any bruising to the back of her mouth. An oral exam at the dentist would provide an opportunity to examine the gums and throat properly and also rule out the possibility this was an oral rape.

"I've got to stay like this," she informed me then reopened her mouth.

"No you don't. Not anymore. Speak freely and tell me what happened when you had to stay like that."

M: "She can see it better on the TV…"

"See what?"

M: "The globbery," she said, with emotional control now, covering her eyes and intermittently spreading her fingers to "peek."

"What is the globbery?"

M: "It's in my neck," she said impatiently.

I assisted her to the end of her traumatic memory then reinforced, "Remember, whenever you want or need, you can go to your 'Safe Place' in your imagination."

To close, I guided her to what Thomas and I called, "Return to Security and Comfort." According to Melissa, this was not until she returned home from the ultrasound procedure and was snuggling with her cat. This positive closure is critical to the calming and healing process. It allows for the creation of new pathways in the brain to improve flexibility, adaptability and resilience.

Next, to help her process her experience in words but without having to reenact with her body, I gave her the task of drawing what she had seen in her mind's eye. As if re-seeing them, she drew the details from the procedure in the order she had experienced them. As she explained each drawing, I labeled them to clarify her vague language with specific words. For example, "lady" was nurse; "stuff" - gel; and "thing" - wand.

And as she talked about her drawing of "the *globbery" I carefully wondered out loud, "Was that a 'cyst?'"

"Yeah," she remembered, "that's the globbery."

Then she drew the final object she had seen during her "Return to Security and Comfort." It was her cat Gertrude, similar in size and artistry to the previous rendition, except this end of the assessment drawing validated a healing because the neck was without shading (Figure 10).

"All better," she confirmed, with a smile that matched the big smile of her 'after treatment' cat.

Melissa's healing was also demonstrated in her altered perception, the cat's orientation, now walking to the left, considered to be in the direction of 'forward in time' "Here, this is for you."

Figure 10: Drawing of Her Cat
Black Marker, After Treatment, Melissa

"Thank you Melissa," I said, filing it in my bag with her other drawings. We walked out together, she ran past her mother into the clinic's playroom.

Thomas greeted me while the head supervisor, the other and the therapist were silent behind him, tense, arms crossed and I would soon come to learn, united in the prior findings. I told them the "good news: Melissa's reenactment was not a sexual violation." I explained, "it was the traumatic procedure of an ultrasound wand over conductive gel on her neck. I detailed how Melissa had been upset not only by the callous, abrasive, female technician harshly enforcing she keep her mouth open but also by seeing the image on the monitor of what was in her neck." I offered, "I could see how Melissa's reenactment with her vague language could result in your misunderstanding." (I was being generous.)

Children should be given age appropriate information before, during and after examinations and procedures, and parents should insist on being present.

I went on, "Melissa can master this trauma through play therapy and, given her vague and made-up language, she should be assessed for *dyslexia and…"

"Alright, thank you very much," the head supervisor interrupted as if he had tolerated me long enough. "That will be all," he dismissed us and the other two nodded in unison.

"Oh, wait, there is more," I said, my excitement overriding my awareness of their staunch position. As I reached in to take Melissa's drawings out of my bag, Thomas grabbed my hand. I quizzically looked up into his deep brown eyes. And all the events rapidly came together clearly.

Thomas, still holding my hand, led me out. We considered the mother's motivation for alleging sexual abuse during her bitter divorce. Unfortunately, all sorts of false accusations are common during divorce proceedings due to revenge, seeking more money or wanting full custody. We talked about how the mother did not disclose any information about Melissa's ultrasound or surgical procedure; then we even questioned if she had deliberately sent her daughter in wearing a roll neck sweater to conceal her scar.

I phoned the state and reported the case by the name of the clinic and head supervisor, as I did not have a last name of Melissa's family.

I followed up 48 hours later. Then they told me that their investigation indicated no record that I had been involved in a case there. I explained I had done the work pro bono and though I did not have a written check of payment or any evidence my professional involvement, I deemed that irrelevant. After all, anyone can make a report. I wrote up a report attached the explicit drawings, (inadmissible in court), and mailed copies to the state, the clinic's chief physician, the head supervisor who had requested the second opinion, and the therapist.

Next, I phoned the head supervisor. He confirmed that, "the claims of sexual abuse were being pursued."

"This is a mistake. Let me explain," I said.

He responded with no curiosity, "The decision has been made."

"You must know the truth. Read the report I sent you and call me back."

He did not return my call.

I phoned him again… and again.

No response from any of them on any of it.

Thomas and I discussed this case numerous times. We were powerless. As psychotherapists, it is difficult for us when do not get to follow our cases through to a healthy closure and especially given this scenario.

One night we stayed up later than usual. He briefed me, "The Navy was fully informed about your assessment and about you." He said, "We have done what we can. The Navy has its own process, they handle their own. Let it go 'Sweetness-Kindness-Niceness,'" his nickname for me, in a world that had not shown him such things.

Thomas awoke that night, back in Vietnam, heart racing, body reacting to sights and sounds I could not see or hear. Despite controversial research and political denial, my Tommy suffered from Combat-Related PTSD. Judith Hermann would describe this as *Complex-PTSD in her groundbreaking work this year, *Trauma and Recovery* (1992).

"Tommy, I am turning on the light," I warned just as we had planned. We even purchased a dimmer lamp providing softer lighting, specifically for this. Little did we realize that the "chakchak" sound of the off/on dial in the silent Vietnam night was like the cocking of a shotgun. He dove off the bed. He sought shelter on the floor, breath shallow, body motionless.

I reassured him he was safe and attempted to ground him with his name in the present day, at our location, and with me.

"Tommy. You are having a memory."

"Tommy… notice where you are, you can look around and you can see you are safe because you are on American soil. You are home with me."

"Tommy, Tommy, have some of my water." I was inviting distraction, movement, and a temperature change.

"Tommy, here, let me put your blanket around you." It was a weighted blanket I made for him, unable to find such a product in this time before Amazon. I sewed dozens of pockets to evenly distribute several thousand popcorn kernels totaling 10% of his body weight. This comforting blanket was designed to counterbalance the physical sensations he experienced.

Smell is our most powerful sense and can be a part of a flashback (or even activate one.) So because Thomas had complained of the "stench" during a past flashback I added the strong fragrance of lavender to the blanket pockets to attempt to counter that offensive smell. Also, lavender was from a recent sweet memory together. "Remember when we walked the beautiful, purple meadow (avoiding trigger words like fields, he associated with killing fields) and picked these lavender flowers.

Breathe in their comforting smell, feel the calming effect of the lavender. Remember, the flowers even made the bees tranquil."

Soon, I guided Thomas to the "Safe Place" in his mind's eye. For Tommy, this was an internal, pristine place where he was at one with God. He remained there for a while and when he was ready, he nodded, and just as we planned, I guided him to "Return to Security and Comfort." For Thomas, this was not until he was back on American soil.

He was ice cold. I asked if I could stroke his forehead and tell him a story. He nodded and I told him a beautiful story from our weekend. This soothed and lulled him back to sleep. This larger than life man who loved his country, a brilliant doctor who helped so many by day, slept the remainder of the night on the floor, curled in a ball.

The next morning he awoke, numb, back here in 1992, his memories of the war waiting, neatly folded back into the tightly tucked sheets of our freshly made bed, waiting… for him to come to bed with emotion and without alcohol to block his REM sleep, waiting… for him to dare to enter REM sleep where fragments of trauma awaken, waiting… until next time. Since Thomas had given me ongoing permission to speak with his psychotherapist.

I phoned Dr. Gary to update, confer and also to receive my own support. Gary, who was tortured in Vietnam, had been trained by Thomas on how to use hypnosis to manage his physical and emotional pain.

Their deep camaraderie from the anguish over the atrocities experienced in the war created a profound connection that made each the ideal doctor for the other.

Gary thoughtfully uses the word 'set-off' rather than triggered with military veterans. He explained to me that while Thomas' had excellent control over his daily life he was most likely set-off by feelings of helplessness. This began for Thomas when he was a Navy SEAL captain and survived but was unable to save the lives of the other members of his team.

Last night, his feelings of helplessness were activated when we were left to conclude that Melissa did not get the treatment she required for her traumatic ultrasound experience; Melissa's father's reputation, Navy career and family life were destroyed; and this innocent girl would grow up falsely believing a story told her, that her father had molested her.

After my call with Gary, Tommy and I discussed an expression from William Shakespeare's *Merchant of Venice*, "Truth will out."

Truth lives in Melissa, in her tears when she refuses further examinations, in her mind where she remembers someone teaching her about a "Safe Place" she still goes to, in the sensations of being touched on the neck, in her slumped posture forming a question mark beckoning to be answered, and in her heart where ultimately she knows who her father really is.

While I do not have PTSD, I keep praying…thinking… *reworking…

Nowadays Addendum – 2018

Upon finishing the writing of this chapter I took a deep breath in through my nose then out, long from my nose. My mind wandered. I found Melissa in my daydream. Somehow, someone mentions this story to her, the details, the drawings. She touches her neck scar and suddenly it all resonates 'true for her.' This begins her journey and her father's, all these years later, into healing and home to Truth.

Addendum - Celebrating with Davisman - 1992

It was my thirtieth birthday. I was out to dinner with the Musketeers and a few other friends. Thomas and I had broken up.

After dinner in a private moment, Davisman gave me a red velvet box. I opened it slowly.

"Oh my God, it's beautiful, it's…it's incredibly extravagant. Davisman, I want this, but I really cannot accept it." I was flustered.

"What? Wait, oh Jules, you know, they're not real diamonds, right? He said looking nervous.

Oh I laughed awkwardly, of course." My breath caught, "Of course," I repeated, "you threw me there with the extravagant name brand and fancy box…"

"Yeah, yeah, I got that box from Ma, red like your lips." He was red like my lips.

"Why are you embarrassed?" I smiled, "I love it, it's perfect." He put the bracelet on my right wrist and I never took it off.

CHAPTER SEVEN, 24 YEARS AGO, 1993

The Internal Family

"You don't know my story.
You only know the page you met me on."

-Unknown

"CAN YOU COME DOWN TO THE COURTHOUSE RIGHT NOW?" begged his desperate mother, phoning from Juvenile Court. "I am worried he is not going to behave." We talked for several minutes and, based on what she told me, I put forth a plan.

"I will be right there," I said, responding to her urgency. Then I stopped along the way and bought candy.

A 12-year-old, nicknamed "Gangsta" was caught spray-painting graffiti down by the mall. I observed him in the hallway outside the courtroom; his forehead was wide, eyes deep. I did not know this boy. He looked so different. He saw me, pushed roughly through the crowd, transforming as he approached me. He embraced me tightly. He was shaking. It was Bart.

His was now at my height "It is okay," I whispered in his ear though I was not sure it was. "We are going to help you" that I was certain of. His mother looked on and attempted a smile.

From my recent work with several dissociative patients, my phone conversation with his mother, a flood of memories from our sessions and my brief observation here, it was evident Bart had Multiple Personality Disorder (MPD), that is, until next year when it would be renamed, Dissociative Identity Disorder (Diagnostic and Statistical Manual of Mental Disorders (DSM-IV-TR).

Once we were in the courtroom, I fed Bart the peanut butter cups I had just purchased to keep Bart present. The plan was to prevent the identity, "Gangsta," from coming out during the hearing and causing further trouble.

After Bart's hearing began, the judge put down the records and addressed me, "What is going on here? Is this like ADHD or something? My grandkid has that."

"Yes, your honor," I agreed, figuring at least one of the identities could have been diagnosed with Attention Deficit Hyperactivity Disorder. And that was it.

Bart, confused and innocent, was sentenced to 20 hours of community service, cleaning up graffiti around the city. Further, he was mandated to attend twice-weekly therapy sessions with me. Of course, the identity "Gangsta," was scot-free, at least until I caught up with him in therapy.

DID is characterized by the presence of two or more distinct personality states. This condition results from extreme and repetitive trauma in a child five years of age or younger. Typically, it is not until the teen years that a patient begins reporting the loss of time. When they are younger, the parts are less distinct and children are less able to explain what is happening, while adults are more likely to think the child is pretending to be someone else.

From our past work, my relationship with Bart was already strong; he felt safe expressing himself and had previously remembered and processed many painful memories. So the next step was to begin work on identifying identities, "reconnecting" and building their inner relationships. The ultimate task would be for all the identities to integrate into one, well-functioning individual. There was one caveat; Bart knew nothing of any of them.

Bart and I began our first session back together with my usual three drawing request, H-T-KFD. Right before he finished drawing his kinetic family drawing, he shifted in his seat and drew a slash on the arm of his illustration of himself. He shifted again. I would have missed this if I had not been sitting directly opposite, observing.

Specifically, another identity came in, drew a quick slash towards himself, indicative of self-harm, exited and it was Bart again.

"Roll up your sleeves," I said with concern.

He complied and sure enough, just as the drawing and gesture informed, he had superficial lacerations all over his arms. Bart was shocked.

With a stern voice I called out this identity, "Who did this?"

His eyes flickered, he stood up and gestured in an unfamiliar fashion, "Me. It look coool." I would soon understand his accent and mannerisms to be Latin American.

"And you are?"

"Terror," he said in a taunting manner.

"No *cutting the body, Terror." I said firmly, making it clear that I was in charge and unimpressed. It was vital I came across authoritatively, especially as I did not know how aggressive or dangerous this identity was.

To my horror, he reached into his pocket and pulled out a knife. Then, to my surprise, he slammed it down on the table. With a shaky hand I took it. "Any other weapons?" I demanded, way beyond any training I had ever had.

"Nope," he said while patting himself down for effect.

Given Terror said he cut for looks, I gave him a red pen and told him, "From now on, if you must, then draw it on. Now, sit down." I was acting tough, not really my nature, underneath I was terrified.

I maintained eye contact as I proceeded with my plan to have him draw me an "inner map" of sorts, a map that represented identities, status, control and any other details he could provide. I steadied myself as I took a piece of paper and wrote "Terror" on the left side about ¼ of the way down. "Terror, do you know Bart?" I asked saying Bart's name quietly, careful not to inadvertently call Bart back out.

"Niiice," he responded. I added Bart's name to the

top, center of the paper.

"Terror" I continued, deliberately using his name to confirm it was him and to keep him present, "Do you know Gangsta?"

"Si," he laughed with contempt. Noted but I remained focused.

I wrote "Gangsta" on the right side, ¼ of the way down also. I slid the piece of paper and pencil over to Terror.

"Terror, fill this in to include everyone." I was hoping this format would be effective in getting started in the identification of his "Internal Family."

Without looking at me, Terror picked up the pencil with Bart's right (non-dominant) hand, crossed out the names, drew a radiating sun and centered himself underneath it. He renamed Bart, "Nice" and relocated Gangsta below both of them, at the bottom of the hierarchical structure. Finally, he proceeded to draw numerous bubbles with slashes connecting them. It was messy, yet the locations appeared specific. This was his Internal Family Drawing (IFD). These bubbles would come to represent eighteen different identities!

I stared at his work, astonished, "Tell me about this?"

"I don't know." I looked up recognizing the change to a prepubescent voice.

It was Bart again, confused, his frequent daily experience. "What were we talking about?" I asked to see how long he has been present or aware.

"I don't know," he repeated as if he had just

returned, because he had.

Over the next month, unbeknownst to Bart, Terror continued to visit, detailing what he knew of his internal family. Then Terror requested to illustrate "everybody" on a six-foot-long piece of blank newspaper (Figure 11). The placement, the groups, and the number of identities in each category were an exact match to his initial pencil diagram.

At the top, crowned with a halo, kneeling on fire, was The Almighty Power. Months later when Almighty Power visited, he explained his hand mudra in the sun connects human consciousness with the cosmos, where all is one. This bond brings in universal power, which runs through him and collects in the other hand where healing magnetic energy can then be emitted. This powerful identity, Almighty Power, went on teach me a great deal about working with energies. He began with basics such as telling me to sleep facing North for peace and insisting on moving my desk to work facing east west. He went on to teach me about breath work and swallowing air and he also advanced my skills of protection and healing.

There was a curious fold with excess paper underneath, between Almighty Power and Terror. Terror explained, "Almighty Power floats on air." And to my amazement, Almighty Power would show me how though opening and closing his nostrils, which he did at will, he could lift off the ground. As remarkable as this was, I was still concerned that additional hidden identities were occupying that hidden space, unbeknownst to

Terror.

Underneath Almighty Power and Terror were three groups of identities: "The Children"; "The Protectors"; and "The Other Guys." These groups were then further divided into distinct identities. Some of the individual details can be seen in the illustration on the next page, such as emotion, handwriting and hand dominance.

Amongst the group Terror called "The Children" was Nice/Bart, a baby named Little Boy, and even a dog. "The Children" were sheltered from the knowledge of the aggressive identities by PTKE, The Person Who Knows Everything.

Some of "The Children" were missing lower body parts. While certainly this is an indication of victimization and the inability to get away, it can also suggest they were like hand puppets, controlled by other identities. Not knowing the explanation, but wanting to safeguard "The Children" during Terror's third of the four weeks that he was working on this internal family drawing, I asked him (with the prior permission from his mother) if I could hypnotize him and we could create another identity to aid in protecting "The Children." This nineteenth identity was female, the only female identity. She was named Guardian Angel and assigned to parent, nurture and take care of "The Children's" needs, to keep them safe from inappropriate outings and misuse. For example, she was to keep Little Boy from attending Bart's eighth-grade school and "The Children" from absorbing other identities' alcohol and drugs. The creation of Guardian

Figure 11: Internal Family Drawing
Colored Markers, Terror

was a deliberate iatrogenic treatment, considered controversial at the time. Nevertheless, her guardianship was profoundly effective.

Alongside "The Children," Terror had drawn a cluster known as "The Protectors." They were five identities separated by degrees of rage and vengeance. Their expressions, skin colors, and weapons were thoroughly detailed. They were originally created to defend against threats to Bart's body and mind when he was younger. Their names, according to the single emotion each represented, were Mad, Angry, Crazy, Psycho, and Violent. These "Protectors" were created and responded out of necessity during Bart's past traumatic exposures.

Bart no longer required the intensity of "The Protectors." However, they kept reacting to events with the same extreme emotion causing daily havoc and destruction everywhere in Bart's life. My initial work with each of "The Protectors" was to teach them how to sit quietly with strong emotion and ultimately, to bear witness to the hurt, pain and fear that drove their intense feelings and behaviors. Each learned to separate the past from the present and to protect Bart in a manner commensurate to daily life without trauma.

The lowest group in the power structure located underneath "The Children were "The Other Guys" diminished even by their name. They were a group of three identities, Gangsta, AC en Artist and Master Mix.

AC en Artist was the only identity besides Terror who was drawn in profile. A drawing of a profile suggests evasion, which clued me in, because sometimes when Terror was drawing, I believe AC en Artist, who presented mute, would come in and take over the project. I noticed this because he would transfer the paintbrush to the other hand.

As I reflect on this I can appreciate how intense it sounds. It was. I lived alone at this time and ran Creative Therapies out of my home, yet I was not concerned for my safety. Even my family and friends, who did not know anything about Bart, warned me, someone could just show up anytime, unexpected, uninvited.

I laughed with confidence and, well, ignorance.

Now, Terror enjoyed being what he called a "prankster" and was humorous until he would go too far. I came to recognize Terror easily by the extra movement in his shoulders, they would move up and down, as if laughing to himself or perhaps with others inside.

"Ha, ha, ha," his shoulders moved as we talked about his skill of mailing me a whole, raw egg, cleverly packed so it did not break. To his delight, I responded by giving him a hatched, little toy bird.

"Ha, ha, ha," he amused himself, after a session one evening, as I watched him sculpt bunnies with the freshly fallen snow along my path. When he returned a few days later, he was ecstatic to see I had fed each of his snow bunnies a carrot. "Ha, ha, ha," I imagined him laughing at my 'surprise' when I returned home one night to see he had not only shown up from a nearby event, uninvited, but had spray-painted his name in bubble letters on the concrete below my porch. That night my family and friend's warnings rang through my head and the next day my concerned neighbors, kept showing up - unexpected, ringing my doorbell and wanting more information.

"No, no, no," I responded setting boundaries when Terror arrived in the next session. I handed him a brush and a bucket of my house paint and kept him talking to ensure he did not have another identity do the work for him.

As Terror painted over his graffiti, he confessed it was he who was the spray-painter. So, in court that day, Bart was blamed, Gangsta was covering and Terror had actually done it (it's dizzying, I know). And I think AC en Artist was involved also, whether Terror knew that or not.

Then one night in the late spring, I was jolted awake by a knocking on a downstairs window. I peeked through my bedroom curtains and could tell from the silhouette, sporting his trademark hat, it was Gangsta. It was happening again, another after office hour's unexpected visitor. From my bedroom window I pointed to the office entrance. He backed out of the bushes and strutted around to the office steps.

I changed clothes and hurried through the house to meet him. I was scared. Now wide-awake, the phone in my hand and with only the screen door between us, I attempted to model calm, "Hey Gangsta. What is happening?"

His presence was stronger than usual and his silence louder in the dark shadows of the late hour. Concerned by his lack of response and for my safety, I asserted, "I am going to call your mother so she knows you are here and safe with me."

Still, no response.

I did not let him in. I went back in the house to make the call. When I spoke to his mother she said she did not know he had snuck out, let alone how he traveled the seven miles, across town lines, and found my home. While we were on the phone together, she walked into his bedroom and pulled back the blankets to reveal pillows shaped like a body and a note that read, "You will never see you again."

The usual parent-therapist formalities had dissolved between us, long ago. We were remarkably in tune with quick, clear communication about what to do for his safety and his mental and physical health in a variety of atypical situations. So I came right to the point, "What style is the…

"Graffiti" she responded.

"Ahh, Terror wrote that, which means Gangsta was threatened and must have come to me for protection." Now that I understood he was scared, I was no longer scared myself. In the future, I would remember that while Gangsta looked intimidating, he was more vulnerable inside and I should be more careful about prejudging him.

We agreed Gangsta would stay awhile and I would support him in feeling safe.

After I hung up the phone with his mother, I walked back through the waiting room. An art history book on my coffee table reminded me of the time I observed Gangsta hunched over it, hidden in his clothes, recognizable only by his hat. Where does the hat come from? How does this work? Do the others carry it for him?

I walked back out to the screened-in porch, put down a bucket of art supplies. "Would you like to paint?" I gestured to my porch wall in lieu of canvas.

He opened the screen door, stepped inside and peered into the bucket. THUD! He dropped loudly to his knees and dug through the bucket.

Soon Gangsta was blending paints and mumbled to someone, "These paints make me feel good."

There was so much I wanted to know, even just wanting to know who he was talking to but supporting his calm was all the therapy I planned to do, in this circumstance, at this hour.

After a while I told him I was going inside to call his mother back. I left the door open so he could hear me as I reassured her and reinforced him with details of his ability to calm down.

In this phone call, I was washed over with a feeling of what it must be like to be his mother. In an instant, that empathic experience changed me forever.

Suddenly he called out, "Can I stay over?"

Over the years many children made this enthusiastic request. Which, of course, would be utterly unorthodox and I would never allow. Well, again the exception, in this case, his mother and I agreed he could.

I smiled, "Oh, if my family and friends could see me now."

I returned to Gangsta with warm chamomile tea and

a tin of midnight, well, after-midnight, snacks. Yes, it included peanut butter cups, just in case.

This night, as he painted and we talked, I got to know Gangsta. I found he had this unexpected, incredibly tender, way about him. He grew very dear to me.

Gangsta must have painted most of the night because when I woke up, not realizing I had fallen asleep, there was a painting of a completely different style than I had seen from other identities. My entire 15-foot porch wall was not the art of young Bart or the cartoonish, bubble work of Terror. It appeared that Gangsta must have a photographic memory, because there on my porch wall was a remarkable reproduction of Leonardo Da Vinci's, *The Last Supper.*

I put a blanket around the boy with soft facial features, sound asleep on a porch lounge chair. This was Bart. When he awoke, once again, he looked confused. Without overwhelming him with details of identities he had yet to know of, I comforted him. I explained that his mother and I agreed to have him sleep over. I would take him home to get ready then I would drive him to school. He rarely questioned anything. Also, what I did not say was I had made this offer to his mother so she could be on time for her work. Her job was in jeopardy due to her habitual tardiness and absenteeism from the demands of parenting Bart et alia.

As we walked out of my home, he paid no mind to the masterpiece on my porch wall. When we arrived at his home, Bart ran off to change while I waited in the den. Ahead of me, I saw hundreds of peanut butter cup wrappers, intricately stacked high in the form of a tower. The wrappers were piled up in 5 columns inexplicably counterbalanced by leaning into one another.

As Bart entered the room, I asked, "How did you attach all these…?" and as I reached out in curiosity to answer my own question, the extraordinary creation fluttered to pieces in a delicate crash.

"Nooo," yelled Little Boy bursting into tears. He and I had recently celebrated his third birthday, and with this new stage of development he was generally more apt to smile and ask a question than previously when he would drop into a "*Happy Baby pose." At this moment, however, he was clearly distressed.

"Oh, I-I am so sorry" I stammered wanting to manage his upset while not showing him my own. "Shall I rebuild it?" I asked, unrealistically.

"No." It was Guardian responding, now. She was easily recognizable in just a word with her warm, soothing, female voice. And of course, as the implementer of rules. she said, "Nice has to go to school."

"Oh, of course," I said, hoping I was keeping up with who was who.

"Oh, of course, what?" It was Bart again. He stood in front of me, touching his face, surprised to find tears.

As I wiped those Little Boy tears away, I informed Bart I had accidentally knocked down the tower and I was very sorry. He brushed it off like it was no big deal, more likely an indication it was not Bart's tower or moreover, he did not even know about it. I was left wondering, *who built it? Who knew about it? How many would be upset? And not for nothing, but how on earth was it built?* Many nights I was kept awake by questions like these and more. I would write in my journal until my mind quieted enough to fall asleep.

Putting these thoughts aside for now, I called out, "Race you!" And we both ran out to my car. I drove Bart to his new alternative school. He had the passenger side window down again, head out, wind blowing through his hair, taking in the morning sights and smells. The sun warmed on his smiling face.

When I pulled into the school parking lot, Bart asked, "Was I at your house because something in my head scared something in my body?" I was thrilled with this question because for the first time he was asking me about a perceived separation: of different parts (identities) within himself. He was awakening, experiencing a breakthrough in his awareness, where previously there were only inexplicable, absences of time.

By summer, in therapy, we were building relationships between identities and developing their ability to recognize, get along and care about one another: problems were admitted, choices explored and new healthy actions taken. I scripted them with techniques such as a "Three-Step What-Where-Clarification": 1. What do you feel? 2. Where in your body do you feel that?" and "3. So, what you're saying is…did I get that right?" These techniques aided the identities in being found, known, accepted and united. This work soon progressed to where the identities were able to do the process in-between sessions amongst themselves. For example, Terror had been having self-esteem and anger outbursts in response to no longer being the gatekeeper, controlling who came out.

However, Gangsta was no longer afraid of Terror's empty threats, and he began reporting to me the following "Three Step What-Where-Clarification" technique:

I asked Terror, 1. "Terror, What do you feel?"

"Tension, fury, I want to cut you." While this was alarming to hear, Gangsta was no longer afraid of Terror. He knew now Terror had not cut since entering treatment and besides he did it for looks, not to harm. Though all threats must be taken seriously, this appeared similar to "a near discharge regression or test" or actually in this case, "a near integration," than something he was actually going to do.

Meanwhile, Gangsta bravely remained on task with the three steps. 2. "Where in your body do you feel that?"

"Wherever you are," Terror hesitated, laughed and reneged, "I know, I know, it you, too."

3. "So what you're saying is, you are tense and furious and want to cut, but my body is your body? Did I get that right?"

"Si," Terror softened.

"Then let's go for a run! It'll help," Gangsta encouraged and Terror accepted.

As I listened to this report, their separateness intermingled with blurred voices and blended mannerisms. Over a short time their ability to communicate built an understanding and trust that resulted in an unexpected friendship that flowed into Gangsta and Terror's spontaneous *integration.

For two years we built relationships and integrated identities. Of course, integration was their choice and sometimes identities were not willing to give up their separateness. However, the more communication and subsequent healing that happened, the greater the identities' desire to be known, accepted and eventually agreeable to being strengthened by integrating into one.

The work continued after integration to develop meditation skills, regulate behavior and manage a full range of emotions, including his *grief from a lost childhood.

Then, and only then, did the Self feel safe to emerge. He requested to be called by the name, One.

I told One and his mother, who smiled these days, that while he had the skills of awareness, he could still split under stress and must, therefore, continue his healing work every day. Also, he would without a doubt, require additional therapy soon, as a young adult and throughout life. Through the years he would have to seek out care and support to maintain a healthy integration, reinforce old skills and adapt with new coping mechanisms. He was also to continue self-care such as manage his susceptibility to stress, use no alcohol or drugs, beware of overstimulation and exhaustion, and of course, he was to avoid scary movies.

When it was time for One to walk out my door for the very last time, now taller than me he bowed and let me kiss his forehead.

I liken that moment to a passage in Hermann Hesse's beautiful book, *Siddhartha.* "Govinda kissed Siddhartha and saw an unending stream of people Siddhartha had been, from many lifetimes. Govinda saw their faces and images of pain and joy all shifting into one another."

One walked out free and peaceful. He turned back and the last words he said to me that remarkable day were,

"Every One needs some one like you."

The Davisman Addendum - 2018

"Mmmmm," he said finally getting to reexamine Terror's Internal Family Drawing.

"…What about the dog?"

"Max," I smiled. Max is in both Bart chapters. I did not mention him at the time, because I did not know it was him. And I was concerned readers would not find him believable.

"You must tell."

"Well let me ask you this, did you catch him anywhere? "

"Was Max the one who bit your arm?"

"Yes."

"Where else was he?"

"It was Max who ran up and down the hill in my backyard and ate dog biscuits with Grover."

"Max was the one that bit and buried the demon I made out of polymer clay."

"It was sweet Max who had his head out the window, sniffing his location, when I thought I was driving Bart to school."

"I also learned later, it was Max with AC en Artist who defended Gangsta from Terror that night Terror threatened Gangsta. In a time before GPS one might assume Max had used his powerful doggy sense of smell to follow his scent back to my home. However, Almighty Power explained it was actually Max's sensitivity to the Earth's magnetic fields. Either way, when Max found my home, AC en Artist, who was mute, took over, disguised as Gangsta, and knocked on my window to seek my help. Gangsta did not actually 'come out' until I invited AC, thinking it was Gangsta to paint."

"What?"

"See what I mean? It is complicated and I can appreciate, hard to follow let alone- believe. But all the same, finally, one sad yet so beautiful day in my garden, Max, with the support of homemade Doggy-People Biscuits, was integrated, amongst the crisp leaves that remind me of him every fall."

"You have to put this in, let your reader decide it's validity."

Davisman snuck me a piece of paper.

I raised an eyebrow, "That's a curious fold," I whispered implying it could also be hiding something.

As I went to unfold it, he reached for and held my hands. With our hands intertwined I leaned forward and one of his hands long and hard, leaving him with a beautiful red lipstick kiss.

When I was alone, I read what he wrote and it made me cry…it still does.

A Third "Out of the Dark" Visitor – 1993

I was, as I often was, working on my computer in the kitchen nook, late at night, when one more unexpected caller showed up without invitation. It was after midnight. There was a light tapping on the kitchen back door. Alarmed, I looked around from the nook and saw the doorknob jiggling.

My heart pounding, "Who is it?" I called out deepening my voice.

"Jules?"

"Day…H-Hulk? I asked coming towards the door.

"Come out."

"It's too late," I replied.

"Let me in."

"I am not dressed for company," I said standing there in a pretty, little nightie.

"Maybe you are," he flirted. "Can I, can we…"

I hesitated, then unlocked the door, stepped back and let the Musketeer in. He walked in slowly. He was different, alluring, emitting a sexual energy. He reached out and put his hands on my shoulders. I had not been touched by a man in, evidently, far too long. His touch was sensual, playful, warm, yes getting warmer…

"Are you in love with Davisman?"

"What?" I short-circuited.

He whispered his own secret.

I retracted from his touch, suddenly uncertain how to move or what to say. I stumbled over my words, "Oh! Thank you for telling me, I mean, I'm glad you told me. I mean…"

Clearly that was not the response he was looking for. He turned away from me, "Forget it," he defended quietly and left back into the dark.

I called after him, "Hulk, don't go."

He was gone.

PART TWO, Two Years Later, 1995
Because I Knew You – Heart and Soul

"Then, when I experienced a potentially threatening event in my own life, I found strength in Gangsta's familiarity, protection in Almighty Power's lesson on light, and healing in an exercise I had created for supporting integration into One. "

A YOUNG MAN WHO REMINDED ME OF GANGSTA STRUTTED TOWARDS ME. I had been holiday shopping in the city and was returning to my car, balancing shopping bags and boxes of wrapped presents. I was walking by myself through a construction area where a sidewalk had been made for pedestrians, though walled up more like a tunnel, and blocking the view of drivers, or any other witnesses.

Only as he came closer did I realize there was no one else around. He had Gangsta's look, attitude and even his walk. It did not escape me that Gangsta meant "gang member," and in this moment I was going to be mugged.

However, fortified by knowing Gangsta, I did not freeze, rather I smiled at him with familiarity.

He responded, eyes cast down, "What's with you?"

"Oh," I said deliberately seeking eye contact to prevent his attack, "you look like someone dear to me."

He stopped in my path, standing wide and far too close.

So… I passed him my boxes.

"Oh thank you," I blurted out. "I appreciate your help." I suggested as my favorite bag fell off my shoulder into the crook of my arm where we both watched it dangle in a time warp, slowly b-a-c-k and f-o-r-t-h.

Here is what happened in the next few seconds of my perceived distortion in time.

First. I began listing items in my mind, *What is in my bag?* To manage my anxiety and with the awareness that it all might be stolen. *Wallet, cash, ugh, the renewal of my license, the inconvenience of calling the credit card companies, my favorite lipstick—do they still make that color?—oh no, my little jar of pearls from my energy lessons with the Almighty Power.*

Next, still talking to myself. *Ahh, protection, that is what I need, protective light.* So, with every breath, albeit fast and shallow, I expanded my inner pearl of light to fill and overflow me. And because Universal energy goes where it needs to go it extended beyond me to create a single, pulsing bubble of light that encapsulated this young man as well!

And then. Instantaneously, he turned around and without a word, off we went, walking as one to my Audi. And hopefully, he would not be high jacking that, as well.

Time reset. We continued along in this construction tunnel when from around a hidden corner suddenly ahead of us, two more men appeared. This terrified me as I remembered hearing about three muggers who worked in tandem to injure, snatch and relay away with the goods. My knees were buckling above my previously awesome, suddenly ridiculous high heel shoes.

I just kept moving, listing… *silver teaspoon, worn clipping, Tiffanies pen…* And then I observed peripherally this young man, carrying my packages, ever so subtly, shake his head at the two approaching men, "No."

They stomped, hissed and gestured but passed by… *watercolor pencils, Rescue Remedy – I am going to need that.* And finally, we came out the other end of the tunnel.

As we continued to walk he broke the silence between us, which masked the noise within me, "Do you really know someone who looks like me?" He seemed genuinely interested.

"Yes," then turning towards him, "I know all the parts of him and love him very much."

This evoked in him an admission at the root of it all, "Nobody ever loved me."

"Their loss" I said, uncertain I should have added that. We stared at one another. He looked like a rejected little boy. He was sad. I was sad for him.

There are times in therapy when the anger a patient is experiencing is becoming so great that I will deliberately aid in care and management by moving the patient beneath to the sadness. A technique that can also be used in reverse to create energy where there is apathy. In this case, a potentially violent young man had been assuaged towards sadness.

"There's my car!" I revealed on an overdue exhale and pointed into the distance. This revealed from under my glove sparkling diamonds, which unbeknownst to him, were cubic zirconia and to me, were priceless.

He put the gift boxes in my car and closed the trunk.

"Thank you, you are a gentleman."

I opened my bag.

"We're cool," he assured me, perhaps thinking I was going to tip him.

But instead of money I took out my little jar of lustrous pearls and tapped one into his welcoming palm. He cradled this delicate, iridescent ball of light in his soiled, large hand and it found its way like a tiny grain of sand, into the thick palm crease of his short life line.

I said, "This represents the pearl of light that lives in your…

"…My soul?"

"Soul" I repeated. I was going to say 'heart' but wow, soul, his beautiful soul.

"This pearl is a reminder to keep its image within you. Then, anytime, as you breathe you can expand its protective, healing light until it fills you up and overflows around you."

"You are never alone," I said to this abandoned boy, who had not been taught to live in relationship with life.

He looked up from the pearl in his hand and searched my eyes. Something meaningful had resonated with him. I wondered, if he had sensed that we just basked in that light. He closed his hand around the pearl and shook his fist with determination.

He lowered his head and backed away.

I don't remember the drive home. I walked in my front door and collapsed.

I reported the safety concerns of the tunnel to the police. Then, I phoned Davisman, still in the city, in his second of four years of residency. I told him everything.

He reprimanded, "That was dangerous of you to predict a mugger's intentions by reading his emotions and what? Based on his similarities with Gan…esha…whateva."

I was tender and his strong reaction hurt because I needed his support in this vulnerable moment. I quietly corrected, "Gangsta."

There was silence. I continued, "I understand what you're saying, Davisman. You know, one of my life challenges is managing my empathy versus, I don't know, versus I don't even know what the opposite of that would be."

"Dis-en-gage Jules. That's what it is, discharge, vacate, scram, take your pick, but exit stage right Scrabblepuss."

"Ok, ok, but we need another name for 'mugger.'"

"What?!" he spewed. Clearly, his upset was magnified by his personal issues, which were poorly managed due to his 30-hour shifts at the hospital.

"I do not see him as a 'mugger.' You are going to have to honor my belief system, Davisman. You know the power of words and their impact on health and also how critical my perception is in the prevention of PTSD right now. You accidentally referred to him as "Ganesha," who is the deity of learning, so that's what we are going to call him."

"That's it!" exclaimed Davisman, his throat tightening and with that he made his exit. He hung up.

A few minutes later my phone rang. I picked up, "I

am listening."

"Hey, it's me."

"Who?" I asked, expecting Davisman with my apology. "Hulk!" he said, as if we had just chatted yesterday. It had been over two years.

"Hulk? Hi, Hulk. So, so Davisman asked you to call me..."

"One for all and all for one." He said sounding much happier than he felt." Let me help you," he said cutting through all the unspoken words between us.

I exhaled, suddenly able to let down and I gratefully accepted his offer. During this call we planned out a therapeutic process, which included the identification of my 'point of trauma.' For me, that was when the other two men approached in the tunnel.

The following Sunday, as planned, when the sun was rising, Hulk came over to my home and let himself in the kitchen entrance. When I went to embrace him he smiled exposing a lemon wedge.

"What are you doing there Hulk?"

He slurped, eyes watering, "Baking thoda in a lemon 'toof tway.' It's a toof whitenur."

"I think after a short time it's an enamel eroder."

"Oh thit," he spat the wedge into his hand. "I'll put this down your garbage disposal. It'll freshen it." He said this oozing white foam, spitting in my sink, rinsing and spitting again. Then he stood tall, flipped the switch and smiled his pearly whites.

As adorable as he was, I still thought for him to come over after all this time, in such a display, was an intimacy barrier.

Shortly thereafter, as we had arranged, I drove us back into the city. I parked in the same spot, vacant with the early hour. Then we walked to 'the tunnel' to work through my traumatic experience. While there, we role-played through the events as they had happened. It was wonderfully cathartic. Then we repeated them at a fast pace and in reverse to make the events malleable until I mastered the experience. For me, this included working through the fear, resolving helplessness and other strong emotions, assimilating, integrating, establishing control and finding meaning. For me this was found in exploring how my conversation with Ganesha opened my heart and soul and I hoped, his also.

Finally, Hulk and I sang and danced through the tunnel tossing pearls of light wherever we felt inclined. We then did the mind's eye return to "Security and Comfort," which for me was when I had returned home.

Thereafter whenever I thought about that event, just like I taught others, I remembered:

It is vital to train your brain so that every time you recall a traumatic event, you fast forward through it in your mind's eye to the time after the trauma, when

you were secure and comfortable.

We drove to Creative Therapies. I showed Hulk the playrooms. Then we sat in the Family Room. I wanted to talk about us, what he told me back in my kitchen. How sad and lonely it was for me when he transferred down south to complete his doctorate soon after that exchange.

He responded, "Let it go. Let's talk about something else. Tell me about your practice."

"I will let it go… for now." I said. After all, we both knew it was not gone.

We spent the remainder of the morning discussing psychotherapy and treatments in our practices. I told him about various therapeutic cards I created and, in particular, about a revised set inspired by my work with a patient with DID.

I picked up four index cards. For example, I shared with Hulk, how we all have our own "Internal Family," typically not comprised of separate identities, but created as a result of unresolved childhood hurts at different ages and stages. I called this healing technique, "What, Where, Show and Tell."

As I explained it, I wrote the script for the technique on the card then passed them to him. "I'll go first," I said thinking we were going to take turns. We were not.

Hulk read the first card, titled, "What: What do you feel?"

I closed my eyes and took a deep breath, excited to be doing this for the first time—and with Hulk but what I wanted to explore were my feelings of being frightened.

"Scared," I said out loud.

With expertise, engagement and ease Hulk softly continued with the second card filling in the blank with my description. "Where? Where in your body do you feel *scared*?"

"In my heart," I said with certainty, as my inner Witness who hears my thoughts informed me with immediacy.

Hulk read the third card, which began with honoring my feeling, "Show: Thank you 'Scared' for your protection. Please show us who or what you are safekeeping *in her heart.*"

"Oh…it is little me," I whispered to Hulk, and I did not say anything more to him for the remainder of the process.

There, in my mind's eye, I could see my quiet, little, 8-year old self, sitting alone on a playground, frightened by those around me. My heart skipped a beat.

The children teased me for my English accent, whispered about my dresses and excluded me. They ran off with my Smile Bag, which contained the few childhood treasures I had arrived in America with: a red diary; a little white bear my Mum had sewn; and my three Spirograph pictures.

"Oh! How could I have forgotten her?"

After a while, Hulk finely attuned with my body language, knew just when to gently read from the fourth and final card entitled, "Tell: When you are ready, have your 'adult-wise-self' step in and tell her how you can help *her*."

I greeted my abandoned little girl with a welcome that no other face had offered, and told her, "I will keep you safe."

Suddenly, I became aware of a need in Hulk. Though I was not reconciled in the healing with my 8-year old self, I stopped the process prematurely, put her back in my heart, and figured, *She'll be back*, not realizing she would return years later with fervor.

I opened my eyes and when I did, I caught something in Hulk's, retreat. I think the process had stirred his childhood pain.

"Hulk," I asked,

"Who would we be if we were never abandoned as children?"

I asked, casually tossing him a pearl from the oyster shell on my side table.

He caught it. "Thanks" he said not answering my question. He was irritated.

I made another attempt, wanting to meet in our hearts, just for this moment,

"What if we offered unconditional acceptance to our inner feelings?"

He jumped up, there were tears in his eyes. "I gotta go," he said apologetically. "Can I have these?"

"Of course." I stood up also. "Hulk, thank you for all your help today. It was really good to see you."

He busied himself crumpling the four cards into his pocket avoiding a hug, then left as awkwardly as he had arrived.

Maybe, I should not have pushed, I thought to myself. He was home now, but with this emotional disconnect, I was missing him more than ever. I was pained by his boundaries and confused that as two therapists, with all our skills, we had not been able to have the emotional, intimate conversation I wanted to have. And that was the point – it was only me who wanted to have it. I had to accept he was just not ready.

CHAPTER EIGHT, 23 YEARS AGO, 1994

Star-the-Adopted-Seal
A Family Awakens

"Enter into children's play and you will find the place where their minds, hearts and souls meet."

-Virginia Axline

"ACCEPT HIM AS HE IS."

"That's it? That's your parenting tip here?" The mother's words quickened, "We need serious help with this kid and that's all you got. Thanks a lot." Rita was quick to get frustrated and to attack with sarcasm.

Needless to say, my initial intake with Lester's parents, Sam (35) and Rita (39), was not going well. It had begun with Rita's projections of her disappointments and inadequacies laden onto Lester, then the school, the previous therapist, and now she was honing-in on me.

This had not been the typical heartfelt first meeting I was used to. There was a detached frostiness to this mother and an unabashed drowsiness to the father. The joy and love in being Lester's parents was missing. They shared no heartfelt stories, nor described any real understanding of, or curiosity about, him.

While Rita answered all my questions, even those directed at her husband, she was not forthcoming and she frequently responded abruptly with a *negative explanatory style. This attitude in mothers often rendered children vulnerable to pessimism and, as teenagers, depression. This orientation in Rita was so strong that all issues were Lester's fault. She was fraught with the emotional distress of blaming and shaming which like a caul would only temporarily protect her gestating sadness.

In response to my questions she described Lester as "lost," "disconnected," "unaffectionate," "weak," and "lazy." She said he "never smiled," "still wets his bed," "always ruins dinners," and "keeps us up late at night always interrupting our sleep." And, she said, he is "soooo jealous of Christopher," his brother. It was all about what was wrong and needed correction, with no connection. Rita said Lester had "ruined our lives." She seemed on the cusp of wanting him re-homed.

Rita wasn't ready yet for my questions about this sense of disconnection between her and her son. I wondered, *How was Lester's withdrawal his way of giving his mother what she wanted (as children often do at the expense of self)?* And, *How is his presentation a reenactment of his mother's past with presents for her to resolve?*

Rita and Sam were told they could not have children naturally so they adopted Lester, a dark-skinned, 18-month old boy from Ecuador. Thereby, Rita did not have the experience of mother-infant intimacy where precious bonding connects the baby to the mother through feelings of safety she provides him and the mother to the baby through the reassurance he provides her.

This initial bonding at the beginning of an infant's life, is where parents are invited by the infant to become aware of the present as-is moment: "bond with me," "sleep by my cycles," "feed me immediately," and "change my diaper…many times a day. This essential bonding when parents allow the infant's needs to supersede theirs and they accept that "it is what it is," they are gifted with the awakening of their own consciousness.

However back then, what happened next, once the pressure was off, to their great surprise, was Rita got pregnant. It was just one year after they brought Lester home, that Rita had Christopher. Christopher, a fair-skinned, blonde-haired, blue-eyed, father-son lookalike. "Then we had one real son and one adopted." Her tone, let alone her statement broke my heart for Lester.

Flash forward: Rita was told by the school several weeks ago, that Lester, now seven years old, must attend therapy. Rita said to me, "Can you just teach him some social skills!" She rolled her eyes, "*Asperger's." *(Diagnostic and Statistical Manual of Mental Disorders, 2000, DSM IV-TR.)*

Most patients arrive for treatment with a diagnosis in hand. Often young children who have been adopted, arrive with the label *Reactive Attachment Disorder. While at Creative Therapies we read all the paperwork and consult with the diagnosing physician, our treatment is without labels. They get in the way of the true care of the whole person, create self-fulfilling prophecies, and live on in families, schools and big insurance companies' computers, even despite treatment and healing.

Besides, Rita's behavior during our visit included poor social skills, a narrowed interest, a lack of empathy, misinterpretations of her son's condition, and rigid thinking to the extent that she herself could have been considered a candidate for Asperger's Syndrome. Ultimately, without being boxed in by a diagnosis, we would soon come to understand and accurately treat Rita's pain and disconnection also.

Rita made two spontaneous comments: "Do you know we just fired another shrink after two visits?" And, "can you believe he had the audacity to take phone calls during sessions?" Despite the construction of the sentences as questions, these were statements of warning.

During Lester's first session he drifted through the playrooms, at my new and expanded second office. My window shade was halfway down, he intently stared at the solar system glowing on the *Sun Room ceiling. He smiled, looked at me, pulled the shade down a little further, checked in with me again then pulled it all the way down. At the beginning of every session he would pull this shade down, setting the stars aglow and giving the room an evening feel.

This first session, as he bent his neck back, eyes unblinking and took in the night sky, it struck me, he was lonely.

"The stars remind us we're all connected," I said.

He continued staring at them.

My phone, which I ignore during sessions, rang. Perhaps because, like many children, Lester was unaccustomed to an adult not picking up a ringing phone, he ran off towards the sound, "I'll get it!"

"Freeze!" I said. Based on my expectation from his mother's description of him, I was surprised: he followed my instruction and actually froze.

I walked to him, bent to his height and smiled warmly, "Lester," I paused, assuming eye contact would be a challenge, but he responded to his name by looking directly at me. "This is our special time together. We are not going to pick up the phone." He watched me turn off the ringer so we would not be further distracted. Then I playfully called out, "Thaw."

He was not at all like I had been prepared for. I was anticipating inflexibility but instead he laughed and laughed, releasing emotion that needed to be healed. He was friendly and able to give-and-take. He was not socially awkward. He was perfectly capable of attachment and bonding. So while he failed to meet the diagnostic criteria for Asperger's I passed his test by demonstrating my interest in him.

During this session I also passed Rita's test. She repeatedly phoned me. I imagined that she had hoped I would pick up so she could fire me. After Lester's session, I checked my answering machine. Even though this was before the days of caller ID, I knew it was her. There were 57 missed calls!

I am fascinated how children find exactly what they need in the therapy rooms. During our session, Lester searched through the puppets with distress. He was clearly suffering as he examined different puppets and moaned, "I don't know," and tossed them aside. Then he put his hand in the puppet pouch of a brown mother seal and pulled out a little brown seal, I had sewn and placed in her belly a while back. Lester squealed with surprise, "I found you, Star-the-Seal."

Lester wriggled on his belly as he swam this pup towards where he had thrown the ram and ewe puppets. These sheep starkly contrasted the seal as white, fluffy land animals. As he did this, he made a heart-wrenching sound until he wriggled Star-the-Seal away. Lester then repeated his painful story, as is typical of post-traumatic play.

Many children at age seven ponder if they have been adopted. This quandary was not relevant to Lester. He knew he was. Nevertheless, the timing of him receiving care, regardless of any developmental push, was ideal because he was literally re-enacting the traumatic moment of removal from his caregiver and placement with new parents of a different race. A child's upset will not necessarily be the same issue as reported by the parents. However, I have found usually in the first session

the upset is revealed symbolically.

In instances where I missed it, upon understanding later, I could usually recall it was there. (In a twist, this is true of what upsets us about our partners today; it was there on our first date.)

When I asked Lester if he would like to come back, he exclaimed, "Tomorrow!" His response, like his mother's speech style, was a statement, not a question. I scheduled to see him the following week, same day and time. By accepting him as he is, being present for him and allowing him to be who he is, the journey began.

Typically, the next morning is the scheduled phone conversation with the parents. However, given their general detachment and overall resistance to this therapeutic process, I was concerned that when I revealed the details of Lester's traumatic play, they would feel I was complicating their situation. After all, Rita wanted me to "just teach him some social skills." I hoped to teach the parents that through the child's process, in the child's timeframe, the goals of the grown-ups (parents, teachers and therapist) would eventually and naturally be met. I encouraged them to be patient, because fast is slow and slow is fast. With this in mind, I decided I would strive to connect and improve my relationship with Rita by doing the home visit first before that phone conversation. The home visit is primarily an observation.

All psychotherapists should do a home visit with every new family entering care. It is an opportunity to assess how the *identified patient's EBIPS impacts the family.

Home visits reveal valuable,

information that might otherwise not be uncovered.

As I arrived for our visit, I overheard Rita and her son Christopher through an open window. She was unexpectedly engaged with a saccharin manufactured voice and artificial laughter. It was painful for me to hear this difference in how she treated her sons. Despite how troubling this compensatory, extreme attention was to me, and surely to each of the family members individually, and in relationship to one another, it did demonstrate Rita's ability to connect. I knocked on the door. My plan would be to focus on turning Rita's positive skills toward Lester.

After this home visit, and with the findings from Lester's session, I now had what I required for a successful phone call with Rita and Sam. I love these *Phone-Ins and typically, in time, the parents do also. Parents are educated about what is happening during their child's session, concerns are addressed, recommendations are given and lively discussions ensue. Additionally, 'Phone-Ins' hold the parents accountable for the assigned, *therapeutic homework. This engagement and level of parent commitment expedites the whole family's healing process.

Shortly into the 'Phone-In', I began, "Rita and Sam, I understand you have trust issues with therapists, and I see your resistance to the school's pressure, but I think you omitted, from our initial intake, some really important information about Lester's adoption. I think your opposition" I hesitated, "is deflecting your shame."

For the first of many times, Rita burst into tears. She sobbed as she described how the day of the adoption had been an excruciating process. Lester was given to them in a little basket. By the time he was legally permitted to leave with them, night had fallen and as painful as the sounds of the weeping foster mother were, Lester's cries were unbearable.

Sam interjected, "We felt like we were stealing him in the night. The trip home was long and, despite finally arriving home, every nightfall Lester would grieve himself into hysterics."

Sam continued by explaining, this was Rita's first experience mothering. Without apparent acceptance from her newly adopted 18-month-old son, any possible attachment to him waned. Soon, as disappointed as she was, she became commensurately overjoyed with the news of her ability to get pregnant after all. Upon Christopher's birth, Rita became fully engaged with Christopher while she showed Lester (then two-and-a-half years old) little interest.

After Sam and Rita's cathartic 'Phone-In,' Rita arrived at Lester's next session with more energy, though this would not be reliable or a constant until she did her own therapy work. She waved a friendly "hello" and rather than sit down, she was perusing the parent and bibliotherapy library. At the end of Lester's visit, I was delighted to see that she had signed out three books on adoption.

Lester ran ahead of me to the Sun Room, despite the offerings of the *Water Room and its symbolic relevance to seals and their habitat. Without greeting me he went immediately into play, an urgency indicative of unresolved trauma. He pulled down the window shade and as before, he played alone with the baby seal.

I played alongside him in what is referred to as parallel play. I looked for an entry point. When I puppeteered the ewe (representing Rita, his adopted mother), he rejected my attempts to engage. I had to allow him to lead, entering into his play; his theme, and his rules. So, I asked, "Which one can I be?"

"I want you to be my mom."

He handed me the mother, the brown seal, which I later came to understand represented Lester's foster mother.

It was not uncommon in play therapy for children to call me, "Mom." Here though, it was more of a confirmation of the connection Lester felt for his foster mother, which magnified the detachment Lester felt from Rita.

By the end of the session, Lester and I were seals, swimming about while holding our puppet seals. I copied him. We wriggled on our bellies and sometimes on our backs, staring up at the stars. I wondered: *Was all this 'tummy time' indicative of before he could walk?* and *Were the stars and water his comfort when he was young?* But assessment time was over – we were in play therapy now. Once play therapy begins, the role was to follow his play, not take him out of it by asking my questions.

The next morning Rita began the Phone-In fuming. She was hurt, jealous and resentful that Lester had difficulty separating from me and didn't want to go home with her. She said, "It's like the adoption all over again. He just doesn't want me."

Her upset had to be handled delicately or once again it could render Lester's care vulnerable to a premature ending.

I assured her that as we worked together exploring and understanding her own abandonment issues and insecurities, healthy feelings would develop and a profound mother-son healing would transpire.

Her homework assignment was to be present and mindful with Lester. She was to put aside her hurt and strive for a high degree of patience, support and enjoyment of him, whether he reciprocated or not. She was encouraged to focus on the long-term benefits because Lester was capable of attachment. I assured Rita that with her developing skills, he would one-day bond with her. Even though Rita responded with reservation, she agreed to this assignment and also to participate in Lester's next session.

In preparation for the session, she was given the additional assignment of reading an excerpt from **The 'Why and How' to Develop the Play of Children.* This e-book contains ten "Playworks;" activities that progress to develop his play and their bonding. Rita's initial work included finding entry points, sharing a common focus and using curative language. The reading of this material prepared her for a deeper understanding of the mother-son session and primed her for her ongoing therapeutic homework assignment, *U 'n Me Playtime (Appendix D).

When it was time for that session, Lester ran up the stairs ahead of Rita, who entered shortly after huffing and puffing. Meanwhile, Lester was off to the Sun Room to set the stage. He pulled down the shade and found Star-the-Seal, the ewe and another seal.

Rita, still out of breath, cut to the chase, "Where do you want me to sit, Less?"

"Star" he chastened.

Rita never called him "Less" again.

(I wondered, *had Lester come up with "Star" from the root of Less-Star?)*

"Where?" she asked again encouraging him to lead. Her inquiries suggested she had read her assignment, but her tone lacked enthusiasm and the nature of her questions implied she was not going to be involved.

"There," he pointed and stated without warmth or eye contact.

She dispassionately plopped down, behaving rejected and looking withdrawn. He tossed the ewe in her general direction. Their mother-son relationship was one of poor behavior, defiance and contempt on both sides.

"Here," Lester handed me a puppet that was not the 'Mom' he gave me last session.

Symbols remain constant in play; the language of children.

By handing me a different puppet, it meant I would be role-playing someone else.

"You are Soul," he said and soon transferring this name from the seal directly onto me. I thought Soul was a profound name given by a seven-year-old, but inquiring about it would be my need, my therapy, and so the answer was not to be known.

Lester repeated his play theme from last week: Star-the-Seal swam towards the ewe/Rita. He howled that heart-wrenching sound and then retreated. After he did this three times, I interrupted the maladaptive pattern by having Soul swim by his side. The effect was the same. We swam towards Rita. Lester wailed. We backed away. He quieted. Rita was silent throughout.

Later Rita confided, "it couldn't be possible. Surely he was too young to remember, and yet his wailing in the playroom was identical to when he was a toddler, that night he was adopted."

I attempted another pattern interrupt by having Soul offer Star-the-Seal power and the opportunity to witness another way. "How about I swim over while you count to three, and then I swim back?" I offered this to give him the power.

He nodded slowly and then counted to three quickly. I never left his side. I only had time to do an exaggerated lean forward and then immediately sit back up. He was enjoying having control over the event. Soon he began experimenting, counting progressively slower, permitting Soul to reach, meet and greet the ewe before having to bolt back in a lively fashion, to his delight.

"Rita," I whispered, to engage her in the moment. Then, each time I swam over with Soul, I would quietly give her an instruction, such as, "Imitate my greeting," "Match my emotion," and "Copy my tone," from her upcoming reading assignment, **Curative Language* (specifically, pacing, skill #5).

As she participated in the play therapy, particularly sharing in Lester's focus, the social climate warmed. Lester delighted by her attention, dropped the seal and the counting and walked over to greet his mother. They began talking directly to one another and responding to each other's positive energy by becoming more and more welcoming. This was the reworking of the night they first met.

After more than a dozen of these verbal exchanges, Lester accepted a suggestion from Soul. "Do you want to shake hands?"

They shook hands and continued the warm greetings. Rita was elated after years of rejection and clearly wanted to grab and cuddle him. I patted the air down to privately remind her to slow down.

She smiled sheepishly, having intentionally interrupted the play to control this impulse, "Um…Am I still the ewe?" She bleated at me.

I looked at Lester for direction. He turned towards her, "Be my Mom."

Rita, controlling her elation remained seated, below his height. She set the ewe down gently (the manner in which everything in the playroom must be treated, as we never know what meaning the child has given an object) and waited. I followed suit and placed Soul nearby.

"Do you want to hold hands with your Mom?" I asked inviting that which was not natural between them. Lester reached out to her with both hands, he giggled, she giggled, they held hands.

"Do you want to hug your Mom now?"

Rita, crossed her legs so he could come closer and opened her arms to him.

Lester responded like an eighteen-month-old boy, "Me do it." He fell into her long awaiting arms and moved around until this big boy was nestled in her lap, home.

She stroked his hair out of his eyes, "I love you, Star."

"I love you, Mom." Their hearts were open, comfort seeped in, his eyes closed and hers filled with tears.

As Rita continued to hold him, to our astonishment, sleepless Lester fell asleep.

In play therapy, children will spontaneously go back to the time of their trauma, reenact it and, with support, rework it. This process results in new understandings and resolutions. Then the child journeys forward, reprocessing and healing through each of their developmental stages before arriving in the present, truly healed.

With this in mind, it was no surprise to Rita when they arrived home after their session that Lester, as if still that 18-month-old little boy, had wet his pants. She did not reprimand him when he pointed rather than spoke, acted possessive or behaviorally demanding. Rita accepted, respected and loved him through it all. Their warmth, connection and laughter reportedly continued from the session and furthered Lester's ability to reprocess and heal each developmental stage. Soon Lester entered the "terrible two-and-a-half's." He threw tantrums, became resistant and then clingy while Rita remained calm and connected. And just like a 2 ½-year-old, he began for the first time returning kisses.

Rita believed she had been given a second chance. She championed for Lester at his school: getting his classroom seat moved near some gentle girls, working with the gym teacher to organize more successful recess time, and helping establish programming at lunch so no child sat alone.

Rita requested her own session and began a deep dive into how her childhood issues were impacting her parenting. She described a lonely childhood, the daughter of two parents who were disconnected from her and one another. The father left when she was two-years-old and soon after her mother remarried. The little attention her mother had given Rita, was then devoted to this new male.

As Rita described her family history, I drew a *Genogram. Then I superimposed names from her present family over the names and roles of her unresolved childhood family to have her see the similar psychological themes of her relationships now and then at a glance. "Sam" represented her disconnected father, "Rita" her unavailable mother, and "Christopher" represented the new male the mother doted upon. Then I placed Lester's name over the young Rita's. She saw how they both were ignored and superseded. Rita's past was determining not only her present but his. While Lester, abandoned by his biological mother, was already vulnerable to a lifetime of feeling rejected, he was reliving Rita's childhood wounds.

She understood it was not Lester's issues but her own unexamined childhood pain and suffering that was triggering her reenactment, including contempt and withdrawal. She wanted to learn to manage her emotions so she could handle his appropriately. She started a "Let Go List" of her rules, judgments, disappointments and expectations. We identified her "Warning Tells" when she was about to react, including nostrils flaring, body tightening, and words speeding up. And she learned to notice her constant inner critic whom she quieted with her developing inner calm, which led to a clear head and an acceptance of the moment "as it is."

We created a 3-step plan for consciously mothering herself first so she could effectively mother her children: 1. I will catch my warning "tells" 2. I will pause & witness my inner critic with my inner calm and 3. I will breathe, allowing the wisdom of "present moment awareness" to guide me.

She considered Sam who was also reliving feelings from his childhood. She said, "Sam thought he had married the opposite of his intense, angry, out-of-control mother. But much to his chagrin, since we have had Lester, I act just like her." She elaborated, "When I was little and upset all I could do was withdraw, but now my rage has a voice because I have the power of size. You know, when Sam ignores me, rejects me…" She trailed off, recognizing another pattern. She gasped, "Oh my God. He's going to replace me."

We are unconsciously driven to attract those who will reenact the dynamics of our unresolved issues with our parents.

This awareness created a readiness and willingness to do what she had to do to restore their relationship. That night she asked Sam if they could work together on their communication and build a secure, warm connection. He liked the idea of becoming a team. He agreed that when they fell into their old criticizing and *stonewalling mode of communication, either one would call a "Back to Our Love, Pause" and they would both engage in a 20-minute "feel better time" of individual physical activity. Sam would go for a bike ride and Rita, had begun mindfully practicing yoga. When they reunited, with the benefits of good feeling chemicals released through exercise, they would seek a positive connection using their developing communication skills to build their connection and resolve their differences.

Sam, despite holding two jobs and previously presenting as exhausted, soon improved in energy, mood and engagement once he re-experienced the warmth, healthy communication and consequent affection of his wife. He later said, "Who knew foreplay was kindness throughout the day."

Sam's therapeutic assignment required him to spend one-on-one time with Lester, swimming like seals at their pool club. As Lester's relationship with his father improved, Lester was no longer wetting his bed, often a metaphor for boys over six years of age who are "pissed" at their fathers. Furthermore, Lester's increased strength and coordination from the swimming led to a confidence to do other physical activities, initially with his younger brother but soon including the neighborhood children and his playground schoolmates as well.

Sam was loaned the bibliotherapy library book, *Guess how much I love you* to read to Lester. Lester asked for this book night after night for weeks. Sam and Lester's bond strengthened over the call and response words from the story, "I love you to the moon" and "I love you to the moon and back."

As Rita's heart opened, she was developing her own self-acceptance, awareness and desire to engage in right action. She began meditating, journaling and reading self-help books from 9 am until noon on the days her children were at school. This newfound inner harmony dissipated her feelings of inadequacy with Lester as well as her compensatory indulgence of Christopher. She confessed her favored child was behaving spoiled from being mollycoddled. "He'll need therapy next."

He did not.

Rita's commitment and transformation healed both her children. She was now caring for them according to their temperaments and needs rather than her upbringing. She helped connect the children to their inner selves by offering them daily art expression, time in nature, mindful conversation and moments of quiet.

She was one-pointed in her one-word; the intention to: Awaken

She was less triggered and more genuine, giving and interested. One day, Rita exclaimed, "I got it! I ACCEPT THEM AS THEY ARE." This was evidenced in the joyous ripple effect that reached each member of her family.

During this time, Lester's developmental progression continued. He began singing little Spanish verses from his preschool years. He was recalling songs the bilingual nursery school teacher, Maria, taught him back then. In support of blending Lester's two worlds, I collected on an IOU The Boy Named Sue had given me in exchange for keeping his beautiful singing voice a secret until he was ready. Late that evening at my home, The Boy Named Sue ate 5 multi-candied-chocolate drizzled cookies and recorded Raffi's children's song, *Baby Beluga* in Spanish, changing the character to "St-ar the Se-al."

As I watched, listening to The Boy Named Sue sing in his native tongue, without the struggles he had speaking English, I had an entirely different experience of him. At the end of the recording, he sweetly leaned into the microphone and whispered in Spanish, "Moon is shining and the stars are out, Good night 'Star-the-Seal' good night." This is when I began calling him by his given name. Despite his own hard beginning and rough edges, he was my gentle giant, Spanish Mosquetero, Suelita.

Only then did it occur to me, "Suelita, why do you not date?"

He stared at me.

I gave him "let me in" nods of encouragement. He remained hesitant. So I offered up a possibility, "Is it because of your past?"

He took a deep breath, as if inhaling the most beautiful of fragrances, "I have angel, and she fill my heart. I come to America for clean sober start sober, good education, beautiful life. She to join me in holy matrimony."

"Oh no, what happened?"

"She stop writing… I write, I ask, I beg for understanding. She no respond. Her mother neither, they ignore my letters. I have no one in Spain to help me understand." He hesitated and then let out a wail, similar to the sound of Lester's pain of separation.

"Suelita, I am so sorry, I had no idea. Perhaps there is a way to resolve this in your heart."

"No, like my own padre, she no want me."

"You…we…could find out what happened, and, and, that information could help you, maybe you don't have to make a commitment to a solitary life from a…an assumption. We will all help you." I volunteered everybody.

He sobbed.

"You must be lonely," I said, acknowledging his pain.

"My longing keeps me company."

I put my hand on his heart. "Thank you for sharing this with me."

He put a hand over mine, squeezed tightly and looked up to God with a finality to our conversation that could not be opposed, although his suffering should have been addressed. He abruptly changed the subject "See you at Ma's." And then for the first time ever, he initiated a hug.

"Thank you for making this tape. It means a lot to me. The boy is absolutely going to love it!" I said, handing him a cookie for the road along, with a tiny homemade fortune cookie-like note sticking out of it.

"What's this?" He asked unfolding it.

"It's me working on expressing myself outside of the therapy walls."

He read the note. "I accept," he said.

"Um, is that how you reciprocate in your country?" I said, looking for more.

"Yeah." He smiled and very happily put the note in his wallet in the clear plastic window in front of his license.

I do not think he understood what I meant by reciprocate.

The next morning, Rita picked up the cassette tape, with a red velvet holiday ribbon threaded through the tape reel holes and tied into a bow. Suelita phoned to let me know he had canceled going to Ma's for Christmas Eve due to an impending storm. Him being alone over the holiday got me thinking again about his predicament—maybe there was a gentle way to soothe his pain and help him move forward.

After the holidays, Rita left a phone message reporting that Lester "was ecstatic, 'swimming' and singing around their home, throughout the day." She reported that by bedtime, this physical activity and emotional support allowed him to finally fall and remain asleep throughout the night. The success of this Spanish cassette tape inspired Rita, her jealousy now replaced by security as Lester's mother, to hire Maria to teach the whole family Spanish.

I phoned her back overjoyed at the success of the Spanish cassette. "Rita, what do you think of having Suelita and Maria 'accidentally' run into one another at your home and see if sparks fly?"

"Yes," she agreed, using her proclaimed new favorite word. She was delightfully enthusiastic these days.

We coordinated so Suelita would drop off a duplicate cassette tape to Maria, next time Maria was at Rita's.

Soon thereafter, Rita phoned me back, "Nada."

We laughed at ourselves and how our busybody plan of matching up the only two people we knew from Spain had fallen flat.

This entire scenario was outside the confines of numerous psychotherapist codes: initiating calls, socializing on the phone, setting up mutual friends—it was all wrong, wrong, wrong.

And yet…

In these very real moments, outside the traditional care box, Rita and I deepened our bond.

"I have to tell you a secret," she whispered into the receiver. "I don't even know why I continued to withhold it from you. I am such a different person now."

"You are," I validated as a witness to how her increased consciousness had naturally resulted in a more genuine and loving self.

She continued, "Do you know why Lester calls you Soul?" I felt her radiant smile through the phone. Without waiting for my response she burst out with it, "It's not S-o-u-l," she spelled each letter. "It's S-o-l. He is calling you the Spanish word for Sun."

"Oh Rita, I am a part of Lester's! That means the world, no the Universe to me. And Rita, Sunshine is one of my favorite nicknames from years ago. Thank you for telling me."

"Well," Rita said, of my *self-disclosure, "then I must call you Sol, as well."

We were comfortably quiet as we held the stillness of this authentic, beautiful moment together.

Next, the school rescinded their concern that Lester had any disabilities at all. His supposed disability was actually development delays that caught up. They reported he was an "on target, seven-year-old, second grader" and gave details using the EBIPS booklet, now an app.

E-Emotionally, his mood was even; he was thoughtful and he could manage transitions and last minute changes.

B-Behaviorally, he was controlling himself; he was self-reflective and comforted by routines.

I-Intellectually, his concentration had improved and his reading skills had progressed by leaps and bounds beyond the pages of his grade material.

P-Physically, he was strong, balanced, coordinated and holding his own at gym and recess; his first six baby teeth had fallen out (an indication his etheric body was freed); also a sign of readiness for formal education including to begin reading.

S-Socially, he had developed friendships; he had three best friends and one girl who was particularly interested in him.

Usually, at this point, everyone is thinking it is time to wrap up therapy. The therapist is recommending discharge planning and the child begins complaining. The care is suddenly too babyish; they want to do other things after school; something is wrong with the play therapy rooms or worse, something is wrong with the therapist. This is a natural part of the child's intuition, indicating that they have received the healing available and it is time to move on. So, while it appeared that all goals were met, Lester was demonstrating he still had unfinished business and continued to work hard in his play. He was searching for something.

I appreciated that his parents were educated and trusting enough, at this point, to continue with treatment, allowing Lester to enter deeper waters. I arrived in the

Sun Room after him. He had again set the stage, as usual, with the shade pulled down, the stars aglow and blue silks that represented the ocean spread across the floor.

"Come on Sol," he looked up to include me,

"Meet me where I am."

I loved this confident invitation, its own 'entry point' to join him in his play. Meeting children where they are, accepting who they are, is critical to the success of play therapy.

On a side, I wish this invitation, "Meet me where I am," would be accepted between adults when one is struggling. This would be a way of asking another for a connection. "Please support me. Listen rather than get defensive. Don't add to my upset or make it about us. It's an ask: for compassion between equals, with non-judgment, patience and kindness; to walk in my shoes; to strive to understand me before offering advice; and to be gentle yet honest. It's a request to turn towards and with opportunity to bear witness to my very essence. To let me know you are there for me. After meeting someone where they are we can provide them with validations, such as, "You sound sad," "That must be painful," and "I don't know what to say, but I am grateful you told me."

As Lester's therapy session wound down for the day, he was play swimming on his belly and engaged in a search. I turned towards him, "It's nearly time to go."

He howled as if the time pressure had injured him.

"What is it?" I asked recognizing the sound of this

pain from our first sessions.

"I don't know." He moaned.

Here. I offered him a folded piece of paper. It could have been a map or a place where secrets could be found. He pushed it back at me.

"Telescope?" I offered him the idea by showing him how I rounded my fingers to touch my thumb and then put this completed circle to my eye.

"I need that," he said pretending to take it from me. Then he put his rounded fingers of his hand to one eye, looked through them and pointed, "Ecuador!"

Here, he revealed it: "How will I know what my mother looks like?"

I placed a mirror in the "water" in front of him, "Your mother is in your reflection."

And what happened next, to this day, still gives me goosebumps. Lester abruptly grabbed the mirror and sat up. He touched his face. He touched his reflection. He tilted his head left, right, down and then lifted his chin high up to the stars and laughed a big, loud, joyous laugh. "I fou-hahaha-nd her!"

He stood up, tall. He was old enough now to process something he had not before, "She was only fifteen." He said with a relief that seemed to include an understanding of why she could not possibly have kept him. He laughed, spontaneously pulling up the shade and sunbeams burst through the room.

The discharge process while always a thoughtful lesson in healthy goodbyes, is particularly important with children who have been adopted or have lost someone significant. His *Check-In voicemail the day before his next session advised me, "I want to play intramurals after school. I have playdates and, and I am getting married." He was describing typical social activities of healthy seven-year-olds with an underlying message of readiness for discharge.

During the session that followed he explained,

"Everything used to be out there. Now it's in here," he touched his heart.

He easily transitioned from weekly to every other week to three weeks between visits. At Lester's graduation from therapy, I gave him a glow-in-the-dark star to put up in his home. I then handed him a second star representing him, to place somewhere in my playrooms. He said, "Put me next to you." I climbed up a ladder to my solar system ceiling.

"Here?" I asked.

"Closer," he informed.

"Here?" I asked again.

"Closer," he repeated. "Right next to Sol. Yep, always connected."

Post Therapy Addendum

During my six-month phone follow-up, Rita reported: "I NOW STRIVE TO ACCEPT ALL OF LIFE AS IT IS." She said, "I understand how my transformation ended a legacy of disconnection that will no longer be passed along to my boys."

Then Rita informed me that as she grew to accept herself, she expanded in love, resilience, and noted even respect for how she cared for and fed her body. Then something she didn't even know we were treating got treated; when did the work to release her traumatic childhood pain her chronic pain released, also.

Several years later I ran into Rita and a very tall Lester. They looked remarkably alike, wonderfully connected and, by the way, they were bilingual.

During our conversation, Rita referred to Lester, as "Estrel."

"Estrel?" I asked.

"He has asked me to call him that" Rita said, "It honors his 'E for Ecuadorian' heritage and Estrel is an anagram for Lester from the Spanish word estrella, star.

"That's remarkable," I said, completely enraptured.

"Estrel, tell Sol what you and your father are studying."

"Oh yeah," he said, speaking with the conversational style of the teenager he had become. "Dad and I got a telescope and we study the stars." Then he looked me in the eyes, perhaps recognizing or remembering something between us, and he reached out and hugged me.

While Lester may not remember, and we may never know for sure where his connection to the solar system came from, his connection with his mother allowed all other connections to shine.

Lester's Poignant Fifteenth Year

As could be predicted, Lester met with me for what we called a "tune-up" during the year that correlated with the age his biological mother gave him up for adoption. He came for three sessions. At this higher developmental stage, he reprocessed his adoption in psychotherapy.

Many children who were adopted and brought to therapy for the first time during their teenage years, present with mood and behavioral issues, as well as substance abuse issues. This was not true of Lester. He initiated the care, presented as emotionally intelligent and well adapted. His astral body, sometimes called the stars, was fully penetrated.

He liked the sentiment that I had retired Star-the-Seal from the Sun Room to the side table of my talk therapy room. I did this despite believing that "Toys in the therapy room, stay in the therapy room." even when old or broken. After all, we might not know what meaning a child has placed on an object.

Before he left, he asserted, "Can I have him?"

"Fifteen is too young," I toyed with the belief.

"I know," he said following the metaphor and accepting it is what it is. "I have to grow into my own life before I am responsible for another's. I don't have the time or the true interest, yet. Can I have him when I am 32?"

"Yes," I said, knowing 32 was the age his mother adopted him.

He kissed my cheek. "Sealed with a kiss," he laughed.

"See you when I'm 32." He said, and ran off to be a teenager.

In memory of Dermot, 2018

Lester had inspired me in maintaining connections with others with the placement of his star at Creative Therapies. I put up a star representing my Grandad, Sue and Igor. Then, my three interns that year while in joint supervision expanded the theme of remaining connected by requesting, to have their own star, to be remembered. Each selected the placement of a star in an area that was meaningful to them and our relationship: by the phone, on the welcoming sign and on my desk. This tradition of remaining connected continued over the years. Today, I am placing Dermot's star on my bag that goes everywhere with me.

Coming Soon

Psychotherapy Tales

Volume Two

Appendix A

A Healthy Lifestyle Plan

On the following page is a balanced, nutritionally sound, Healthy Lifestyle Plan, originally created for Mary and approved by her medical doctor and the hospital's dietician. Through the years the plan has been adapted to meet the individual and varying needs of teenage girls and women. Despite all the fad diets that come and go, this solid, sensible daily "Plan" (intentionally not called a diet) is as good for the body, mind and spirit now as it was then.

I started with the *Metropolitan Life Height -Weight Tables* based on mortality scales, which were not suitable for children and added height for heels. Then I transferred to an easily calculated minimum weight based on a height-weight ratio. A five-foot tall, female teen is to weigh a minimum of 100 pounds and for every inch thereafter to weigh 5 pounds more: 5'1 - 105lbs, 5'2 - 110lbs, 5'3 - 115lbs and so on. Ideal weights are higher.

The focus is on whole foods with no artificial flavors or colors. This supports mood, strength, healthy complexion, energy level as well as ideal weight. Individual adjustments to the plan are made for a variety of reasons, including height, small-to-large-boned frame, weight goals and amount of daily activity.

This plan is based on the recommended 2200-calorie intake for ideal health of the still growing body, mind and spirit of teenage girls. This caloric information is for the doctor's knowledge. We do not talk calories, negotiate butter as a dairy, review calories per serving compared to our list or otherwise engage with patients having weight-related issues. These conversations are discouraged because they fuel the patient's need for control—to be exacting and more restrictive rather than insightful as to what is really challenging them. For the doctor and/or nutritionist overseeing the plan, the caloric equivalents are roughly as follows: carbohydrates 80, protein 100, dairy 100, fruit 50, vegetable 50, and fats 100. Also, it is recommended that consideration is made for alternative whole foods not listed on the plan and to ensure proper supplementation, especially of iron and calcium. The boosts, previously called snacks, were extra treats if necessary or required to gain weight faster or lose weight more slowly. And everyone was required to eat whatever was served for dinner—again this was to support flexibility.

Additional encouragements were the two sections: for a "Daily Power Statement" or positive affirmation and for "Journal" for the identification and expression of feelings.

For variety, balance and nutritious eating, the selection of meals should vary with the repetition of foods less than once every four days. Through the years as allergies have become more prevalent. This also helps in the prevention of overexposure to particular foods, intolerances and consequent gut imbalances.

Once weight goals were met and healing in body, mind and spirit was evident, we were no longer in charge of serving the meals and snacks. Then we could soften to approximations over the rigidity of measuring. We kept an eye on the weekly scale and eyeballed portions: A fist is a cup; a palm is 3 ounces; a handful is an ounce of fruits and nuts; 2 handfuls is an ounce of crackers or chips; a thumbnail is a teaspoon of fats.

Healthy Lifestyle Plan

Name______________________________Day _____________

8-8oz Glasses of Water 0 0 0 0 0 0 0 0

Type and amount of exercise____

Circle foods below to plan your day after eating
Then color in the circles after eating each serving

5 Servings of Carbs
0 0 0 0 0

½ c cooked pasta
½ bagel
1 c cereal
½ c cooked rice
½ c granola
2 pancakes
1 baked potato
4 c popcorn
1 slice of bread
1 English muffin

5 Servings Vegetables (Before Cooked) 0 0 0 0 0

lettuce, celery - free
cucumber – free
2 c chopped cauliflower
12 baby carrots
2 c chopped
16 cherry tomatoes
¼ c avocado
2 c kale
1½ mushrooms
1½ c green beans
5 c arugula
1½ c broccoli

5 Servings of Fruits

0 0 0 0 0

2 ½ c prunes
small banana or pear
1 ¼ c grapes
medium apple or peach
medium mandarin or nectarine
10 strawberries
1 ¼ c diced watermelon
¾ c pineapple
1 c blueberries
¼ medium cantaloupe
1 c honeydew
¼ c dried fruit
1¼ c raspberries
½ c mango
¾ c apple sauce

4 Servings of Oils/Fats

0 0 0 0

1 T butter
1 ½ T dressing
1 T mayonnaise
2 T maple syrup
5 T ½ & ½
2 T honey

6 Servings of Protein

0 0 0 0 0 0

1 large egg
2 oz meat or fish
1½ oz chicken
1 T peanut butter
½ c legumes
12 almonds

3 Servings of Dairy

0 0 0

1 slice cheese
1 c yogurt
¾ c kefir
¾ c frozen yogurt

Boosts____

____

Daily Power Statement

____

____

____

Journal____

____

____

____

____

____

____

____

____

____

____

____

____

____

____

____

____

Appendix B

Our Persona Manifested in Our Soulmate(s)

Love and abuse were intertwined wicks
creating a twin flame of destruction.

"But he's my soul mate," she persisted, as if everything before the word "But" was irrelevant. It is not uncommon for a woman who has been abused to use this very argument, perceiving her abuser as her 'one and only.'

We all have more than one soul mate to help us grow towards wholeness by exposing our deep and vulnerable soul wounds. Sure they are our "match," which means they will not be emotionally healthy and mature if we are not. Our internal emotions and wellbeing are reflected back externally in how they treat us and where we must develop.

So the abused attracts a relationship with the abuser as the abuser attracts a relationship with the abused. In this case, the match of his soul will light her childhood wounds aglow with increasing amounts of gasoline until she is forced to wake up to the lesson, grow and move on…or stay, fall back asleep and endure the nightmare of a problematic soul mate.

Before Sabine could be a match, to ignite the flame of a higher, healthier soul mate, she required good psychotherapy for at least two years to encounter her unprocessed pain and integrate these shadows from her childhood. The deeper these shadows were hidden, the darker and denser they were. Otherwise, even with the end of an abusive relationship, she would be destined to repeat the pattern in the next relationship. The alternative is to be willing to be open and honest and then to dive deep into a difficult, psychotherapeutic journey where progress would be reflected in future relationships. This would be where upsets and soul wounds arise and her authentic, True Self would then be able to offer and receive healthy and supportive cultivation with encouragement toward further growth.

I will *always remember* Sabine

Every spring when the wind blows through my pink cherry blossom tree, inviting me to rest a while under a rhapsody of petals, I reflect on the seasons of Sabine. I met her during her desolate, heavily weighted down winter. Her trunk was thick, her roots exposed and her branches stunted like they had not grown the way they should have, or they were pruned back way too much in proportion to her needs. I watched her bud, bloom and blossom with caring attention, healthy connection and quality nutrients. Then she transitioned from her pale, spring green surroundings into the lush, rich green of summer. But, as happen in the life of the season's cycle, leaves fall and bare branches become exposed and vulnerable as a cold winter comes back around. However, rings get older and keyholes become stronger with the knowledge of past healing, good support and personal power pulsing through her veins. She can be confident that the sun will return with a promise of a fresh dawn and a new season.

Appendix C

Divorce: Important Considerations on Behalf of Your Children

These recommendations are inspired by the corrective work I provided divorcing parents and their children through the years. Additionally this work is in response to comprehensive clinical interviews with adults who reported their own childhood trauma and difficulties since their parents divorce many years ago.

Consider the vulnerabilities of what it can be like for a child who lives in two homes

Living two different lives in two different homes creates a divided self.

Torn loyalties are created from having to choose sides, keep secrets or assumed secrets, even when not asked.

At any time a child can feel rejected when one parent criticizes the child for being like the other parent.

The child will take on the inappropriate responsibility of being a peacemaker to hold the broken family together.

Put in the position to take care of both parent's emotions. Having to listen and understand adult issues at a young age.

Having to take on adult responsibilities such as keeping track of time, cooking and laundry.

Scheduling becomes around the parents' needs rather than the needs of the child.

Going between two homes compromises a child's attachment to either parent because the child is regularly leaving one or the other.

The child is not able to express emotions of separation such as sadness, anxiety or attachment to, when leaving the other parent.

The child becomes distracted from academics and social life.

Because of all of the above vulnerabilities a child does not get to just be a child and these conflicts live on in their body, mind and spirit.

Your children will forever be affected by your divorce and how you went about it.

So if you must divorce, here is how to do it mindfully.

Between the Parents

According to the research, marriages can improve with psychotherapy and even simply with the passage of time. Therefore, unless there are abusive issues, the best chance for health and happiness for the family is for the parents to do what they can to work out their differences.

The greatest gift we can give our children, our partner and our self is to heal, to become our best self. Parents who are thinking about divorcing are encouraged to begin psychotherapy as an opportunity to consider this move as a symptom of something deeper. This self-awareness of our own unresolved wounds that keeps us blaming, shaming and guilting stems from our very first intense relationships with our own parents. We must come to understand that when we are hostile, oppositional and resistant, it is because our partner has triggered something within us from our past. Unfortunately, without awakening to this understanding and resolving it, we are destined to repeat it with the next and all future partners. As we develop self-awareness, we can still divorce if we wish, but it can be amicable and respectful, whether our partner is or is not.

Due to the imitative nature of a young child, a healthy emotional relationship between the mother and father is essential. This absorption in the child affects their health and happiness in their own relationships and into adulthood.

Do not allow the children to overhear you argue because they will copy the anger becoming argumentative themselves or the opposite becoming more sad and passive. Agree with your partner, if a fight begins in front of the children, either one of you can call a "Pause" to talk away from the children or to continue later when privacy is possible. If the children have overheard you arguing, the best way to decrease their stress levels is by informing them thereafter that the disagreement was resolved.

Before the children are informed

Be discrete about who you tell before you inform your children. While it is recommended to wait to tell the children until the plans are all set and the move-out day is upon you, there is a risk, if you are not discrete, that they will hear it from one of the children of an adult friend you told.

Hire a child psychotherapist to help the family, first to meet with the parents to discuss plans and needs. Next, have the therapist meet the children individually.

Most likely, if you are considering divorce, the children are already affected by the climate in the home. It is recommended that you hire a child psychotherapist for the children in advance of telling them your plans to divorce. This way, rapport can be established, an initial baseline of the child's state of mind can be measured and the development of emotional skills can begin, such as learning to identify, express and manage feelings.

The psychotherapist will also require parenting sessions to assist in the creation of the best Parenting Plan possible, rules for both homes, scheduling, and other agreements deemed necessary. It is important to iron out parents opposing views as winning at one house means trouble for them at the other. The familiarity with all family members will help the therapist make the best recommendations on behalf of the children.

Do not underestimate the need for treatment, as children are troubled even by a low-conflict divorce. When the serious news of a divorce comes to them completely unexpected, they determine that the world is not predictable. Consequently, they become insecure and anxious, believing life can fall apart at any moment.

During these parent sessions, it will also be important to discuss and anticipate how each child will react when told, what parents should say, and what strategies to put in place to support each child. It is also important for the psychotherapist to educate the parents about the ever-expanding worlds of children who live in and have to bridge between two homes where parents make new lives, grow further apart and separate.

The psychotherapist can script the parents where there are differences and recommend joint responses, such as if any of the children accuse or blame a parent. This would require both parents to be prepared to stand united regardless of their own anger and blame. When a husband and wife divorce, ironically, their maturity, parenting and communication must be stronger than ever, regardless of all the reasons for the divorce. It is important to remember that any time a parent assigns blame upon the other parent the heart of your child is wounded. Your child is half you and half your spouse, and any criticism of your spouse harms the self-esteem of your shared child.

It is also important that the teachers and the school counselors be informed of the divorce shortly before the children return to school. This is so these adults can be supportive and compassionate in noting any behavioral concerns or emotional changes in the children.

When and how to tell the children

Regardless of age, the children must be told.

The ideal for most children is to inform them only a few days before one parent moves out, provided it is not an abusive situation.

A good day to tell the children is on Sunday in the

early afternoon (not before sleep) so that the next day they return to the structure and support of the school.

It is desirable to inform the children in a neutral room, for example, not in a public place (where they might inhibit their feelings); not in a bedroom (to keep it a place of peace and a good night's sleep); and not in a kitchen (so traumatic news is not associated with food).

It is preferable that both parents together inform each of the children one at a time. This allows each child their own time to react to the news in their own way. Otherwise, they may copy or react to their siblings' responses. Their siblings will naturally respond according to their own personalities and needs, for example, based on emotion ("I want to die"), temperament ("It's about time, I'm good"), development ("It's my fault"), experience ("Jimmy's parents got divorced and it's bad"), gender ("I'm living with Dad"), and others responses based on birth order, age, intellect, previous trauma, processing time and more. Schedules must be orchestrated so that no child hears the news from their siblings and that no siblings are asked to keep it a secret.

Keep it simple and gentle: "We have come to the decision that your father/mother and I are going to get a divorce/separation/not live together anymore." Pause here. Allow your child to express what he or she is feeling.

Mostly, listen. If the child asks a question, keep in mind that just because he or she asks does not mean it is appropriate for parents to answer it. These questions can be responded to with, "That is between your parents."

Also, when children ask, "Why?" it is often a developmental concern indicating, "Why is this happening to me?" more than simply a request for details. And the common get-back-together fantasy in children resides in the understanding that life would be so much easier for them if we all lived under the same roof.

If a child asks, "Who wanted the divorce?" it is important not to set up a good-parent, bad-parent dynamic. The healthiest response for your children is to hear, "We came to this decision together." It is important to avoid blaming the other parent or your children will learn to do the same and then, when they become teenagers, they will switch that blame to you.

It is important not to volunteer a concern or suggest issues the child has not brought up. For example, parents *should not* make the following statements:

Parent: "We will both still love you."

Child: "Wait, was that a problem? You guys might not love me anymore?!"

Or, Parent: "Mom is leaving me not you."

Child: "So she might leave me one day?"

Or, Parent: "You didn't do anything wrong, it's not your fault."

And the child thinks: "Oh, yes I did. I can fix this."

Finally, the parents close the conversation with: "As questions or concerns come to you, bring them to us."

Immediately after telling the children, it is best to stay around the house. Children may feel emotional, lonely, have further questions, and/or need your support for a sense of security.

The next day after telling the children

The next day, it is important that the parent who is leaving move out. This will prevent prolonging the children's healing process, the confusion, denial and the fantasy of the parents reuniting. Also, the parent moving out should take belongings now preventing children from witnessing or experiencing difficult discussions, behaviors and emotions.

This day and date to children, is the day they consider to be the divorce. Don't confuse or burden them further with court dates, details or any final official notices, thereafter.

Remain available so that your children can continue to bring their questions and concerns to you over the days, weeks, months, years, and into their adulthood.

Parenting Plan & custody agreement considerations

The Parenting Plan must be as specific as possible, acknowledging that the plan is to be revisited as the children grow.

Be flexible. Keep asking yourself, *what is best for each child?* This is because, unfortunately, in divorce, the children's needs are usurped by the parents' schedules.

It is recommended that children spend all school nights in the same home. This is because the children's executive functioning skills, the ability to plan and organize in particular, are still maturing and vulnerable to compromise due to the challenges of living in two homes. Examples of overseeing the children's planning and organizational skills in both homes includes working together using color-coded kitchen calendars of everyone's daily plans, separate checklists of the children's routines and responsibilities, and individual check sheets for necessary backpack contents. Additionally there are apps available to help with this planning and organization and the communication between parents.

It is highly recommended, in non-abusive divorces that both parents sign a waiver agreeing not to call the psychotherapist into the court. Otherwise, one parent typically becomes angry with a decision made, blames the psychotherapist, fires him or her and the children's care is compromised.

Appendix D

U 'N' Me Playtime

I tried to teach my child with books,
he gave me only puzzled looks.
I tried to teach my child with words,
they passed him by often-unheard
Despairingly I turned aside,
"How shall I teach this child?" I cried.
Into my hand he put the key,
"come," he said, "play with me."

-Author unknown

This is a Playwork strategy from the training E-book, ***The 'Why and How' to Develop the Play of Children*** (available at creativetherapies.net/store/)

Messages: I am here! I am your witness! I understand! I care!

1. Schedule one, two or three 20 minute, one-on-one blocks of playtime daily. This is ideally with the same rhythm each day, such as after breakfast, lunch and/or dinner. Ideally, your time together is relaxed and your attention continuous. Strive to be calm, in the moment, and not preoccupied with any outside interference or distractions. All screens and other potential interruptions, including alerts are turned off. Inform your child, "It is now time for our special U 'N' Me Playtime ." No screens or store purchased games.

2. Allow him or her to enter or continue to play. Let he or she take the lead; decide what to do and how to play. Observe until you find an "entry point," meeting the child where he or she is in his or her play. It is okay to use "How?" and "What?" for clarification: *"**How** many trains shall I have?"* or *"**What** do you want her (my doll) to say?"* Trust the journey, allowing him or her to take you along on the exploration, discovering and reworking issues regardless of where you may think they are.

3. Plan for this to be a non-directive, ideally non-corrective interaction. During the U 'N' Me Playtime it will be tempting, but you must refrain from questions, suggestions, commands, interpreting, evaluating, giving directions and teaching. This is critical to the effectiveness of following what flows from within the child.

4. Describe exactly what you see and what he or she is doing using Curative Language Skill #1, Tracking: observe and narrate the ongoing play in positive terms. This language is kept simple and generally under 10 words per statement. As you progress over the first few experiences, you will decide when to add in other Curative Language (see e-book). During Creative Therapies training, clinicians found it helpful to write the language reminders, color-coding them by skill, on index cue cards they stuck on the play therapy walls, for instance, ***"You are..." "You are pretending to..."*** and ***"Right now you..."*** were in red representing, Tracking.

5. Provide concise, non-judgmental statements, occasionally noticing positive behavior, especially those behaviors you'd like to reinforce in hopes of seeing more of! Remember, whichever behavior you put your attention on, he or she will give you more of, so encourage accordingly. For instance, other Tracking examples are, ***"I notice...****how cooperative you are being;* **"I see...***you are flexible;" and* **"You are...** *generous... kind... thoughtful... gentle..."*

6. Ignore mildly inappropriate behaviors. If he or she continues, turn away for a moment then return to playing. If the behavior becomes disruptive, destructive, or worse, state *"I will return to play with you in 6 minutes"* (or whatever is the equivalent number of minutes as he/she is years old). Set a timer and absolutely reenter the play as you said you would. Do not mention the previous behavior and finish only what is left of the twenty minutes.

7. The first few U 'N' Me Playtime experiences can be challenging because of the unfamiliar process, orientation, and the language that is sometimes described as awkward. Keep at it. Initially, caregivers give too many commands. They want to teach and say fewer positive comments. It takes practice, but the benefits to you and your child are for a lifetime.

8. Other benefits include the rebuilding of your relationship; the improvement of listening skills; a reduction in your criticism and negative feedback; the increase in your child's feelings of self-worth, confidence

and security; the development of a more positive attitude toward one another; the child will be calmer; and time together will be more enjoyable.

Glossary and Other Commentary

*Abreact: Abreaction is a psychoanalytical term for expressing and releasing an emotion through reliving a traumatic experience.

*Acting Out: To act out is to behave poorly or socially inappropriately as a means of venting painful emotions, typically in a self-defeating manner.

*Adverse Childhood Experience (ACE):. The ACE Questionnaire is available online. The higher the score on types of abuse, neglect and other hallmarks of a rough childhood, the greater the risk of health problems as an adult. Those with high scores can reduce health risks with the help of a good psychotherapist.

*Asperger's Syndrome, (AS): AS would no longer exist in the updated DSM-5, 2013. It would be replaced for some, but not all, with Autism Spectrum Disorder. The diagnosis AS included marked impairments in children's social interactions (such as nonverbal behaviors, missing social cues, difficulty with reciprocity, monotone speech, obsessions, poor eye contact, limited pretend play), poor coordination, sensory issues (such as light, clothing, and noise sensitivities), and behaviors (such as difficulty transitioning, self-stimulating, repetitive mannerisms).

*Atop: Atop means on or at the top (1650). Most people are familiar with the word atop from the poem of Humpty Dumpty, who was illustrated as an egg in *The*

Looking Glass by Lewis Carroll. However, historically, Humpty Dumpty was actually the nickname of an English Civil War cannon atop the wall, surrounding Colchester in 1648. While initially powerful and effective, "he" toppled to the ground when the wall collapsed underneath him. This is a foreshadowing to the eventual "resignation" of Kolten. It was worse for Simon; he was simply asked to clean out his desk one morning and he was apparently gone within the hour.

*Autism Spectrum Disorder, (ASD): This is a new diagnosis as of 2013 (DSM-5, 2013). ASD encompasses a broad range or spectrum of social communication and interaction difficulties, as well as restrictive, repetitive patterns of behavior. The severity levels vary from requiring 1-support, 2-substantial support, and 3-very substantial support.

*Bibliotherapy: Bibliotherapy is the reading of a theme related storybook to help resolve children's challenges. The stories can be helpful to learn to cope, increase conversation and experiment with new solutions all to develop mastery over trauma to support healing.

There is a bibliotherapy list at creativetherapies.net. The books are alphabetized by therapeutic theme or category (Adoption, Anger Management, Attention) and available for lending to Creative Therapies patients. Children often request the reading of a relevant book over and over again until the issue resolves. A few favorites include:

The Crocodile and the Dentist for children under 7 who have fears of going to the dentist.

The Invisible String for children 9 and younger, struggling with separation anxiety. The message reminds us that we are always connected. Playing with a real, then imagined string between the caregiver and the child imitates the concept of the book, brings further understanding, comfort and laughter.

Molly's Rosebush, reading level age 4-7, message up to age 10. After her mother has a miscarriage, Molly's grandmother provides support through a metaphor in nature and with a gesture for a child's healing.

<u>*Check-In:</u> The day before a child's session at Creative Therapies, the parents are required to "Check-In" by leaving a voice mail describing the successes and challenges since the previous session, how the therapeutic assignment went and any other relevant information about their child. This allows for the psychotherapist's best preparation and also prevents the parent, at drop off, from attempting to pull aside or talk about 'issues' in front of the children. This also conveniently, confirms their appointment.

When the children in therapy reach a particular level of sophistication and emotional intelligence, they also begin their own "Check-In." Now, not just the parents but also the child is leaving a voice mail. This supports the children's own identification and communication of concerns, topics for the upcoming session and reporting of successes between sessions. This also instills the experience of phoning in to the psychotherapist should the need arise after graduation. This skill is not expected with younger play therapy patients.

*Cheeked: Cheeked is slang for pretending to swallow medication in front of a caregiver, when in actuality the patient has hidden it in a cheek or under the tongue.

*Compassion: Compassion is a feeling of sorrow or pity for the hardship of another and a desire to alleviate that suffering. See *empathy.

*Compassionate Strategies of Inclusion: This was the inspired beginning of what would become CSI a Creative Therapies school program for promoting social resilience, emotional intelligence and a connected community. Of course, thereafter it would become better known as the abbreviation for a primetime television series Crime Scenes Investigation.

*Complex Post Traumatic Stress Disorder (PTSD): Also known as Complex Trauma Disorder. Judith Hermann, M.D. in her 1992 book *Trauma and Recovery* was the first to propose this disorder. She distinguished PTSD from Complex PTSD patients who reported repeated traumatic experiences with little to no opportunity of escape. While her diagnosis is included in the International Statistical Classification of Diseases and Related Health Problems, 11th Edition (ICD-11), it is not in the Diagnostic and

Statistical Manual of Mental Disorders (DSM).

*Creative Therapies (1990): A unique psychotherapeutic treatment center with a variety of playrooms and services for children and their families.

*Curative Language Skills: The child therapist's essential healing language of eight identified skills provided with sentence examples. This e-book is from training sessions with clinicians, students and other caregivers, and is for therapeutically talking with children in play. It is available in the store at creativetherapies.net

*Cutting: Typically, cutting is distinguished from a suicide attempt. While the reasons for self-mutilation are diverse, Terror's explanation for superficially lacerating the body was for appearance. Regardless of the reason, this behavior requires psychological care and support.

Remarkably, Terror willingly agreed to switch to slashing the arms with a red pen. Over time he transitioned to making red slashes in a notebook, and eventually to journaling about his feelings with a variety of different colored pencils. This is what worked for Terror in treatment. Depending upon the individual and why he or she cuts, other distractions and communications would be more effective. For example, painting, listening to loud music, throwing rocks in a pond, crunching on ice bits or eating a chili pepper.

*Death by Suicide: This language was updated to reflect

the change since the Suicide Act of 1961, when "committing suicide" was a crime. Back then, if the attempt failed, then the person could be prosecuted and imprisoned, and if he or she succeeded, then the families could be prosecuted and imprisoned.

*Domestic Abuse Council: DAC provides free information, counseling and some legal services for victims of domestic abuse. The DAC also has a 24-hour crisis line and staff available to meet victims at the hospital and courthouse.

*Dyslexia: A specific difficulty in understanding written or spoken language in storing language information and in organizing and retrieving this information. Go to Checklists at creativetherapies.net for a dyslexia checklist categorized by age.

*EBIPS: The word EBIPS is my acronym for Emotional, Behavioral, Intellectual, Physical, and Social. Nowadays it is offered as an app to help parents follow developmental milestones, to photograph, to document and to organize their child's life in memories, from birth to age ten. Educating parents about their children's development provides understanding that encourages patience, tolerance and compassion. The free parenting app also provides helpful, developmentally appropriate activities, "Just for Fun."

*Empathy: This is the actual experiencing of another's thoughts, feelings or attitudes. It is used more broadly these days and often confused with compassion.

*Entry Point: An entry point into a child's play is found by observing to see where one can follow the child's lead in play. This is similar to when adults find entry points into other adult's conversations by listening to the conversation already in progress before joining in.

*False Self: In this book, 'The False Self' is the superficial, defensive, idealized shell that builds up over time and can become like a protective armor.

*Fog: It takes less than a cup of water to create a fog so dense that people can barely see around them for more than one-acre in circumference by one-meter deep.

*Four Walls: An expression we Musketeers made up in school to request confidentiality. Davisman and I continued this ritual during supervision of one another, though after a while an understanding of confidentiality between us was naturally in place. It is a privilege to be granted the privacy to say anything in support of being human, managing our feelings and being able to support each other in being the best possible psychotherapists we can.

*Genogram: A graphic representation detailing family relationships, patterns and themes amongst individuals and across generations. Genograms can include family life cycles, beliefs, rules, alliances, triangles, stories, secrets, times of stress, symptom bearers, medical histories.

*Gift: In the "policies and procedures" form at Creative Therapies it states that only homemade gifts and cards can be accepted. The reason for this gift policy is due to ethical considerations and complications. A gift changes the relationship, whether due to monetary value, entanglement, motivation, conflict of interest, preferential treatment or other pressures.

*Globbery: I did not know if "globbery" was a word Melissa made up, substituted for "globular in shape," or mispronounced from an overheard diagnosis such as thyroglossal, a type of cyst. Ultimately my understanding came from the combined, repeating theme found through her reenactment, drawings, surgical scar and her recognition and validation of the word "cyst."

*Graduation: Healthy discharge planning is an important aspect within the entire therapeutic process. It brings up grieving along with other emotions, memories and associated feelings of loss. Patients benefit from participating in a planned closure over a number of sessions, rather than repeating awkward or abrupt endings that have happened, to most, in other areas of their lives. Then during the final session, a special celebration is planned which includes discussions of their growth, healing, skills learned, techniques to carry forth and signs of when to seek help, if relevant.

Patients draw their final H-T-KFD and receive a meaningful letter highlighting progress and skills learned, along with and a small therapeutic memento, tool or book relevant to the work they did. If the patient was a child, the parents now also feel equipped with the tools essential to their child's well-being.

*Grief: Grief is discussed here as relevant to the healing of trauma. Grief is described as "mourning" in Judith Herman's 1992 book *Trauma and Recovery*. She identified Three Stages of Trauma Recovery: Stage One - Safety and Stabilization, Stage Two – Remembrance and Mourning, and Stage Three – Reconnection and Integration. Of course, when working with different identities, who was in which stage at what time varied.

*Happy Baby: This is a yoga pose that mimics a position taken naturally by young children when they lay on their backs, bend their knees into their chest, and hold the outsides of their feet. Every now and then it would be good for our body, mind and spirit if we dropped into the "Happy Baby" pose for our health, joy and higher consciousness.

*He: Please note the use of the pronoun 'he' is for the reader to identify self or someone they know. The domestic violence statistics indicated that, 1 in 4 females and 1 in 9 males are victims. This educational piece written with the understanding, of course, that it could alternatively be a 'she' who is abusive. At that time, the local domestic violence hotline found 3 out of every 10 calls were male victims. This figure is much higher than those men who would actually go on to fill out a report. Some of the reasons domestic violence against men is not reported is because it gets minimized, police do not take it as seriously and men do not want to look or feel emasculated.

*Identified Patient: The person in the family who has unconsciously been chosen as the one to act out the family's inner conflicts.

*In-Home Care (1990): The In-Home Care program changed its face over the years, becoming an addition to a child's weekly session when more than once a week care was indicated. The service was staffed including trained interns and at no additional fee to families. While not as experienced or knowledgeable as the hired staff, the quality of the interns often exceeded them in terms of their energy, enthusiasm, fresh knowledge, ability to take supervision and willingness to go the extra mile.

Observational details were gathered: The home was quiet, cluttered, chaotic, spotless, routined; The parents physically present, emotionally available, rigid, protective; The family interactions kind, frustrated, dysregulated, unusual; The children cooperative, structured, disciplined. Observations also varied in time and location including weekend, breakfast time, family dinner, school and extra-curricular activities. All treatment plans including In-Home Care was created with measurable and observable goals.

Of course, we also reveal ourselves based on how we present in our own office. For example, are we tidy, cluttered, detail-oriented, disorganized, are the plants nurtured. The patient wonders, *how are you going to take care of me if this is how you take care of your environment?* What are we disclosing about ourselves by the pictures on the walls, our family photos and the books lying around? The patients thinks, *Oh you have a teen my age then you know…oh you only have boys, then you don't know.*

*<u>Initial Phone Inquiry:</u> The initial phone inquiry is a 15-20 minute mutual interview phone call. The objective it to determine if psychotherapy could help and if the individual or family was appropriate for Creative Therapies programming and treatment. If the treatment was for a child, the initial inquiry was also an opportunity for the psychotherapist to assess parent cooperation and to screen out abusive, neglectful or otherwise inappropriate parents.

By today's standards with years of experience, I would clear in my expectations with Rita from this beginning phone call. Furthermore, her attitude would have been confronted, expectations would have been set forth, and (yikes!) if she had not been more cooperative, I would have referred them on. While this is my prerogative, it surely would have been my loss to have not had the opportunity to know this family and witness their transformation.

*<u>Initial Intake:</u> The initial intake/interview is the first visit scheduled for the patient seeking help. During this initial intake information including a thorough background, concerns and other details is gathered about the patient.

This assessment sometimes includes requests for specific drawings, finishing sentences and telling stories from pictures before beginning treatment. This is where the psychotherapeutic relationship begins. Sometimes this evaluation is scheduled for ninety minutes other times it is completed during the first one to three session.

*Integration: The process of combining of identities into one. The identities are not banished or dead but rather combined into a harmonious, strong and flexible whole personality.

*Label: The awareness of labels extends beyond clinical. The deepest and clearest perception of a person is not in any label and its symptoms but rather it is in the very essence, body and soul. When a caregiver, who is connected with their own inner self, meets the patient with genuine interest and warmth, a connection happens. As this connection deepens, the true answers come from the patient's very nature: their expressions, dialogue and what is essential to him or her. Treatment from this understanding, going to this depth, is where healing awaits.

*Miniatures: Children find or create what they need in the playrooms, including finding the miniature they require for their Sandtray, "Two-House Therapy" or any other play. Typically, miniatures are organized by themes. At Creative Therapies, miniatures were labeled drawers instead of on open shelves that stimulate and overwhelm. The drawer themes and contents were inspired by Carl

Sagan's "everything that is, was and will ever be." This included miniature animals, buildings and barriers, fantasy items, food/containers, furnishings, humans figures, nature items, religious/spiritual figures, symbols, supplies and treasures.

*Negative Explanatory Style: A negative explanatory style of the person in the mothering role renders children vulnerable to pessimism and, as teenagers, toward depression. This language is described by Martin Seligman as permanent ("I am never going to get this"); pervasive ("It's all my fault"); and personalized ("This undermines every aspect of my life"). Further explanation with examples can be found at https://creativetherapies.net/ebips/fifteen-months-old/or EBIPS The Parenting App.

*Nose: Breathing in and out from the nose is the correct and optimal manner for the body to breathe. The benefits of nose breathing include: fights infection; increases circulation; improves lung function; maintains body temperature; and reduces stress. At rest, functional nose breathing is a silent, eight to ten breaths a minute led by the diaphragm.

**PATH, edition 8*: The PATH, Prevention, Anticipation, Taking Charge and Healing is a solution-oriented e-book from the creativetherapies.net store. A caregiver's program for "how to help children" who are quick to temper. The e-book provides skills and techniques for implementation with children ages 5-10.

*Phone-Ins: I could not imagine dropping my child off anywhere and not knowing about their visit because of "confidentiality."

One way Creative Therapies is different from traditional therapy is that the child's confidence is not held, rather the family's confidence is by the therapist and the therapist's confidences is held by the parents. Therefore, parents can only be accepted who will use the information revealed about their child's session in positive, healthy cooperation with the psychotherapist's recommendations and not against the child.

The therapist will discuss their child's session, quotes from their child, therapeutic observations, strengths and weaknesses, treatment, plans and sometimes the homework that has been given to the child. Also, during this call, parents are given their own homework, which they are held accountable for in the next phone-in.

Phone-ins are scheduled for the next business day morning after their child's weekly session at a set weekly appointment time. There is no additional charge. The parents initiate the 10-15 minute call and, if necessary, in a conference call fashion.

Phone-Ins are provided to parents of children through age nine. Thereafter, as children are striving for independence, it would not be appropriate to have this degree of involvement.

This after session call is a critical piece of the successful progress in the treatment and healing of their child and often because of the parents' positive involvement results in a shorter amount of time needed in therapy.

*Point of Trauma: I coined "Point of Trauma" as the identification of the most overwhelming detail in the patient's retelling of a traumatic event, as determined by where the eyes flickered.

*Process: The process is "how" we communicate rather than the content, which is "what" we communicate about.

*Projecting: The defense mechanism projection is the denial of an unconscious impulse while attributing it to another.

*Reactive Attachment Disorder (RAD): According to the DSM-5 RAD is a trauma and stress-related disorder with age, persistence and severity specifications. The first three criteria are: A - both rarely seeks or responds to comfort when distressed (at least two of these three); B - minimal social and emotional responsiveness, limited positive affect and unexplained episodes of irritability, sadness or fearfulness (at least one of these three); C - social neglect and/or deprivation of basic emotional needs for comfort, stimulation and affection met by caregiving adults and/or changes of primary caregivers and rearing in unusual settings that severely limited attachments.

*Reported: Anyone who even suspects a child has been harmed can make an anonymous call. However, caregivers are legally obligated to report even suspicion of abuse – physical, emotional or sexual. This mandatory reporting to Child Protective Services usually results in at least one of the parents rejecting the therapeutic relationship and unfortunately, though typically, the termination of that therapist working with the child and family soon thereafter.

*Reworking as a Sign of Secondary Traumatization: I did not understand this at the time; I was suffering from Secondary Traumatization. This is found in caregivers exposed to the retelling of a patient's trauma or from cumulative exposure to a patient's traumatic stories. Secondary traumatization can sneak up on caregivers who often deny or minimize the effects on themselves. I specify "patients" here, but I am also referencing family, especially mothers and, in my case, as a girlfriend.

While signs and symptoms can be transitory, they must be taken seriously because untreated Secondary Trauma can lead to long-lasting psychological issues.

Below are some EBIPS warning signs and symptoms for caregivers, including mothers who tend to wait until their child is "better" before becoming symptomatic. Through the years and various experiences, we reworked this list to support each other and ourselves. In supervision, Davisman and I would say,

"Scale it 1-10."

E – anxiety and depression (ubiquitous in mental disorders), anger, dreading work, fear, guilt, helpless, hopeless, inadequacy, overwhelmed

B – avoidance of responsibilities, cynical

I – negative world-view, reworking, ruminating

P – burnout, disturbed eating, disturbed sleeping, exhaustion, intrusive imagery, nightmares, numbing, decreased exercise, substance abuse, teeth grinding

S – avoidance of friends, disconnection, reduced compassion for others

*Self-care: It is healthy practice for caregivers to participate in regular supervision with a close, trusted colleague that you can say anything to. Additionally, research supports that having a religious or spiritual connection is most effective and of course self-care is a must including exercise, adequate sleep, hobbies, mindfulness activities, time in nature and socialization, are important.

*Self-disclosure: As a psychotherapist, one must be careful about sharing their personal views, emotions and experiences. A self-disclosure must be with a clear purpose and goal in support of improving the patient's mental or emotional state.

While thoughtful sharing about self can reinforce that we are relatable, human and that we do understand it is typically more appropriate for when the individual's treatment advances from self to others. This often leads to a warmer connection and can encourage the patient towards further disclosures and resolutions.

My disclosure to Rita modeled genuine emotion and supported her developed skill of bonding, at a time close to family discharge. This was a time when her ability to self-nurture and not require my approval was intact.

Alternative response options could have included the three D's: deepen, diverge or disregard. Deepen: "I know this had been hard for you. What was your thinking in keeping it from me?" Diverge: "How else does your jealousy hold you back?" Disregard: Which for Rita could open her childhood wound of being ignored.

*Seven Generations: In the oldest living democracy known on Earth, the Iroquois Confederacy philosophized in the Great Lau of the Haudenosaunee, "In our every deliberation we must consider the impact of our decisions on the next seven generations."

*Slate/Blank Slate: In psychology 'blank slate' has two meanings. The first definition is from English philosopher John Lock's theory that knowledge is developed by sensory experiences rather than determined biologically. The second meaning, and the one referenced in this volume is from Psychoanalysis. Freud believed that the psychoanalyst must initially be a tabula rasa, blank slate to allow for patients to transfer their feelings from childhood onto the psychoanalyst. This task of blank slate is a striving not a possibility as Freud said of silence "betrayal oozes out every pore." We continually give color to our blank book through our being and our surroundings, such as through our EBIPS presentation, and our office décor.

<u>*Solnechnysvet:</u> Noona, Igor's wife called me "Sunshine."

<u>*SOAP:</u> An acronym for Subjective, Objective, Assessment and Plan. This is the standardized method of clinical note taking. Subjective notes are what we think; objective notes are the facts of what we measured and observed with our senses (they can include quotes). Assessment notes are the findings, diagnosis or differential based on the subjective and objective. The Plan is the documentation on what we will do next, including treatment, medicine, goals and referrals.

<u>*Stonewalling:</u> This occurs when the listener withdraws, shuts down and stops responding to their partner. According to John Gottman's research, stonewalling is one of the four communication styles that predict the end of a relationship: contempt (meanness, including body language, especially eye-rolling which is considered the single greatest predictor of divorce); criticism (most common); defensiveness (blaming); and stonewalling (withdrawal).

*Suicide Prevention: Let's create positive, solution-oriented programs, rather than a fundraiser such as a "Walk for Mental Health." We must be responsible in our advertising and educating of the public as publicized suicide information (to those under 25) gives ideas, creates copycatting and can elicit a contagion. This is also true for bulimia, cutting and mass shootings (for 13 days after a high profile mass shooting).

*Sun Room: The Sun Room is the name of one of the themed playrooms at Creative Therapies. It is a warm, spacious, yellow room painted with the Lazure technique that invites openness of being. This room included a glow-in-the-dark sun, nine planets (Pluto had not yet been downgraded), a remote control moon light, a room window shade (to adjust the play to nighttime), a sensory swing, beanbag chairs, very large pillows, a huge stuffed teddy bear, mats, a tunnel where secrets are hidden, a large closet filled with therapeutic toys and games and a vast array of puppets selected with consideration for where the hand enters into the puppet, never from underneath.

*Therapeutic Homework: Assignments given to support a patient's progress and healing. Homework is also given to the parents when the patient is a child.

*True Self: Donald Winnicott, a British psychoanalysis coined this term in 1960, when he connected this concept to narcissism, I am using this term more generally: The True Self is the real self, the original, authentic, vulnerable, spontaneous self. Also see *False Self

*Two-House Therapy (2-HT): A Creative Therapies discovery. Children would change the owners of the two wooden houses to meet their individual needs. In children whose parents had split up, one house would become moms and the other dad's. In other scenarios' one of the houses was home, the other school, church, or the grandparents' house. Then, of course, there were the wealthy parents from such large homes that their children would turn both houses into their one huge home. This technique is now applied around the globe.

*U 'n' Me Playtime: This is a Creative Therapies parent homework technique for therapeutically playing with a child. It is described in Appendix D and listed as a Playwork strategy in a course training turned e-book, *The 'Why and How' to Develop the Play of Children, 6th edition,* available at creativetherapies.net/store/. This e-book provides nine additional strategies that progress to U 'n' Me Playtime and is appropriate for caretakers with ages children four to seven, and older when the child is developmentally delayed, does not play or for older children when the parent-child connection could benefit from strengthening.

*Waiting Period for Gun Purchase: This law varies from state to state. Where I am, there is no waiting period and a firearm could be purchased upon passing the few minutes of a background check or in a "default proceed," meaning three business days if the background check is not immediately completed. A stringent waiting period would serve the potentially life saving function of an increased time to "cool off." This cool off time could protect against impulsive acts of violence towards self or others.

*Water Room: The Water Room is the name of one of the themed playrooms at Creative Therapies. It is painted in soft blues with the Lazure technique, which invites breath. This room included a water tray, sand tray, 2 wooden houses, many labeled drawers filled with miniatures, a huge fish tank, an arts and crafts area, a play kitchen, a real kitchen and my ivy plant.

*Werther Effect: When a suicide creates a spike of emulation suicides. David Phillips, a researcher, coined the Werther Effect after a character in Johann Wolfgang von Goethe's novel, *The Sorrows of Young Werther.*

References and Recommended Reading (some references are from the time period of the book, despite age)

Aronson, J & Jones, E. (1992). "Inferring abilities after influencing performance." *Journal of Social Psychology*, 58, 1062-1072.

Brown, S., Vik, P., Creamer, V. (1989). "Characteristics of relapse following adolescent substance abuse treatment." *Addictive Behaviors.* 14(3):291-300.

Caroll, L. (1871). *The Looking Glass.* London, England: Macmillan & Co.

Cavoukian, R. (1980). *Baby Beluga.* Santa Monica, CA: A&M Records.

Chodron, P. (2017) *The compassion book: Teachings for awakening the heart.* Boulder, CO: Shambala.

Cohn, J. (1994) *Molly's rosebush.* Illinois: Albert Whitman & Company.

Cooper, J.A. (1988). *Childhood sexual abuse antecedent to eating disorders.* University Thesis: Unpublished.

Cooper, J.A. (1995). *Neurotheology: Neuroscientific explanations for religious and spiritual experiences.* University Dissertation: Unpublished.

Cooper, J.A. (2000). "Short-term solution oriented play therapy for children of divorced parents," in Kaduson, H.

& Schaefer, C. *Short-term play therapy for children.* New York, NY: The Guilford Press.

Cooper, J.A. *Curative Language.* E-book: creativetherapies.net/store.

Cooper, J.A. *PATH for Managing Angry Children, edition 8.* E-book: creativetherapies.net/store.

Cooper, J.A. *EBIPS The Parenting App*, App Store.

Cooper, J.A. *The Why and How of Play: When a Child Does Not Play, 6th Edition.* E-book: creativetherapies.net/store.

Dalai Lama. (2002). *An open heart: practicing compassion in everyday life.* Columbus, GA: Back Bay Books.

American Psychiatric Association (1994). *Diagnostic and statistical manual of mental disorders, DSM IV.* Washington, DC: American Psychiatric Publishing.

American Psychiatric Association (2000). *Diagnostic and statistical manual of mental disorders, DSM IV-TR.* Washington, DC: American Psychiatric Publishing.

American Psychiatric Association (2013). *Diagnostic and statistical manual of mental disorders, DSM-5.* Washington, DC: American Psychiatric Publishing.

Breggin, P. *Toxic psychiatry* (1994). New York, NY: St Martin's Press.

Felitti, V.J., et al. (1998). *Relationship of childhood abuse and household dysfunction to many of the leading causes of death in adults. The adverse childhood experiences (ace) study*. Am. J. Prev. Med, 14(4), 245-258.

Freud, Sigmund. (1977). Introductory lectures on psychoanalysis. New York, NY: Liveright Publishing Corportation.

Goethe, J. W. (1774). *The sorrows of young Werther.* Leipzig Germany: Weygand'sche Buchhandlung.

Goleman, D. (1995). *Emotional intelligence.* New York, NY: Bantam Books.

Gomi, T. (1996). *The crocodile and the dentist.* New York, NY: Scholastic.

Hay, L.L. (1988). *Heal your body expanded/revised: The mental causes for physical illness and the metaphysical way to overcome them.* New York, NY: Hay House, Inc.

Herman, J. L. (1997). *Trauma and recovery.* New York, NY: BasicBooks.

Hesse, H. (1951). *Siddhartha.* New York, NY: New Directions.

Holt, J. (1967). *How children learn.* London, England: Pitman Publishing.

International Statistical Classification of Diseases and Related Health Problems, 10th Edition (ICD-10) (1992). World Health Organization.

International Statistical Classification of Diseases and Related Health Problems, 11th Edition (ICD-11) (2018). World Health Organization. This edition is submitted for official endorsement in 2019 and adoption by Member States and effective January 1, 2022.

Karst, P. (2000). *The invisible string.* Columbus, GA: Little Brown Books for Young Readers.

Kassani, A. et al. (2015). "Survival analysis of drug abuse relapse in addiction treatment centers." *International Journal of High Risk Behaviors and Addiction.* Sept 4(3):e23402

Kubler-Ross, E. (1969). *On death and dying.* New York, NY: Simon and Schuster.

Kubler-Ross, E. (2005). *On grief and grieving: finding the meaning of grief through the five stages of loss.* New York, NY: Simon and Schuster.

Lindner, R. (1954). *The fifty-minute hour: five true psychoanalytic tales of patients on the edge.* New York, NY: MJF Books.

McBratney, S. (1994). *Guess how much I love you.* London, England: Walker Books.

Metropolitan Life Height -Weight Tables, 1943, Revised 1983.

Morris, Desmond. (1978), *Manwatching.* London, England: Triad/Panther Books.

Nelsen, J. (1987). *Positive Discipline.* New York, NY:

Ballantine. Now revised and updated.

Putnam, F.W. (1989). *Diagnosis and treatment of multiple personality disorder.* New York, NY: Guilford Publications.

Sacks, O. (1985). *The man who mistook his wife for a hat.* New York, NY: Harper-Collins.

Sagan Carl. (1980). *Cosmos.* New York, NY: Random House.

Seligman, M. (2006). *Learned optimism: how to change your mind and your life.* New York, NY: Random House.

Shakespeare, W. (2008). *Merchant of Venice.* New York, NY: Simon and Schuster.

Shonkoff, J., et al (January 2012). "The lifelong effects of early childhood adversity and toxic stress." *Pediatrics* 129(1), e232-46. doi: 10. 1542/peds. 2011-2663.

Thomas, K.W. (2015). *Conscious uncoupling: 5 steps to living happily ever after.* New York, NY: Harmony.

Wallerstein, J. (2004). "The unexpected legacy of divorce: report of a 25-year study." *Psychoanalytic Psychology* 21 (3), 353, 2004.

Wallerstein, J. (2005). "Growing up in the divorced family." *Clinical Social Work Journal* 33 (4), 401-418.

Williams, M. (1922). *The Velveteen Rabbit.* New York, NY: George H. Doran Company.

Wordsworth, W. (1807). "Ode: intimations of immortality from recollections of early childhood." *Poems in two volumes.* London: Woodstock Books.

Yalom, I.D. (1989). *Love's executioner and other tales of psychotherapy, edition 6.* New York, NY: Harper Perennial.

About the Author

JULIA A. COOPER has a doctorate of psychology and a doctorate of divinity. This combination of science and spirituality blended with the creative use of art is at the foundation of her treatment.

After a 30-year career as a psychotherapist and as the director of Creative Therapies, she now provides individual care by phone, school consultations on campus and family services in the home.

She lectures extensively on topics from her work, including 'Positive Parenting,' 'Developmental Milestones' and 'Trauma.' Additionally, she provides workshops on topics from Psychotherapy Tales.

drjuliaacooper.com